THE ENCYCLOPEDIA OF
FISHES

A Complete Visual Guide

THE ENCYCLOPEDIA OF

FISHES

CONSULTANT

Dr Stephen Hutchinson
Visiting Senior Fellow
National Oceanography Centre
Southampton, UK

FOG CITY PRESS

A Complete Visual Guide

Conceived and produced by Weldon Owen Pty Ltd
59 Victoria Street, McMahons Point
Sydney NSW 2060, Australia
Copyright © 2006 Weldon Owen Inc.

Chief Executive Officer John Owen
President Terry Newell
Publisher Sheena Coupe
Creative Director Sue Burk
Vice President International Sales Stuart Laurence
Administrator International Sales Kristine Ravn

Project Editor Jennifer Losco
Project Designer Heather Menzies
Editors Stephanie Goodwin, Angela Handley
Designers Clare Forte, Helen Perks, Karen Robertson, Juliana Titin
Cover Design Heather Menzies, Juliana Titin
Picture Researchers Joanna Collard, Annette Crueger,
Jennifer Losco, Heather Menzies
Editorial Assistant Irene Mickaiel

Text Stephen Hutchinson, Karen McGhee

Species Gallery Illustrations MagicGroup s.r.o. (Czech Republic)—
www.magicgroup.cz
Feature Illustrations Guy Troughton
Maps Andrew Davies Creative Communication and Map Illustrations
Information Graphics Andrew Davies Creative Communication
Index Sarah Plant/Puddingburn Publishing Services

Production Director Chris Hemesath
Production Coordinator Charles Mathews

ISBN 1-740-89354-9

Color reproduction by Chroma Graphics (Overseas) Pte Ltd
Printed by SNP Leefung Printers Ltd
Printed in China

A Weldon Owen Production

CONTENTS

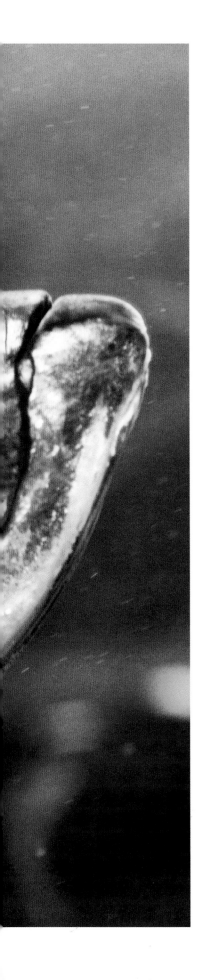

FOREWORD

Some of the first known scientific writing about fishes is contained in the works of Aristotle, who described the biology of 115 types of fishes nearly two and a half thousand years ago. Throughout the ages the abundance, diversity, economic value, and the beauty of fishes have fascinated humans. Long as our interest may seem to us, it is but a brief moment in the history of fishes. For more than 450 million years, fishes have been evolving from primitive, jawless, aquatic animals to become the most diverse group of vertebrates on Earth.

The greatest explosion in numbers of fish species took place 350 million years ago during the Devonian period, which is sometimes called the "Age of Fishes." Today, due to their great range and abundance, fishes remain one of the wonders of the living world. They are found everywhere, from small, icy mountain streams to the bottom of the deepest ocean trenches, from pole to pole and in every kind of water—sometimes even out of it. Among this profusion of body types and lifestyles, we can see glimpses of our own origins as air-breathing land animals with four limbs.

At present, at least 25,000 species of fishes are known to science and new species continue to be discovered. In a recent census of aquatic life, more than 100 new species were found in a single year. This richness of life is, however, seriously threatened by fishing once-thriving species to extinction, pollution, and habitat destruction. *The Encyclopedia of Fishes* cannot hope to document every fish species but it can give an insight into the variety and adaptations of a group of animals that are the most abundant vertebrates on the planet and keystones in the ecosystems on which we depend.

DR STEPHEN HUTCHINSON
Visiting Senior Fellow, National Oceanography Centre, Southampton, UK

HOW TO USE THIS BOOK

The first section of this book provides an introduction to fishes: their characteristics, evolution, classification, biology, behavior, habitats, adaptations, and conservation status. The second section surveys fishes according to their taxonomy. Larger groups, such as the sharks and rays, or the bony fishes, are further divided into subgroups, such as sharks, or eels and catfishes. The book concludes with a comprehensive glossary and index.

Group global distribution
A map shows the worldwide distribution of the group being profiled, followed by text that discusses the distribution of particular groups in more detail.

HABITAT ICONS

The six habitat icons below indicate at a glance the various habitats in which a species or group can be found. It should be noted that the icons are used in the same order throughout the book, rather than in their order of significance. A more detailed profile of each habitat can be found on pages 30–57.

- Polar regions
- Seas and oceans
- Coral reefs
- Mangrove swamps
- Coastal areas, including beaches, oceanic cliffs, sand dunes, intertidal rock pools, and/or coastal waters (as applicable to group)
- Rivers and streams, including river and stream banks

Section and chapter
This indicates the group of fishes under discussion.

Classification box
This shows the taxonomic groups to which fishes belong.

Lavish photographs
Taken by leading wildlife photographers, these portray the habits and habitats of different species.

Feature pages
These explore topics of particular interest and provide insight into fish behavior through text, illustrations, and photographs.

---

70   SHARKS

SHARKS

CLASS	Chondrichthyes
SUBCLASS	Elasmobranchii
ORDERS	8
FAMILIES	31
SPECIES	415

Although less than 2 percent of living fish species are sharks, they are of crucial ecological importance in marine ecosystems because they are apex predators. As a result they occur at naturally low levels of abundance compared with most bony fishes. This, combined with low reproductive rates, makes sharks particularly vulnerable to overexploitation. Most only reach sexual maturity after 6 years, and some not until 18 years or more. They produce few young and embryos undergo long periods of development before birth. Chimaeras are related to the sharks but belong to the subclass Holocephali, which contains a single order with 3 families and 37 species.

Widespread distribution Sharks are found throughout the world's oceans, although very few species can tolerate polar waters. Most prefer shallow marine habitats but a small number of species, such as dogfish sharks, dwell at great depth

"Mermaid purses" Shark eggs are large and yolky. The purse-like outer layer is made of a tough keratinoid (horny) protein and can be up to 6¾ inches (17 cm) long. Each contains a single embryo that can take up to 15 months to mature.

Gatherings Sharks do not school in the same highly coordinated way that bony fishes often do. But many species form aggregations. In the Sea of Cortez, large day-time groups of mainly juvenile female hammerheads form regularly in areas of high productivity (left). Reasons for this remain unclear.

PREDATORY LIVES
Because most sharks are highly active predators, they tend to be strong, agile swimmers, and some species make long migrations covering many hundreds of miles (km) in search of food. As they have slower metabolisms than most fishes, sharks do not need to feed as frequently and only hunt when necessary. Prey typically includes small fishes and invertebrates but larger sharks also hunt sea turtles and marine mammals.

They have no internal swim bladder but other adaptations help to increase buoyancy and enhance their swimming capabilities. The cartilaginous skeleton, which is lighter than true bone, contributes. And large livers with high levels of oil also help keep many afloat. The do need, however, to keep swimming to avoid dropping to the ocean floc

Sharks reduce water loss by retaining urea in their tissues.

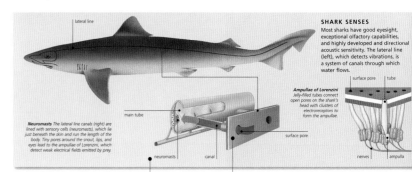

Neuromasts The lateral line canals (right) are lined with sensory cells (neuromasts), which lie just beneath the skin and run the length of the body. Tiny pores around the snout, lips, and eyes lead to the ampullae of Lorenzini, which detect weak electrical fields emitted by prey.

Ampullae of Lorenzini Jelly-filled tubes connect open pores on the shark's head with clusters of electroreceptors to form the ampullae.

SHARK SENSES
Most sharks have good eyesight, exceptional olfactory capabilities, and highly developed and directional acoustic sensitivity. The lateral line (left), which detects vibrations, is a system of canals through which water flows.

Feature box
This support text describes in detail a facet of the species' behavior or biology, and is accompanied by relevant photographs, illustrations, or diagrams.

Detailed diagram
Where appropriate, diagrams are included to illustrate points about anatomy or adaptation.

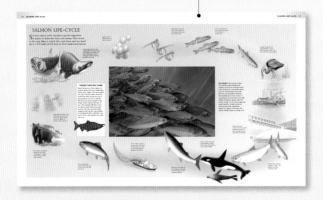

SALMON LIFE-CYCLE

CONSERVATION INFORMATION

Within the fact files, each profiled species is allocated a conservation status, using IUCN and other conservation categories, as follows:

✝ Indicates that a species is listed under the following categories:
Extinct (IUCN) It is beyond reasonable doubt that the last individual of a given species has died.
Extinct in the wild (IUCN) Only known to survive in captivity or as a naturalized population outside its former range.

♟ Indicates that a species is listed under the following categories:
Critically endangered (IUCN) Facing a very high and immediate risk of extinction in the wild.
Endangered (IUCN) Facing a very high risk of extinction in the wild in the near future.

The following categories are also used:
Vulnerable (IUCN) Facing a high risk of extinction in the wild in the foreseeable future.
Near threatened (IUCN) Likely to qualify for one of the above categories in the near future.
Conservation dependent (IUCN) Dependent upon species- or habitat-specific conservation programs to keep it out of one of the above threatened categories.

Data deficient (IUCN) Inadequate information available to make an assessment of its risk.
Not known Not evaluated or little studied.
Common Widespread and abundant.
Locally common Widespread and abundant within its range.
Uncommon Occurs widely in low numbers in preferred habitat(s).
Rare Occurs in only some of preferred habitat or in small restricted areas.

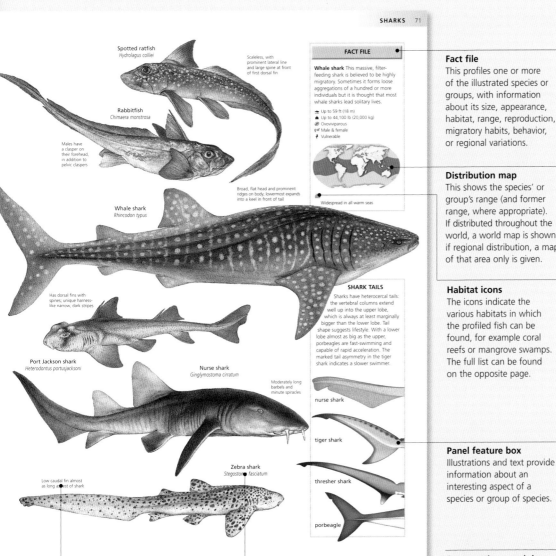

SHARKS   71

Spotted ratfish
Hydrolagus colliei

Scaleless, with prominent lateral line and large spine at front of first dorsal fin

Rabbitfish
Chimaera monstrosa

Males have a clasper on their forehead, in addition to pelvic claspers

Broad, flat head and prominent ridges on body; lowermost expands into a keel in front of tail

Whale shark
Rhincodon typus

Has dorsal fins with spines; unique harness-like narrow, dark stripes

Port Jackson shark
Heterodontus portusjacksoni

Moderately long barbels and minute spiracles

Nurse shark
Ginglymostoma cirratum

Low caudal fin almost as long as rest of shark

Zebra shark
Stegostoma fasciatum

FACT FILE

Whale shark This massive, filter-feeding shark is believed to be highly migratory. Sometimes it forms loose aggregations of a hundred or more individuals but it is thought that most whale sharks lead solitary lives.
⬎ Up to 59 ft (18 m)
🟦 Up to 44,100 lb (20,000 kg)
⊘ Ovoviviparous
♀♂ Male & female
♟ Vulnerable

Widespread in all warm seas

SHARK TAILS
Sharks have heterocercal tails: the vertebral columns extend well up into the upper lobe, which is always at least marginally bigger than the lower lobe. Tail shape suggests lifestyle. With a lower lobe almost as big as the upper, porbeagles are fast-swimming and capable of rapid acceleration. The marked tail asymmetry in the tiger shark indicates a slower swimmer.

nurse shark

tiger shark

thresher shark

porbeagle

Fact file
This profiles one or more of the illustrated species or groups, with information about its size, appearance, habitat, range, reproduction, migratory habits, behavior, or regional variations.

Distribution map
This shows the species' or group's range (and former range, where appropriate). If distributed throughout the world, a world map is shown; if regional distribution, a map of that area only is given.

Habitat icons
The icons indicate the various habitats in which the profiled fish can be found, for example coral reefs or mangrove swamps. The full list can be found on the opposite page.

Panel feature box
Illustrations and text provide information about an interesting aspect of a species or group of species.

Conservation watch box
This provides information about the status of a particular species or group of fishes, according to the IUCN Red List of Threatened Species. These boxes may also outline factors that threaten the fishes' survival.

FACT FILE STATISTICS

Important or interesting facts about profiled species or groups use the following icons and information. All measurements given are maximums.

Length
⬎ Head and body, including tail

Weight/Mass
🟦 Body weight

Breeding
⬤ Viviparous (produces live young)
○ Oviparous (produces eggs that develop outside the maternal body)
⊘ Ovoviviparous (produces eggs that develop within the maternal body)

Sex
♀♂ Indicates separate male and female, hermaphrodite, or sequential hermaphrodite

♟ CONSERVATION WATCH

Of the 221 species contained in the Osteoglossiformes order (i.e. bony tongues and their allies), 4 are included on the IUCN Red List, as follows:

1 Endangered

2 Near threatened

1 Data deficient

Snippets
These highlight distinguishing aspects or characteristics of the species, such as color variations, behavior, habitat, size, and anatomical features.

Name labels
Labels provide the common and scientific names of illustrated fishes.

INTRODUCING
FISHES

FISHES

PHYLUM	Chordata
SUBPHYLUM	Vertebrata
CLASSES	5
ORDERS	62
FAMILIES	504
SPECIES	25,777

With more than 25,000 already described, and thousands more thought to be still awaiting discovery, the fishes comprise more than half of all living vertebrate species. Since evolving in freshwater, almost 500 million years ago, the group has spread to exploit almost every aquatic habitat, from polar seas to tropical ponds. Some even pursue a parasitic existence, while a few can live briefly on land. This extraordinarily diverse group comprises five surviving classes: hagfishes, lampreys, cartilaginous fishes, lobe-finned fishes, and ray-finned fishes—the most diverse of all vertebrate classes.

FINNED LOCOMOTION

Fins immediately differentiate fishes from all other vertebrates. Although a small number of species have lost theirs through the course of evolution, most fishes move by using fins. In many, fin flexibility and fine control enable a range of swimming movements, including hovering and backward swimming. Fins, however, are not only used for swimming. Specialized fins allow some fish species to glide above-water for hundreds of feet. Other fins enable underwater, as well as terrestrial, "walking."

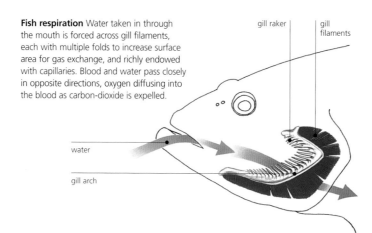

Fish respiration Water taken in through the mouth is forced across gill filaments, each with multiple folds to increase surface area for gas exchange, and richly endowed with capillaries. Blood and water pass closely in opposite directions, oxygen diffusing into the blood as carbon-dioxide is expelled.

gill raker

gill filaments

water

gill arch

SCALES

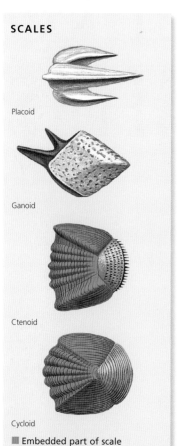

Placoid

Ganoid

Ctenoid

Cycloid

■ Embedded part of scale

Scaled protection There are four kinds of fish scales. Tooth-like placoid scales are characteristic of sharks and rays. Hard ganoid scales provide a form of armor for sturgeons and other ancient species. Most bony fishes have thin, tough scales interleaved like roof tiles; these are serrated (ctenoid) or smooth (cycloid) along their rear margins.

Larval babies In the Red Sea surgeonfish (*Acanthurus sohal*) (right) and most other fish species, larvae emerge from eggs to lead a free-swimming existence before metamorphosing into adult form. However in some, such as the striped blenny (*Chasmodes bosquianus*) (below), young pass the larval stage in the egg to hatch with the appearance of tiny adults.

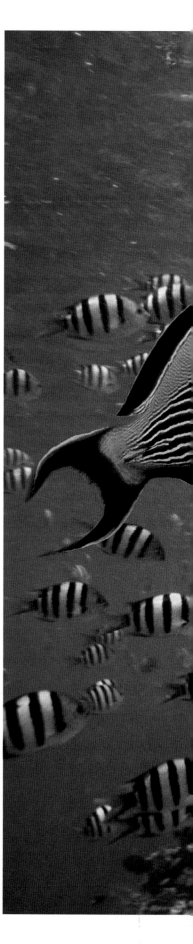

FISHES THROUGH THE AGES

The first fishes were the mostly bottom-dwelling, jawless agnathans. These are thought to have evolved from small, tadpole-shaped filter-feeding animals, similar to today's lancelets, just after the close of the Cambrian about 480 million years ago. Although they lacked jaws, many agnathans were well protected from predators by heavy armor-like plates and scales. Very little is known about their internal skeletons: they had a cranium but it is not clear whether all had vertebral elements. Most appear to have become extinct by the end of the Devonian, 354 million years ago, and today only two groups survive—the hagfishes and the lampreys. Almost 100 million years after the first jawless fishes, jawed fishes, known as gnathostomes, appear in the fossil record. One of the largest early groups was the placoderms.

DIVERSE EVOLUTION

The placoderms' shoulder girdle and head were heavily armored with bony plates. First known from the early Devonian, about 417 million years ago, they became widespread and diverse throughout much of that period. The placoderms died out by the early Carboniferous, about 360 million years ago. They may have included the ancestors of another important early jawed group—the cartilaginous fishes.

This group has skeletons composed entirely of cartilage and includes the sharks, thought to have first evolved about 400 million years ago; and the rays, which appeared some 200 million years later. Right from their earliest evolution, the cartilaginous fishes seem to have been marine predators.

Other significant early fishes were the acanthodians. This now-extinct group was once considered the most primitive of the jawed fishes. At various times it has been placed with the placoderms and with the cartilaginous fishes. Most recently, it has been identified as the sister-group to the bony fishes.

Early fish The fossil below is a species that lived 50 million years ago. It looks remarkably similar to modern bony fishes.

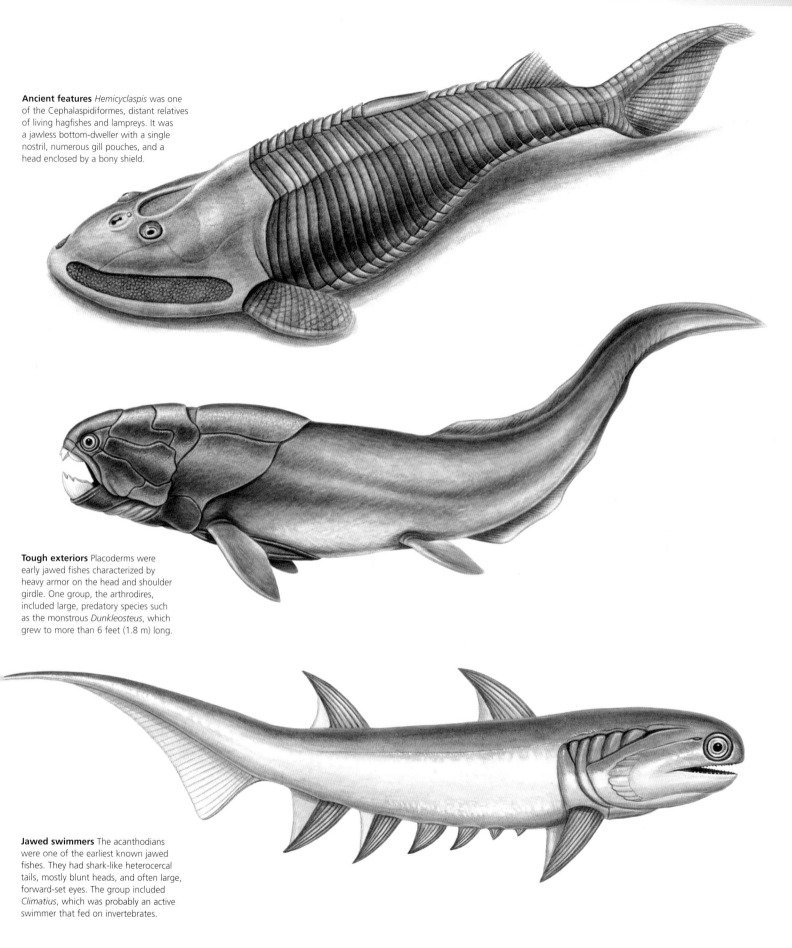

Ancient features *Hemicyclaspis* was one of the Cephalaspidiformes, distant relatives of living hagfishes and lampreys. It was a jawless bottom-dweller with a single nostril, numerous gill pouches, and a head enclosed by a bony shield.

Tough exteriors Placoderms were early jawed fishes characterized by heavy armor on the head and shoulder girdle. One group, the arthrodires, included large, predatory species such as the monstrous *Dunkleosteus*, which grew to more than 6 feet (1.8 m) long.

Jawed swimmers The acanthodians were one of the earliest known jawed fishes. They had shark-like heterocercal tails, mostly blunt heads, and often large, forward-set eyes. The group included *Climatius*, which was probably an active swimmer that fed on invertebrates.

Early ray-fin *Cheirolepis* (above), known from a fossil discovered in mid-19th century Scotland, is one of the earliest ray-finned fishes yet discovered. It lived during the mid-Devonian and is thought to have been a fast-swimming predator. Its shark-like heterocercal tail is a primitive feature lost in later ray-fins.

Prehistoric similarities When viewed in cross-section under polarized light, fossil bone from the mid-Devonian placoderm *Asterolepis ornata* (below left) is surprisingly similar to that of modern fishes. The Haversian canals—the tunnels which carry blood vessels and nerves, and are a distinguishing trait of bone—appear black.

Land-loving fish Watching mudskippers scaling trees on mudflats (below), it is not hard to imagine how early colonization of land may have proceeded. The skeletal structure and associated musculature of mudskipper fins, however, differ markedly from those of the lobe-finned fishes that ultimately gave rise to all land vertebrates.

BONY BEGINNINGS

The true bony fishes—Osteichthyes —are divided into two major living groups: the Sarcopterygii and the Actinopterygii. The Sarcopterygii are the fleshy-finned fishes, today represented by just nine lungfish species and two coelacanths, the latter of which are considered relic species from the age of dinosaurs, about 65 million years ago.

The Actinopterygii, the ray-finned fishes, is the other main living group of bony fishes. It comprises more than 20,000 living species, which accounts for about half of all living vertebrates. A few isolated fossils of scales indicate that the first ray-finned fishes evolved by the late Silurian, about 420 million years ago. But the first complete fossil skeletons of this group come from early Devonian rocks.

A third, once-large but now-extinct, group of bony fishes, the Osteolepimorpha, may have been significant in the evolution of other vertebrate groups. These were lobe-finned freshwater predators and many paleontologists believe some component of this group gave rise to the earliest tetrapods—amphibians.

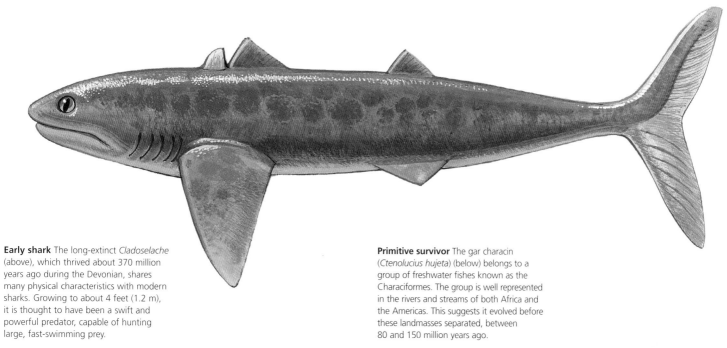

Early shark The long-extinct *Cladoselache* (above), which thrived about 370 million years ago during the Devonian, shares many physical characteristics with modern sharks. Growing to about 4 feet (1.2 m), it is thought to have been a swift and powerful predator, capable of hunting large, fast-swimming prey.

Primitive survivor The gar characin (*Ctenolucius hujeta*) (below) belongs to a group of freshwater fishes known as the Characiformes. The group is well represented in the rivers and streams of both Africa and the Americas. This suggests it evolved before these landmasses separated, between 80 and 150 million years ago.

CLASSIFICATION

Classification has two major purposes. The first is to scientifically describe the planet's species—both living and extinct. This helps categorize and sort the world's organisms according to similarities and differences and gives species universal names that apply in any language. The second major role of classification is to provide hierarchical summaries of evolutionary knowledge of the world's species. This kind of information helps scientists understand the biological history of species, including how and when they evolved, and what sorts of related organisms they may have arisen from, or given rise to. Without classification, biological knowledge would be a series of disconnected facts. Our own evolutionary history would not only be obscured, but also much of our ability to use biological knowledge for conservation, medicine, agriculture, aquaculture, and industry.

Color confusion Outward appearances can be deceiving and need to be considered carefully when classifying species. For example, in the yellowstriped fairy basslet (*Pseudanthias tuka*), males and females have different coloration and could be confused for different species.

KINGDOM
Animalia
yellowstriped fairy basslet, human, domestic cat, parrot, crocodile, stick insect

PHYLUM
Chordata
yellowstriped fairy basslet, all other fishes, human, domestic cat, parrot, crocodile

CLASS
Actinopterygii
yellowstriped fairy basslet; all other ray-finned fishes

ORDER
Perciformes
yellowstriped fairy basslet, all the perch-like ray-finned fishes

FAMILY
Serranidae
yellowstriped fairy basslet, sea basses, groupers, fairy basslets

GENUS
Pseudanthias
yellowstriped fairy basslet, threadfin anthias, sunset anthias

SPECIES
Pseudanthias tuka
yellowstriped fairy basslet

FISHES

Any study of fishes shows that they are an immensely diverse array of animals, differing greatly in the range of habitats they occupy and their body forms and adaptations. As a consequence, most biologists regard the term "fishes," as a convenient name, rather than a closely defined taxonomic entity, that describes aquatic vertebrates such as hagfishes, lampreys, sharks, rays, lungfishes, sturgeons, gars, and the advanced ray-finned fishes. There are a number of classification schemes for the fishes but one of the most widely accepted recent ones recognizes five classes of living species and three classes that are now extinct. The five classes, whose classification is detailed below, are hagfishes, lampreys, cartilaginous fishes, lobe-finned fishes, and ray-finned fishes. These are grouped into two superclasses: jawless fishes and jawed fishes. The three extinct classes are the pteraspidomorphs—jawless armored fishes; the jawed placoderms that were encased in bony plates; and the acanthodians, small true bony fishes with two long dorsal spines.

JAWLESS FISHES
Superclass Agnatha
Lampreys and hagfishes

JAWED FISHES
Superclass Gnathostomata
(includes all the groups below)

Superclass Agnatha, page 67

    CARTILAGINOUS FISHES "Chondrichthyes"
    Class Chondrichthyes
    Sharks, rays, and allies

        Subclass Elasmobranchii
        Sharks
        Rays and allies

        Subclass Holocephali
        Chimaeras

    BONY FISHES "Osteichthyes"

    Class Sarcopterygii
    Lungfishes and allies

    Class Actinopterygii

        Subclass Chondrostei
        Bichirs and allies

Subclass Elasmobranchii, page 85

        Subclass Neopterygii

        Primitive Neopterygii
        (gars and bowfin)

        Division Teleostei

          Subdivision Osteoglossomorpha
          Bonytongues and allies

          Subdivision Elopomorpha
          Eels and allies

          Subdivision Clupeomorpha
          Sardines and allies

          Subdivision Euteleostei
          (includes all the groups below)

Subdivision Osteoglossomorpha, page 98

            Superorder Ostariophysi
            Catfishes and allies

            Superorder Protacanthopterygii
            Salmons and allies

            Superorder Stenopterygii
            Dragonfishes and allies

            Superorder Cyclosquamata
            Lizardfishes and allies

            Superorder Scopelomorpha
            Lanternfishes

            Superorder Polymixiomorpha
            Beardfishes

            Superorder Lampridiomorpha
            Opahs and allies

            Superorder Paracanthopterygii
            Cod, anglerfishes, and allies

            Superorder Acanthopterygii
            Spiny-rayed fishes

Superorder Acanthopterygii, page 152

SCIENTIFIC NAMES

In the early 18th century, Swedish naturalist Carl Linnaeus developed a scheme for naming, ranking, and classifying different organisms according to the presence, or absence, of observable similarities. It still provides the foundations for the approach to classification now used by biologists worldwide.

The principal feature of the Linnaean system, and one which still applies, is that it assigns a unique two-part name to each and every different organism. In this so-called binomial system, the first part of the name indicates the genus to which the organism belongs. It points to other organisms, living and dead, with which the named organism shares its closest evolutionary relationships. The second name is the specific name. Only one species within any genus will be assigned this name.

Common problems The fish at right are known by various common names, including magpie sweetlips, dotted sweetlips, painted sweetlips, and black spotted sweetlips. Confusion is avoided by using the scientific name—*Plectorhinchus picus*—which is uniquely applied to this species.

Family feature Regal angelfish (*Pygoplites diacanthus*) (below) have a spine on the preoperculum—a bone located near the cheek. It is a defining feature of the angelfish family Pomacanthidae.

BIOLOGY AND BEHAVIOR

The evolution of many of the biological and behavioral adaptations of fishes has been driven by the physical and chemical properties of the medium in which they live. Water is, for example, considerably denser than air, quickly dissipates chemical signals, and carries sound waves farther than light. Although their actions and activities are always driven by the same basic requirements, fishes have a broad variety of behaviors. Like that of all animals, fish behavior is governed fundamentally by the need to find food and mates, balanced by the need to avoid predators. Fishes achieve these goals largely by using specialized sensory systems, some of which are not found in other vertebrates.

SENSORY SYSTEMS

Sight is a well-developed sense in most fishes but its use is often limited by water depth and turbidity. Perhaps because of this, many fishes have extremely well-developed senses of smell and hearing. They do not have noses as we know them, but fishes do have nostrils, or nares, with which they can detect even minuscule concentrations of chemicals.

Smell is intimately connected with the sense of taste. As fishes do not have tongues, their "taste buds," or chemoreceptors, are spread right across the face and sometimes even along the entire body.

Many fishes also have a highly developed sense of hearing and some can perceive noise across considerable distances. They use sound not only to locate prey and avoid the paths of predators, but sometimes also to communicate with other members of their species.

As well as these basic systems, all fishes have an extra sense not present in other vertebrates. This is the acoustico-lateralis system or the sense of "distant touch," the organs for which are located on the fish's lateral line—which runs along each side for the length of the body. This sense allows fishes to detect the wake from a swimming neighbor. Schooling fishes use the lateral line sense to regulate distance between neighbors, particularly in muddy waters or darkness when vision is not possible. Sharks, skates, rays, and chimaeras—the cartilaginous fishes—have a highly specialized sensory system not found in the other major fish groups. Using a network of cells spread around the head, these fishes can sense the minute electric fields that emanate from every living animal.

In sight From goldfish to white sharks, vision is often important to fishes for gathering information about their surroundings, just as it is in most vertebrates. Sunlight dissipates rapidly with increasing depth so most fishes can see at light levels humans would call darkness.

Chin sense Like all goatfishes, yellowfin goatfish (*Mulloidichthys vanicolensis*) have a pair of long, sensory chin barbels. They use their barbels to probe bottom sediments in search of small invertebrates and other food.

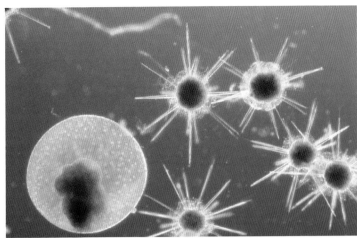

Floating food The eggs and larvae of many fishes are often important components of zooplankton (above)—the base level of many aquatic food chains.

Indiscriminate predators Many fishes devour a variety of prey. However, for most piscivorous (or fish-eating) fishes, mouth-size strictly limits the upper size of prey taken.

Dynamic chain In food chains, such as the one seen below, energy and materials flow from a broad base consisting of many small producers, through levels with decreasing numbers of larger organisms, and finally to just a few top consumers, creating a trophic pyramid. This structure is thought to occur because 90 percent of energy is lost at each level.

solar energy drives the food web

seabirds feed on small fishes (tertiary consumers)

killer whales feed on large fishes and seals (top consumers)

plants trap the energy of the Sun (primary producers)

small fishes graze on zooplankton (secondary consumers)

large fishes eat small fishes (tertiary consumers)

phytoplankton trap the energy of the Sun (primary producers)

zooplankton graze on plants (primary consumers)

seals feed on large fishes (fourth level consumers)

CATCHING PREY

Finding a meal can be a difficult task for any animal, and fishes are no exception. Many have narrow needs, and with each specialized food comes an equally specialized method of capturing it. Fresh-water archerfish, for example, knock insect prey into the water from overhanging foliage by firing well-aimed water jets from the mouth.

Prey availability in aquatic environments is often sporadic and patchy. Many fishes will gorge themselves when food is available and then go for days, or in some cases, weeks or longer before their next meal.

Among fishes that eat only other fishes, there tends to be two types of predatory approach. Some species actively stalk prey while others adopt a sit-and-wait strategy.

In school Swimming together in groups confuses and can even intimidate potential predators. By moving together in unison, many small individuals can appear to be one large animal best avoided.

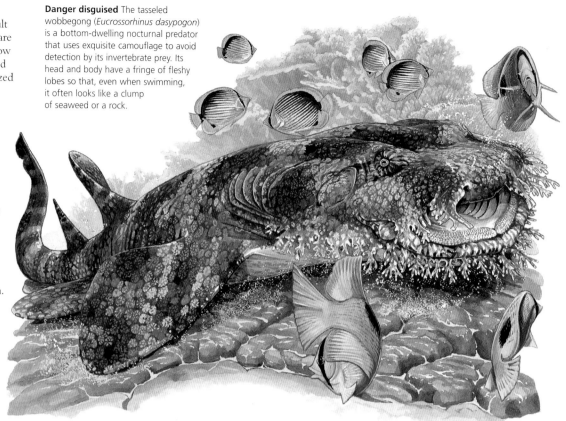

Danger disguised The tasseled wobbegong (*Eucrossorhinus dasypogon*) is a bottom-dwelling nocturnal predator that uses exquisite camouflage to avoid detection by its invertebrate prey. Its head and body have a fringe of fleshy lobes so that, even when swimming, it often looks like a clump of seaweed or a rock.

STAYING SAFE

In evolution's predator-prey arms race, the hunted have made as many advances as the hunters, allowing them to stay, mostly, one step ahead. Hiding is a popular strategy and many fishes seek protection in sea-floor cracks and crevices. Other shelters are more ingenious. Young cardinal fishes, for example, hunker down among the long-spined sea urchin's sharp quills.

Some fishes use chemical defenses to ward off predators. Parrotfishes, for example, secrete and sleep inside translucent mucus bubbles to prevent predators from detecting them. Toughened spines, scales, and skin are other common predator deterrents, but the most widespread strategy is the safety-in-numbers approach of schooling.

Catch and grind A bottom-dwelling reef predator, the coral hind (*Cephalopholis miniata*) (right) feeds on crustaceans and other fishes. It uses grinding plates inside its throat to break up prey.

Aggressive carnivore A torpedo-shaped body designed for speed through the water and a mouthful of razor-sharp teeth make the barracuda (*Sphyraena barracuda*) (below) a formidable predator of fishes.

REPRODUCTIVE RIGHTS

Fishes display an unparalleled range of reproductive systems. Each, however, can be divided into the same four phases; courtship, mating, spawning, and parental care. Some species collect in large mating aggregations to spawn en masse under the full moon, allowing egg and sperm cells to drift and mix unattended, at the mercy of currents. Others rigorously select and defend nest sites, attract mates with elaborate courtship displays, and tenaciously guard their eggs and offspring.

In most fish species, mating and spawning are virtually synonymous. However, in species with internal fertilization—as in all the cartilaginous fishes and a few bony fishes such as guppies—spawning is replaced by birth sometime after the act of mating.

In schooling spawners, such as anchovies, males and females appear identical and do not engage in courtship. But elaborate courtship displays and mating rituals have evolved in fishes in which eggs are deposited in nests or picked up and cared for by a parent. Courtship usually relies on males attracting

the attentions of females and so the males often develop attention-grabbing coloration or patterning, sexual accessory structures on their fins and tails (for battling rival males), and occasionally larger body size.

In cichlids, for example, spawning takes place after an elaborate courtship that can last for days before a suitable nest site is selected. The eggs are deposited in the nest and the fry are raised there, all the time guarded by both parents. Often there is a division of labor—females tend to the eggs while males patrol and defend boundaries of the territory.

Mating systems in which a single male mates with several females (polygyny) are common in habitats where the male can successfully defend resources—such as food or shelter—that females want.

In species such as the cleaner wrasse, which do not use seabed nests but release sperm and eggs directly into the water column, polygynous mating systems operate like harems. A single male controls reproductive access to a group of females, and mates with each of them in turn. This mating system is further complicated by the fact that these fish have the ability to change sex.

Sexual parasites In some anglerfish species, males have become dwarfs that parasitize the females and are incapable of independent survival (top left). Each female produces a pheromone attractant to guide mates to her. She may carry up to three males simultaneously.

Gentle spawners Spawning pairs of mandarinfish (*Synchiropus splendidus*) (left), ascend the water column in close contact as they release sperm and eggs. This species, like most others in the dragonet family (Callionymidae), is sexually dimorphic, with the males bearing an elongated first dorsal fin for display.

Close mates Pair-bonding is very rare among fishes. However, in habitats riddled with potential egg predators, monogamy and shared parental care can be the only way to successfully raise young. The butterflyfishes, including the bluecheek butterflyfish (*Chaetodon semilarvatus*) (right), are among the small number of fishes that form long-term, monogamous sexual partnerships. In some species, these are known to endure for several years. Shorter-term monogamy is seen in some freshwater cichlid species as well as in the seahorses and their close relatives.

TROUT REPRODUCTION

Brown trout (*Salmo trutta*) return to the upstream areas in which they were born to spawn. The female creates a shallow depression—a redd—in gravel substrate using her fins and body. Into this she deposits up to 10,000 eggs over which several males release sperm. The female covers the fertilized eggs with a light gravel layer and the adults return downstream, giving the eggs no further attention. After hatching the following spring, young trout (alevins) initially remain close to the redd, nourished by large yolk sacs.

Female brown trout deposits eggs

Male releases sperm over the eggs

Hatchlings feed on orange yolk sac

PRODUCING OFFSPRING

The males of pipefish and seahorse species and their close relatives have external brood pouches, in which either they, or the females, place fertilized eggs. The males then carry and protect the eggs until hatching.

Although most fish species fertilize their eggs externally, internal fertilization and live birth do occur in a surprising array of species, particularly among the cartilaginous fishes. Live-bearers have dispensed with the need for nest-building and early parental care entirely. Their young are born as fully developed, active fishes. This strategy ensures that egg and fry losses are minimized but also limits the number of young produced. Some sharks, for example, may give birth to just a single pup.

In some live-bearing species, such as guppies, females display superfetation. This means they are able to produce many more than one brood from just one mating by storing sperm and fertilizing eggs in batches that develop in succession.

PARENTAL INVESTMENTS

Fishes display a wide range of parental care, from none to extensive. Many schooling and open-water species broadcast spawn during mating aggregations. Millions of eggs can be released during these events to mix in the water column with sperm before floating away. The overabundance of fertilized eggs ensures at least some survive predators to hatch.

Species that have benthic nests and provide parental care usually produce large, yolky eggs in much smaller numbers than the broadcast spawners, because far fewer are lost to predators. In habitats where egg predation is intense, parents can be particularly attentive. Stickleback males, for example, construct algal nests, into which they entice females to deposit eggs, and which they then guard from predators.

Some cichlids use their mouths, instead of nests, to brood eggs. The tiny fry are released after hatching but scooped up quickly into the protective mouth of a parent should a predator threaten.

Brooding not eating Mouth brooding is widespread among the many species of the tropical marine genus *Opistognathus* (top left). As in other fish groups that protect eggs or young in the oral cavity, it is usually the males that do the brooding. It is thought the phenomenon may have evolved, in part, because it helps males ensure the paternity of offspring.

Devoted daddy The male leafy seadragon (*Phycodurus eques*) (left) incubates eggs in a brood pouch on the underside of its tail. The female may deposit as many as 250 eggs into this pouch. Fry hatch after about two months.

Takeaway food Females of the velvet belly lantern shark (*Etmopterus spinax*), a deep-sea species, produce large, yolky eggs that are retained internally until they hatch. At birth, young are well-developed but draw nourishment (top right) from a large yolk sac until they are able to feed themselves.

Nursery slime In the freshwater Eurasian perch (*Perca fluviatilis*), males arrive at springtime spawning grounds ahead of females. Belly prodding by males encourages females to release eggs, up to 300,000 at a time, in a protective mucus ribbon, often more than 3 feet (1 m) long. These are strung across weeds, logs, and other submerged debris and vegetation. Eggs are fertilized by attending males as they emerge from females, and hatch up to two weeks later, depending on water temperature.

HABITATS AND ADAPTATIONS

Fishes are found in almost every aquatic habitat: from high-altitude lakes and torrential streams to the deepest freshwater lakes and widest slow-moving rivers; from 104°F (40°C) desert springs to super-cooled Antarctic waters of just 28°F (-2°C); from the sun-lit shallows of complex coral reef systems and the wide expanses of the open ocean's surface waters to the dark depths of ocean trenches. A few fishes can even survive out of water. Marine flyingfishes, freshwater butterflyfishes, and hatchetfishes all take to the air; flyingfishes glide, butterflyfishes jump, and hatchetfishes "fly" short distances. Mudskippers make more extended forays out of water onto mangrove mudflats. Some lungfishes can survive months, even years, of desiccation, buried in the bottom sediments of dried-up waterholes. The walking catfish and some freshwater eels can journey considerable distances across land in search of mates, food, or more suitable habitat.

STREAMS
AND RIVERS

It is not surprising that the two driest continents—Antarctica and Australia —support the fewest freshwater fish species. Antarctica has none living, although fossil evidence shows they did occur there in the distant past. Australia supports only 200 species. The biodiversity of freshwater fishes increases toward the tropics.

Streams and rivers provide a large variety of freshwater habitats in which fish adaptations are strongly influenced by water quality, including oxygen content, turbidity, and the pace of flow. The rushing head-waters of a mountain stream, with rocky bottom and cold, clear, highly oxygenated water, for example, require vastly different adaptations to the typically slow-moving, warm, often turbid waters near the mouth of a floodplain river. The trout of mountain streams are keen-sighted, fast-swimming predators that need low temperatures and high oxygen to survive. In contrast, the carp that inhabit the still waters of rivers and ponds are slow-moving, detritus feeders with a tolerance for higher temperatures and lower oxygen levels.

Torrential mountain watercourses in Asia are home to the hillstream loaches in which both pectoral and pelvic fins have evolved into powerful sucking disks designed for clinging firmly to rocks while waters rush over them. Other hillstream inhabitants include members of the carp and catfish families. Among these, large sucking mouths and belly skin with folds and grooves are two adaptations that help survival in this extreme environment.

Regional richness This waterfall in Borneo (top left) is one of many freshwater habitats in the poorly studied Southeast Asian region, which is believed to support more freshwater fish species than anywhere else.

Travel requirements Many fishes enter and adapt remarkably well to extremely different habitats throughout their lives. Some trout (left), for example, regularly migrate between salt and freshwater, which requires radical adjustments in body chemistry.

Biodiversity The Amazon (right) has over 1,500 different fish species. These range from tiny neon tetras to the huge, ancient, air-breathing arapaima which can attain a length of 10 feet (3 m) and weight of 400 pounds (180 kg), making it one of the largest freshwater species.

Specialist habitats The blue waters in Xpuhil cave (left) are part of an interconnected river-and-lake system that flows through limestone channels and caverns beneath Mexico's Yucatan Peninsula. Fishes here cope with low light and high levels of dissolved calcium carbonate.

HOT SPRINGS AND CAVES

Desert springs, in which temperatures can rise above 100°F (38°C), are among the most extreme of habitats endured by freshwater fishes. North America's desert pupfishes and an African cichlid are among the few species that can tolerate such hot water. These fishes usually swim at the edges of springs where conditions are coolest.

Underground water in caves is another highly specialized habitat. Several unrelated families include cave-dwelling species, all of which show similar adaptations. They are typically blind and lack body pigment. Most also have sensory bumps and ridges on the skin which detect pressure waves generated by both predators and prey in the surrounding water.

Experiments have shown that the loss of eyes and pigment is not always an irreversible adaptation, but depends on whether individuals develop in light or dark conditions.

Sightless life The blind cavefish (Astyanax jordani) (below left) is known from just three caves in Mexico. It uses a highly developed sense of smell to find food.

Broad tolerance The spangled perch (Leiopotherapon unicolor) (below), Australia's most widespread native fish, tolerates fresh and saltwater, a pH range of 4–8.6, and temperatures from 39°F–111°F (4°–44°C). Few other fishes can survive such a range of physical and chemical conditions.

PONDS AND LAKES

Some 5 million lakes and many more ponds are scattered across the continents. The older these are the more diverse their fish life tends to be and the more endemic species they contain. The Great Lakes of tropical Africa provide a striking example. Lakes Malawi, Victoria, and Tanganyika support some 1,500 different species of cichlid that have evolved between 500,000 and 2 million years ago. This extraordinary level of biodiversity is thought to have developed from just a few original species in each lake.

Wetland wonder This area is a haven for one of South America's greatest concentrations of wildlife. In the rainy season, the Pantanal (right) spreads to create the world's largest freshwater habitat. Over 250 fish species have so far been identified there.

Ancient habitat Formed 20–25 million years ago and with a depth of 5,320 feet (1,637 m), Siberia's Lake Baikal is the oldest and deepest lake. It contains the world's largest volume of freshwater and supports more than 50 endemic fish species.

WORLD OCEAN

Seawater, in which more than half of all fish species occur, covers two-thirds of Earth and is normally divided into four large ocean basins —the Pacific, Atlantic, Indian, and Arctic—with smaller subdivisions and adjacent marginal seas.

The Pacific is the largest and deepest ocean. It covers about one-third of Earth's surface and has an average depth of 13,127 feet (4,001 m). At its widest point, the Pacific is 11,185 miles (18,000 km) across and reaches almost halfway around the planet. The Arctic is the smallest and shallowest of the oceans. Because all the great oceans are interconnected and exchange water, heat, and organisms, Earth's seawater is often referred to as the "world ocean."

When viewed from the South Pole, the Atlantic, Indian, and Pacific oceans appear as branches of a single system extending northward from the Southern Ocean and between the major landmasses. The Southern Ocean, which has its northern boundary fixed at 60°S, has been recognized only since the year 2000. The Artcic Ocean is almost land-locked by the Eurasian and North American landmasses, and much of it is covered by permanent ice.

The major oceans are subdivided into smaller seas, gulfs, and bays—such as the Mediterranean and Black seas— that are usually defined by obvious geographical boundaries. Other areas are marked by less obvious features. The Sargasso Sea in the Atlantic Ocean, for example, is characterized by the mass of seaweed it accumulates.

Boundaries between oceans are usually marked by the coastlines of the continental landmasses and their margins, or by major under-water features such as ocean ridges.

Not all seas are part of the world ocean. There are large, isolated bodies of saltwater, such as the Caspian and Salton seas, which are actually salt lakes.

Blue planet Liquid water covers 71 percent of Earth's surface. This, and the development of oceans, result from a combination of cosmic factors, particularly Earth's position in the solar system—far enough from the Sun so that the water is not vaporized, but close enough that most remains unfrozen.

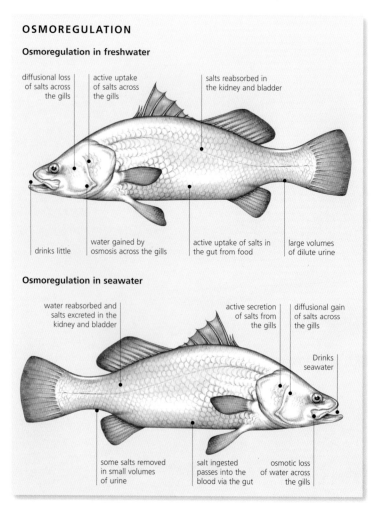

OSMOREGULATION

Osmoregulation in freshwater

diffusional loss of salts across the gills

active uptake of salts across the gills

salts reabsorbed in the kidney and bladder

drinks little

water gained by osmosis across the gills

active uptake of salts in the gut from food

large volumes of dilute urine

Osmoregulation in seawater

water reabsorbed and salts excreted in the kidney and bladder

active secretion of salts from the gills

diffusional gain of salts across the gills

Drinks seawater

some salts removed in small volumes of urine

salt ingested passes into the blood via the gut

osmotic loss of water across the gills

Water control Fishes are osmoregulators—they control their body fluid composition. Freshwater fishes gain water but lose salts. They respond by reabsorbing sodium and potassium from their urine, taking up salts from the water and producing large amounts of dilute urine to remove the excess water. In saltwater, fishes lose water and gain excess salts, which are pumped out by the gills and kidney. They produce concentrated urine.

WATER DISTRIBUTION

The oceans contain virtually all of the world's water. The remainder is distributed between groundwater, ice caps and glaciers, freshwater lakes and rivers, water in soil, and atmospheric water vapor. Only 1 percent of freshwater is accessible to living organisms and 1 percent of this is contained within living organisms.

oceans 97.5%

freshwater 2.5%

ice caps and glaciers 79%

accesible surface water 1%

groundwater 20%

water in lakes 52%

water in soil 38%

water vapor in atmosphere 8%

water in rivers 1%

water in living organisims 1%

Ocean riches Despite its enormous breadth and great depths, fish diversity in the Pacific tends to be greatest in its shallowest waters, along coastlines and around reefs. These locations are among the most productive marine areas. The Pacific's tropical coral reefs (right) are particularly diverse fish habitats.

OCEAN CURRENTS

There are two main strata of oceanic waters: a less dense, lighter, warmer surface layer that usually extends down to a depth of about 650 feet (200 m), sits on top of deeper, denser, colder water. In the narrow boundary between, known as the pycnocline, temperature and salinity change rapidly.

In the surface layer, water currents are divided into open-ocean and boundary currents. Boundary currents flow along the edge of continental margins.

Immediately north and south of the equator, open-ocean currents normally flow westward, driven by the trade winds. In the high latitudes of the Northern Hemisphere, there are eastward-flowing surface currents in the North Pacific and North Atlantic. These are matched in the Southern Hemisphere by the Antarctic circumpolar current. In each hemisphere, interactions between eastward and westward flows cause large circular gyres in subtropical latitudes.

Surface currents affect only the uppermost 10 percent of the oceans. Most water movements are considerably larger, deeper, and slower. The movement pattern of deep-ocean currents is known as thermohaline circulation. This is not affected by surface winds but driven by shifts in water density produced by changes in water temperature and salinity. The huge water masses involved in thermohaline circulation do not mix easily when they come in contact and can take centuries to complete their circulation around the world ocean.

The systematic mapping of the oceans' currents over the past 150 years has revealed not only how they are generated but also their importance in transferring heat around the planet which has a strong influence on climate.

Northward flow The Atlantic Ocean's Gulf Stream is a warm surface current that originates in the Gulf of Mexico and flows northward along North America's east coast at about 4 miles per hour (6.5 km/h). It transfers heat and salt toward the pole and warms the European continent. In this false-color satellite image (below left) warmer waters appear red and cooler waters are blue.

Coastal plumes Rivers can produce strong surface currents where they enter oceans. The eddies visible here (below), off the coast of Alaska and British Columbia, are created by nutrient-rich riverwater flowing into the Pacific, stimulating intense phytoplankton blooms detectable by satellite imaging.

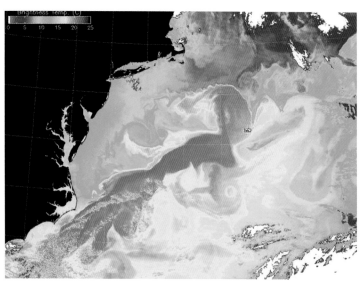

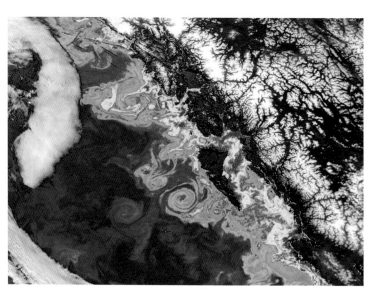

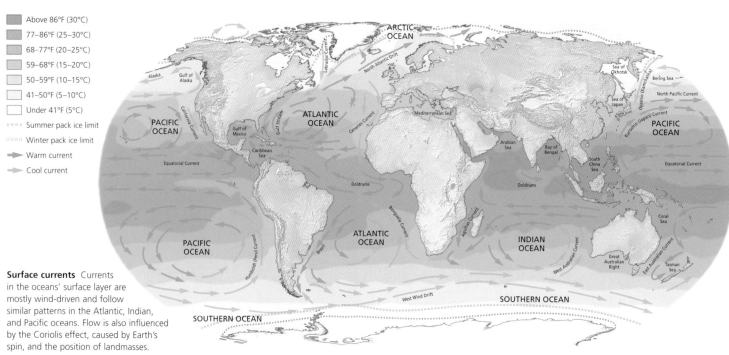

■	Above 86°F (30°C)
■	77–86°F (25–30°C)
■	68–77°F (20–25°C)
■	59–68°F (15–20°C)
□	50–59°F (10–15°C)
□	41–50°F (5–10°C)
□	Under 41°F (5°C)
∘∘∘∘	Summer pack ice limit
∘∘∘∘	Winter pack ice limit
→	Warm current
→	Cool current

Surface currents Currents in the oceans' surface layer are mostly wind-driven and follow similar patterns in the Atlantic, Indian, and Pacific oceans. Flow is also influenced by the Coriolis effect, caused by Earth's spin, and the position of landmasses.

SALINITY AND TIDES

Salinity affects many of the oceans' physical, chemical, and biological processes. Large amounts of dissolved salts in seawater even affect density: seawater is usually slightly heavier than freshwater of the same temperature.

The average salinity of the oceans is 35 (salinity is unitless) with most seawater covering the range from 33 to 37. The reading in any particular area will vary according to the balance between evaporation, which increases saltiness, and diluting rainfall. In partially enclosed seas, the salinity range is often more extreme. In the Red Sea, for example, evaporation produces salinities around 40 but in the Baltic Sea, rivers dilute surface salinity to 7.

Tides, like salinity, also have a profound influence on the behavior and distribution of fishes. Tides are generated by the interaction of the gravitational pulls of the Sun and Moon on Earth, causing the oceans to wash to-and-fro as if they were in a giant bowl. The basic celestial rhythm of the tides is made more complex by differences in water depth, the shape of adjacent land-masses, and the rotation of Earth.

Fish spread Ocean current patterns can have a great impact on fish distribution. The blackfin chromis (*Chromis atripectoralis*) (right), for example, is widespread on reefs throughout the Indo-Central Pacific. Its larvae circulate in the equatorial currents.

Deep-water coral reefs

Warm ocean

Warm-water coral reefs

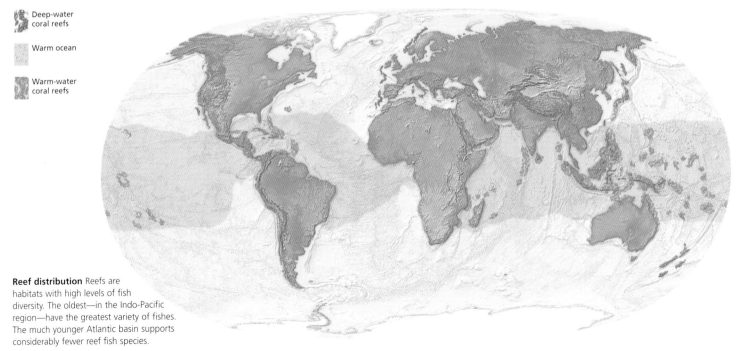

Reef distribution Reefs are habitats with high levels of fish diversity. The oldest—in the Indo-Pacific region—have the greatest variety of fishes. The much younger Atlantic basin supports considerably fewer reef fish species.

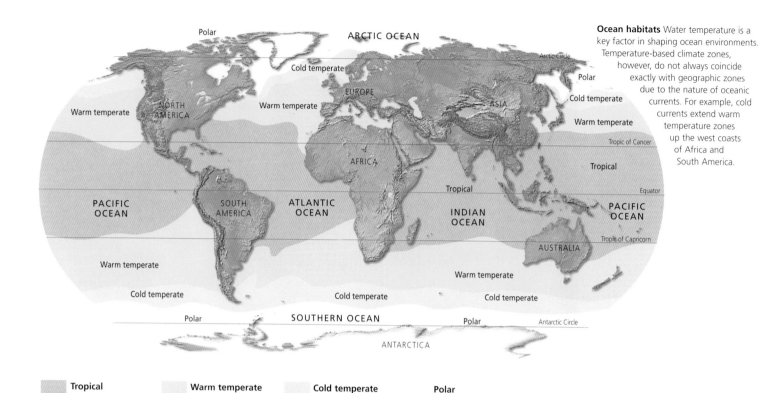

Polar

ARCTIC OCEAN

Cold temperate

Ocean habitats Water temperature is a key factor in shaping ocean environments. Temperature-based climate zones, however, do not always coincide exactly with geographic zones due to the nature of oceanic currents. For example, cold currents extend warm temperature zones up the west coasts of Africa and South America.

Polar

EUROPE

ASIA

Cold temperate

Warm temperate

NORTH AMERICA

Warm temperate

Arctic Circle

Warm temperate

Tropic of Cancer

AFRICA

Tropical

PACIFIC OCEAN

SOUTH AMERICA

ATLANTIC OCEAN

Tropical

Equator

INDIAN OCEAN

PACIFIC OCEAN

AUSTRALIA

Tropic of Capricorn

Warm temperate

Warm temperate

Cold temperate

Cold temperate

Cold temperate

Polar

SOUTHERN OCEAN

Polar

Antarctic Circle

ANTARCTICA

Tropical over 69°F / 20°C	**Warm temperate** 50–69°F / 10–20°C	**Cold temperate** 40–50°F / 5–10°C	**Polar** less than 40°F / 5°C

TROPICAL REGIONS

Most nutrient-rich waters in the tropics lie below 500 feet (150 m), with the highest nutrient concentrations between 1,640 and 3,280 feet (500–1,000 m). As a consequence, the growth of phytoplankton, which occurs only in the oceans' sunlit surface layer, is severely limited in the tropics by a lack of phosphates and nitrates.

There are, however, exceptions to this productivity shortfall. Equatorial upwellings bring nutrients to the surface in parts of the eastern Pacific and help support the anchovy fisheries off Peru. Coastal upwellings also bring valuable amounts of nutrients to tropical coastal regions, such as the northwest coasts of Morocco and southwest Africa.

Coral reefs are tropical sites where nutrients, missing in surrounding waters but supplied by coral polyps, slowly accumulate and are recycled.

Crystal waters Tropical surface waters contain less than 1 percent of the phytoplankton found in temperate areas. This is one reason why the ocean around the Whitsunday Islands (right), beside Australia's Great Barrier Reef, is so clear, affording near-perfect visibility for divers studying reef life.

POLAR REGIONS

Not surprisingly, exceptionally low temperature is a defining feature of ocean habitats in polar regions, where the coldest surface-water temperatures on the planet occur. These are typically below 38°F (3.5°C). While freshwater freezes at 32°F (0°C), the salt in seawater lowers its freezing point to 28°F (-2°C). Polar food chains are essentially marine. Many fish species living in these environments have special proteins, known as glycopeptides, in their blood which act in the same way antifreeze prevents the water in car radiators from freezing. Density increases as temperature decreases so that Antarctic bottom-water is the densest of any water in the world.

South Pole fishes More than 260 different species of fish occur in Antarctic waters (right), none of which form large schools. About 75 percent of these fish species belong to the suborder Notothenioidei (order Perciformes), which is found nowhere else in the world.

TEMPERATE REGIONS

Clearly defined seasons underpin very high productivity in temperate waters. Winter mixing ensures high nutrient levels in surface waters. When light levels rise in the spring, conditions are right for the growth and reproduction of phytoplankton. These tiny, free-floating plants multiply rapidly to create what is known as the Spring Bloom. Phytoplankton is the first level in most marine food chains and its explosion during spring in temperate waters creates similar bursts of productivity among the zooplankton that eats it, among the small fishes that eat the zooplankton, and right up to top order predators such as sharks and marine mammals.

Productive waters Temperate waters support more commercially valuable species, such as the swallowtail seaperch (*Anthias anthias*) (below), than the other regions. This is due to the annual Spring Bloom, which initiates growth up and throughout the food chain.

MANGROVES

Mangroves fortify shorelines in wave-protected river deltas, estuaries, and coasts in the tropics and subtropics. Most tropical coastlines are narrowly fringed with this valuable habitat that is dominated by salt-tolerant, shallow-rooted trees and shrubs. The tangled and extensive root systems of these plants stabilize sediment, capture vegetation, and create an environment in which decomposer organisms, ranging from bacteria to worms, are able to flourish. They also provide substrate and shelter for a wide range of larger invertebrate fauna, from mollusks to crustaceans.

Although large adult vertebrates rarely enter mangrove swamps, these habitats play a critical role as nurseries for a range of fishes at the larval and juvenile stages. There is also one group of fishes—the mudskippers—that thrive, as adults, in this inter-tidal world.

ESTUARIES

Estuaries are areas where the salty waters of the ocean meet the land and mix with the freshwater of river systems, giving rise to environments that support a highly specialized group of animals and plants. These organisms have to cope with perpetually changing temperature and salinity. Depending on what part of an estuary the organism lives in, it may also need to be able to endure alternating periods of exposure and submersion as these tides ebb and flow.

All animals need to maintain a balance of salts and water in their cells, but in an estuary this task is exacerbated by rapid changes in salinity that come with tidal movements. As a result, estuarine communities are comprised of very few species in comparison to adjacent freshwater or marine coastal habitats. Most estuarine species have marine origins.

Those species that can tolerate the extreme environmental conditions of estuaries benefit from reduced competition for space and food. They also have fewer predators to contend with.

Not all estuarine species are permanent residents. Many species of coastal fish, for example, use estuaries as nursery grounds because they are places where vulnerable young can grow and develop in relative safety, away from most predators. The abundance of invertebrates found in estuaries provides these young fishes with a reliable food supply.

Estuaries are also important gateways through which species that move between fresh and saltwater environments to complete their life-cycle must pass. Juvenile American and European eels born at sea, for example, pass through estuaries on their way upriver to freshwater streams and rivers where they will spend most of their adult lives.

Binding effect The trees and shrubs of mangroves (top left) are adapted to life in soft, waterlogged, often anoxic (oxygen-poor) mud that receives a daily inundation of saltwater. They are not so tolerant of temperature change, however, their optimum water temperature being about 66°F (19°C).

Fish nurseries An infrastructure of buttress roots and pneumatophores— erect roots exposed to air—helps make mangroves ideal nursery grounds for the larvae and juveniles of many fishes (left). Various commercial fish species are believed to either spend some time in mangroves or depend on food chains linked to mangroves.

Spawning ground Many estuaries in the United Kingdom, such as this one at the mouth of Devon's River Erme (top right), are entered by Atlantic salmon (*Salmo salar*) during upstream spawning migrations. These fish spend their early lives in freshwater, mature in the Atlantic Ocean, and then return to breed in the streams where they were born.

Drowned valleys Estuaries are defined by the geological processes that created them. These two estuaries, on the west coast of Africa (right), are examples of the best-known form—the coastal plain, or drowned river valley, estuary. These develop when existing river valleys are flooded by seawater, and sedimentation rates do not keep up with rising sea levels. They retain a typical V-shape in cross-section and do not have extensive mudflats.

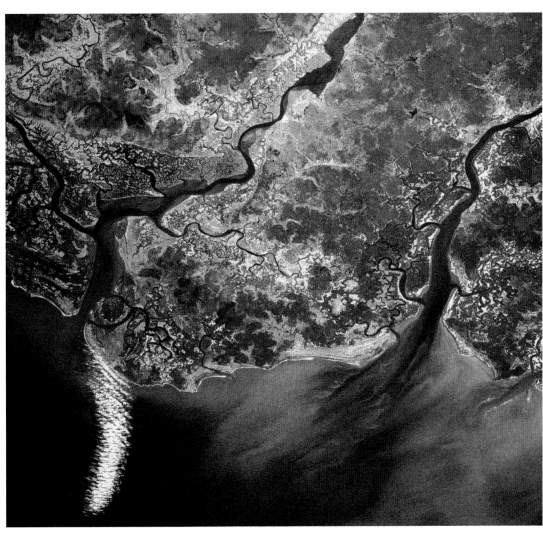

CORAL REEFS

The foundations of coral reefs are formed largely by the hard, external skeletons of small invertebrate animals called polyps, which are close relatives of sea anemones and jellyfishes. Not all coral polyps can form reefs. Those that can are classified as hard corals and live in interconnected colonies in which individuals extrude and sit within hard, protective "cups" of calcium carbonate. As these animals die they leave behind their skeletons and successive generations of polyps build on top of them.

Coral reefs have been growing like this in the world's oceans for more than 450 million years and many are massive structures. The diversity and abundance of organisms they support rivals that of tropical rain forests. Many of the fishes and invertebrates that live among coral reefs are important not only as part of their marine ecosystem, but also as a vital source of food for human consumption.

Almost all reef-building corals are extremely temperature sensitive. They can grow only where the water temperature remains around 70°F (21°C). As a result, coral reefs are restricted to tropical waters—

from about 30°S to 32°N. They are never found on the westward-facing coast of landmasses, as these are areas of upwelling that bring cold, deep water to the surface, lowering the water temperature.

High formation The biggest reef structure and largest biological entity on the planet is the Great Barrier Reef (above). It stretches for about 1,560 miles (2,500 km) along the north-eastern coast of Queensland, Australia, and is an astounding 95 miles (152 km) at its widest point. It is not a single, continuous structure, but comprises thousands of interlinked segments that are oldest and thickest at the northern end.

Serious competitors Reef fishes face intense competition for food, space, and mates (right). This, combined with the need to avoid and fend off predators, has produced fish communities characterized by bright colors, spines, camouflage, venoms, and a wide range of lifestyles.

Fringe benefit Bora Bora (far right), in Tahiti, was once a volcano that emerged from the ocean to form an island. It is edged by a fringing reef that grew upward from the sides of the volcano as it slowly subsided into the sea. As its central remnant subsides further, the fringing coral will continue growing to eventually encircle Bora Bora and create an atoll.

Sex-change experts Hermaphroditism is more common among fishes that live around coral reefs than those that live in other marine environments. These sea goldies (*Pseudanthias squamipinnis*) (left), for example, form aggregations comprised of territorial males responsible for small harems of females. When a male dies, it is replaced by a dominant female that has undergone a sex change.

Reef regulars The cardinalfish family (Apogonidae) includes close to 200 species of mostly small, brightly colored warm water fishes, such as these (below), which are primarily associated with coral reefs. Like the vast majority of coral reef fishes, they belong to the perch order, Perciformes.

REEF LIFE

Tropical marine inshore habitats boast more fish species than anywhere else in the oceans, with coral reefs epitomizing species richness in these coastal areas. More than 4,000 different species of fish have been documented so far in the tropical reef environment. Many families, such as the gobies, wrasses, damselfishes, groupers, blennies, and butterflyfishes, have numerous species living in close proximity to each other, each specialized for a particular microhabitat.

The reason there is such a high diversity of fishes around coral reefs is partly because of their complexity and the many different options they provide for fishes to feed, live, and reproduce. Scientists believe the long period of time that reefs have been providing habitats for fishes is probably also significant. The modern coral reef environment has existed for some 50 million years, since the early Tertiary.

Diversity of fish species around coral reefs has also been enhanced by the changing environmental pressures created by repeated rises and falls in sea level associated with natural global warming and cooling, and resultant ice cap fluctuations.

Despite the species diversity, most reef fish families belong to just a single order—Perciformes—the perches. This group is characterized by a highly protrusible mouth and anteriorly placed pelvic fins. Both attributes enable a specialized type of feeding behavior that involves hovering in place while picking at small individual food items. Such coral reef fishes as damselfishes, butterflyfishes, and some groupers feed in this way.

FROM SHALLOWS TO OPEN OCEAN

Along with coral reefs, other shallow marine habitats include surf beaches, rocky headlands, and the waters of the continental shelf down to about 650 feet (200 m). Most of the best-known marine fishes live in these shallow-water environments, from the gobies and blennies, common in rocky tidepools, to the many and varied white-fleshed fish species found in the fish markets of the world.

The surface waters of the open ocean create a more specialized environment where some of the more familiar fishes live. Mako and blue sharks, tunas and mackerels, and billfishes, such as marlin and swordfish, cruise these waters. They are all fast swimming and well muscled, important adaptations to an environment in which there is nowhere to hide.

A further adaptation in some of the oceanic tunas and lamnid sharks, such as the great white and mako, is an arrangement of the blood vessels in the muscles in what is termed a counter-current heat exchange system. This allows these fishes to retain metabolic heat and maintain their body temperature significantly higher than the surrounding water. The advantage of this is that it gives them a high degree of activity and

lightning-sharp reflexes across a wide range of temperatures. All other fishes are, like amphibians and reptiles, poikilotherms. They take on the temperature of their environment. This is unlike birds and mammals, which can maintain a constant body temperature.

Although oceanic fishes have no place to hide, most species have protective coloration—blue or dark gray on top and white or silvery underneath—to make them inconspicuous to potential predators.

Other typical high-seas fishes include the oarfishes and their relatives, and the huge ocean sunfishes. Some smaller fishes, such as the juveniles of some jacks and trevallies and the man-of-war fishes, have found an ingenious place to hide in the open ocean. They swim among the tentacles of jellyfishes where they are protected by stinging cells. Like the anemone fishes that live on coral reefs, they are unharmed by the lethal weapons of their hosts.

Varied diet Black triggerfish (*Melichthys niger*) (left) commonly occur in large feeding aggregations in the shallows around oceanic islands where they feed on zooplankton, algae, and occasionally phytoplankton. They have also been observed in association with dolphins, feeding on their faeces and vomit.

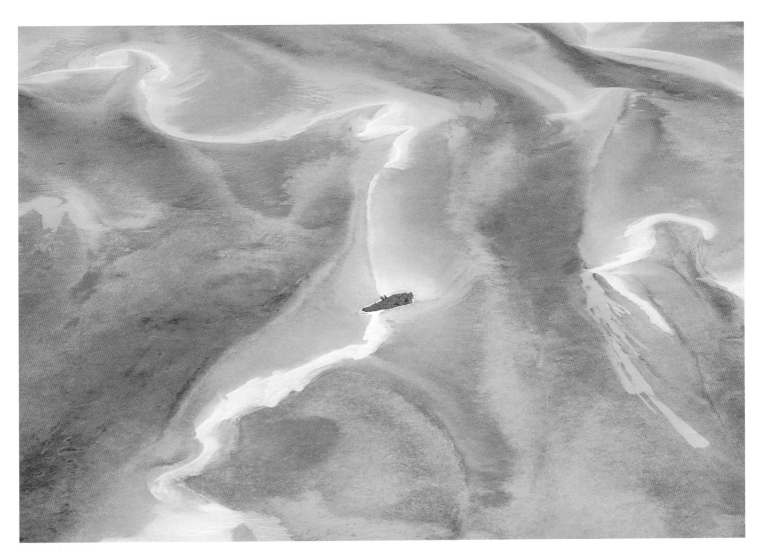

Shifting sands The persistent ebb
and flow of tides, constant surging by
currents, and pounding by waves, make
sandbars (above) unstable shallow-water
environments that can appear, disappear,
and reappear on a daily basis. They are,
nevertheless, well exploited by fish species,
many of which have flattened body shapes
and are patterned like grains of sand.

Camouflage colors Counter-shading,
as seen on this Caribbean reef shark
(*Carcharhinus perezi*) (left) is common
among fishes inhabiting surface waters,
in both the open ocean and shallower
marine environments. Dark dorsal coloration
when viewed from above, blends into the
dark blue of the ocean's depths. A pale
underbelly disappears into sunlit waters
when viewed from below.

Common fishes Maiden gobies
(*Valenciennea puellaris*) (right), like most
gobies, are usually found in pairs. With
more than 2,000 species, the goby family
(Gobiidae) is the largest marine fish family.
All but a few live just above, and often in,
the sediment of inshore shallow waters.

POLAR SEAS

Freezing waters around the Antarctic continent support over 260 fish species. Five families dominate, collectively called the notothenioids. Among these are the Antarctic dragonfishes and icefishes. Adaptations include glycoprotein antifreezes in the blood of some. At such low temperatures, water and body fluids contain so much oxygen that icefishes have colorless blood, having lost the need for oxygen-carrying hemoglobin.

Poles apart The Arctic ice sheet has a central permanently frozen portion. During the winter months, this doubles in area to approximately 5.4 million square miles (14 million km²). In the Antarctic, there is a constant band of drifting sea ice around the continent, with its northern limit in the South Atlantic pack ice that extends to 52°S. Although the South Pole is located on the Antarctic landmass, the North Pole lies in the Arctic Ocean, in a region of sea ice just 6½ feet (2 m) thick in summer.

Unique adaptation Antarctic crocodile icefishes, such as the blackfin icefish (*Chaenocephalus aceratus*) (below), are the only vertebrates that do not have hemoglobin in their blood. This is an adaptation to life in the extreme cold, where most other fishes could not survive.

IN DEEP WATER

The average depth of the ocean basins is 12,430 feet (3,790 m). This figure, however, masks the great variation between and within the five oceans. The Arctic Ocean is by far the shallowest, with less than half the average depth of the others. In terms of both its average depth and deepest point—the Mariana Trench at 36,201 feet (11,034 m)—the Pacific is the deepest of the oceans.

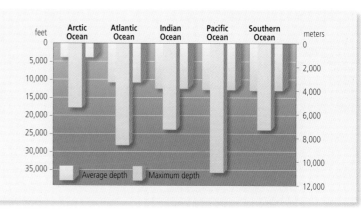

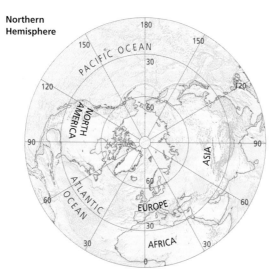

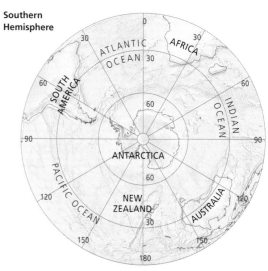

DEEP SEA

Most deep-sea fishes belong to primitive groups, such as the sharks, eels, and other less advanced bony-fish families. The environment is harsh, with low temperatures, no light, and very little food. The latter two features appear to have driven most of the striking adaptations of deep-sea fishes. Some of these include the development of light organs, for both capturing prey and avoiding predators, as well as the development of a large lateral line system to detect pressure waves from swimming animals, which compensates for the loss of vision.

Breaking ice Antarctic fishes are well adapted to the extremely low temperatures of McMurdo Sound (right), where seawater in winter has a temperature of 28°F (–2°C). In spring, as the ice breaks, the water temperature may rise and cause some fishes to die of heat if it reaches 43°F (6°C).

Frozen workplace Biological richness in the Ross Sea (below) is due to a productive water column with upwellings and cold-water currents that release nutrients. These nutrients cause plankton to bloom and form the base of the Antarctic food chain. Diverse marine species feed on plankton, and their predators, in turn, feed on them.

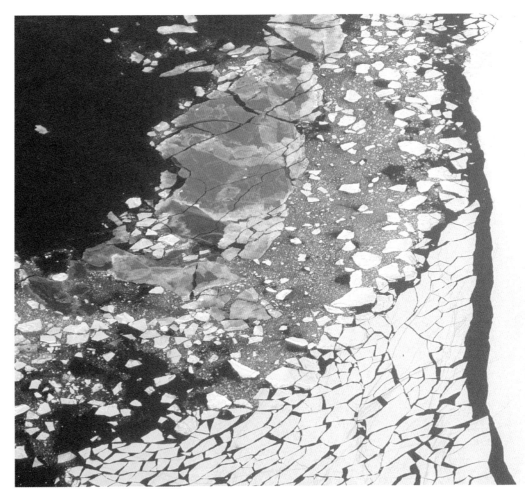

DEEP-SEA LIFE

The deep sea begins at about 660 feet (200 m), where the last vestiges of surface light peter out. Unlike shallower waters, temperatures are relatively constant, varying little from an average of 39°F (4°C). Immense pressure is another feature. Most deep-sea fishes are at the same pressure as their surroundings, so do not have to be physically resistant to the force around them. However, fishes living below 5,000 feet (1,500 m) have subtle changes in cell structure and biochemistry to cope with high pressure.

1. Seaweeds and sea-grasses grow only to a depth of 100 feet (30 m).

2. Butterflyfishes feed on coral polyps at depths above 80 feet (25 m).

3. Anchovy are not found below 980 feet (300 m). They prefer the surface layers that contain their food—plankton and tiny crustaceans drifting in waters penetrated by sunlight.

4. Bonito are streamlined, fast-swimming predatory fishes found no deeper than 660 feet (200 m).

5. Marlin, among the fastest of the open-ocean fishes, are found down to 3,000 feet (915 m).

6. Jellyfishes float in surface waters, grazing on zooplankton and small fishes.

7. Requiem sharks, which prey on large fishes, turtles, and sea mammals, have been recorded down to depths of 1,150 feet (350 m).

8. Dolphins hunt small fishes, squid, and crustaceans, and are found between the surface and 590 feet (180 m).

9. Octopuses are bottom-dwelling stealth predators. Most are found in coastal surface waters but a few species occur down to 3,300 feet (1,000 m).

10. Sperm whales can dive to 9,850 feet (3,000 m) pursuing large, deep-sea squid, which are among their preferred foods.

11. Lanternfishes live between 980 and 3,940 feet (300–1,200 m) by day but migrate upward at night to feed in shallower, more productive waters.

12. Squid are found from surface waters to the depths of the abyss.

13. Hatchetfishes live down to a depth of 5,000 feet (1,500 m). They migrate upward at night to feed on zooplankton in surface layers.

14. Deep-sea rays feed on small mollusks, worms, and crustaceans on the sea floor. They are found down to a depth of 9,000 feet (2,750 m).

15. Viperfishes are found down to 14,440 feet (4,400 m). They are ambush predators that lunge at passing prey.

16. Grenadiers and rattails are scavengers that will feed on dead as well as live animals. They live between 660 and 6,600 feet (200–2,010 m) down.

17. Deep-sea eels are active predators and scavengers found down to a depth of 11,500 feet (3,500 m).

18. Anglerfishes occur at a wide range of depths, from shallow water down to the bathypelagic zone. The deepest dwellers are found at 6,560 feet (2,000 m).

19. Tripodfishes, found at depths between 820 and 18,700 feet (250–5,700 m), are ambush predators able to detect the distant movements of small fishes and crustaceans.

20. Deep-sea isopods are found at all ocean depths. Their greatest diversity, however, occurs between 3,300 and 16,400 feet (1,000-5,000 m).

21. The relative abundances of animals change with depth. The width of the distribution plot is proportional to the number of animals at a given depth.

MIGRATION AND LARVAE

Diadromous fishes move between freshwater and seawater. Most fishes in the salmon family, for example, are born in freshwater, migrate to the ocean, and then return to freshwater to spawn. This type of freshwater-ocean-freshwater migration is known as anadromy. The opposite type of migraton—catadromy—is typical of freshwater eels which spawn at sea.

Diadromous fishes undergo complex physiological changes as they migrate through estuaries. The demands of this process may explain why many with this lifestyle only spawn once. It may also be why there are so few diadromous species.

Migrations also take place within one major habitat and are often undertaken by mature adults, traveling to breed. This type of migration is mostly associated with herring and cod species in the North Sea.

CHANGING PATTERNS
Zebra shark pups resemble adults in body shape and movement but differ in two respects: size and coloration. At birth, their dark brown skin is broken by thick, yellow, zebra-like stripes. As they mature, the background coloration becomes a lighter yellow-brown and the stripes are replaced by dark, leopard-like spots.

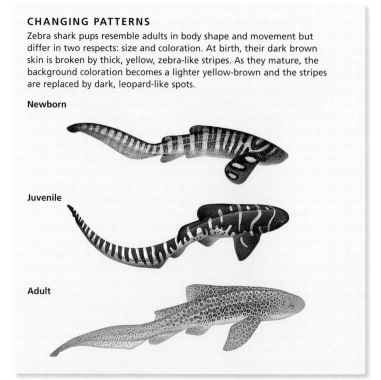

Newborn

Juvenile

Adult

Migration allows fishes to exploit different habitats and resources during different periods of their lives. In many species, larvae and adults also exploit different habitats to ensure they do not compete for resources. In most of these species, this has meant the developing larvae look extremely different from their parents. Most fish larvae, even those of bottom-dwelling adults, are pelagic, floating in surface currents where food is most abundant.

Bubble baby The larvae of many deep-sea anglerfishes (below) float in a balloon-like envelope of inflated skin. These tiny juveniles develop near the ocean's surface and the balloon may help maintain neutral buoyancy so they can remain suspended in waters that are considerably shallower than those where their parents dwell.

Migrating school Herrings (right) spend their adult lives in large schools. They usually breed seasonally or in seasonal peaks throughout the year, often after mass migrations to particular spawning grounds. Some species migrate upriver to spawn in freshwater.

COLORATION AND CAMOUFLAGE

Body pigment has several functions in fishes. It protects the internal organs of shallow-water fishes from sunlight, and is particularly noticeable over the brain of larval fishes. In contrast, the skin of fishes dwelling in deep, dark waters is often unpigmented.

Patterns and colors enable members of the same species to recognize one another and will often become brighter during the breeding season. They can also be important in camouflage and may help a fish blend into the background to avoid the attentions of predators. Some species, in particular the flatfishes, can quickly change their patterns to match that of the bottom sediment on which they are lying.

One of the most noticeable parts of a fish is its black eye, so many species have a dark line running through the eye to camouflage this feature. Others have false eyespots on the tail or back of the fins which can trick predators into striking away from the head.

Transparency tricks The color and texture of the fan coral (top right) can be seen clearly through the almost transparent body of this goby. Transparency is a simple and efficient means of camouflage. It allows this goby to travel over different corals and still be undetected by predators.

Bottom dweller The southern stingray (*Dasyatis americana*) (center right) is a nocturnal predator that lives on sandy and muddy sediments. During the day, it maintains a low profile by lying still on the ocean bottom and sometimes even burying itself in sediment, with only its eyes exposed.

Hidden talents Excellent camouflage is essential for anglerfishes (bottom right), of which there are more than 300 species occurring in a wide range of marine temperate and tropical environments. Without it, their sit-and-wait style of predation and the lures that extend from the head to entice prey close would not work.

Exquisite mimicry Protection from predators often involves blending into the background. The Amazon leaf-fish (*Monocirrhus polyacanthus*) (left) mimics the shape and color of dead leaves that litter the beds of the rivers and streams in which it dwells. This hides it not only from predators but also from prey, which it will strike at as it passes nearby.

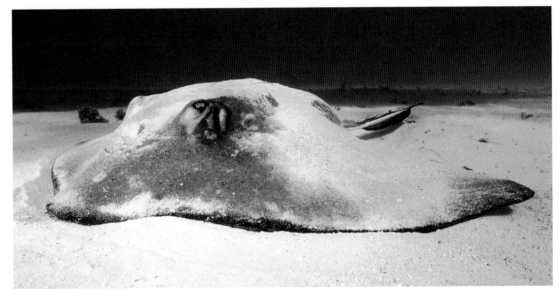

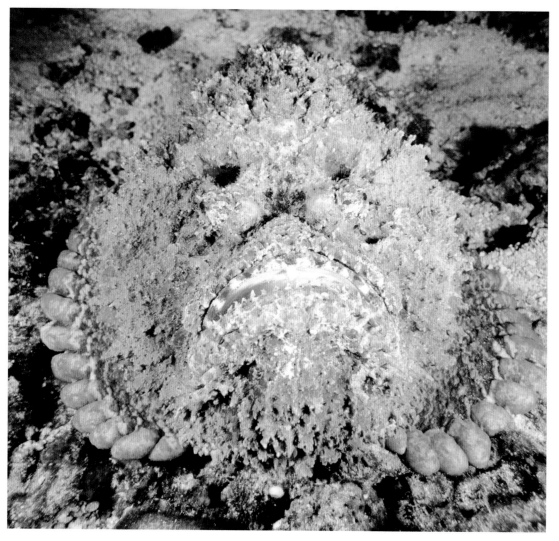

LUMINESCENCE

Living light, known as bioluminescence, takes the place of color in fishes in the dark environment of the deep sea. Surprisingly, it is also present in a number of shallow-water marine forms such as the flashlight fishes, pineapple fishes, ponyfishes, as well as some cardinalfishes and bullseyes. Fishes in these families have a relatively large light organ. In species such as the flashlight and pineapple fishes it is situated externally, on the head. In the others, it is associated with a colony of light-producing bacteria located internally, in the digestive tract.

A small number of shallow-water species, including an anchovy, a croaker, and some midshipmen, have numerous external light-producing organs—known as photophores—in the skin. This is more typical of deep-sea species, particularly those of the twilight zone, such as the aptly named lanternfishes and lightfishes.

Bioluminescence has several functions. In the twilight zone—where the last vestiges of light from the surface fade away—it can operate as a form of camouflage. Fishes will emit light that matches the intensity of the sunlight traces filtering down from above. This obscures their silhouette when viewed by potential predators from below.

Most lanternfishes have distinct patterns of light organs that may be used in recognition for courtship or schooling. The elaborate luminous filaments on the heads of anglerfishes and the chins of dragonfishes lure their prey, like moths to a flame, to within reach of their enormous mouths.

Light show The pineconefish (*Monocentris japonica*) (above left) lives in caves or under ledges and has a light-producing lure, containing bioluminescent bacteria, on the tip of its lower jaw. The spot is orange by day and emits blue-green light at night to attract zooplankton.

Poison fins Among the venomous fishes, the stonefishes, such as this one (*Synanceia* sp) (left), are the most deadly to humans. Their venom glands are located at the base of the fin spines, which have grooves on each side with a duct running to the tip.

Bright dining Large light organs near the eyes are thought to help some fishes, such as this flashlight fish (*Photoblepharon steinitzi*) (right), see their food better.

LIGHTSWITCH

To hide from predators, the flash-light fish covers its light organ with a flap of skin covered with a layer of black pigment cells (melanophores) that acts like a shutter.

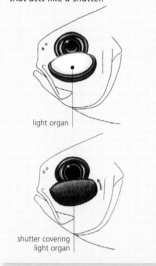

light organ

shutter covering light organ

VENOM AND POISON

One of the most effective ways to discourage predators is to inject them with painful venom. Many unrelated fishes have evolved protective devices to do this, the most effective involving a venom gland at the base of a grooved fin spine. Such venom spines occur in at least 40 different groups, including some sharks, stingrays, chimaeras, catfishes, toadfishes, scorpionfishes, weeverfishes, rabbitfishes, and stargazers.

Some pufferfishes, especially those in the Indo-Pacific region, have an extremely potent poison, known as tetrodotoxin, concentrated in the liver, ovaries, and gut. The poison may also lace the skin and even the blood. It is a powerful neurotoxin, considerably stronger than cyanide, known to cause rapid death in humans.

INSIDE A PHOTOPHORE

Light is produced without heat inside fish photophores when luciferin—one of a group of substances found in bioluminescent species—is broken down inside the cell by the enzyme luciferase. The light is guided in the lantern toward the lens where it is focused into a forward-pointing beam. Pigment surrounds most of the photophore to prevent illumination of surrounding tissues.

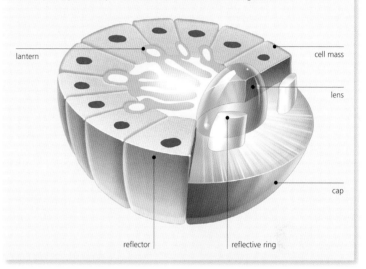

lantern

cell mass

lens

cap

reflector

reflective ring

FISHES IN DANGER

Early this century, a major international report warned that 90 percent of all large fishes, both bottom-dwelling and open-ocean species, had disappeared from the oceans. It was a potent reminder that fishes are under pressure right around the planet, with threatened species now listed from every continent. Declines are occurring in most habitats—from rivers, lakes, and caves, to estuaries, mangroves, coral reefs, and the deep sea. Even in the forests, fishes are at risk because the loss of forest cover affects the amount of water available in the area.

The Cyprinidae—the carps and their relatives—contains at least 160 species at risk, more than any other family. The Cichlidae follows with about 90 species, of which more than 85 percent are found only in mainland Africa. All 27 members of the sturgeon and paddlefish order, Acipenseriformes, are threatened, including 17 that are on the critically endangered and endangered lists.

RESTRICTED RANGES

Many fish species have naturally narrow distribution ranges, which makes them particularly sensitive to habitat change and overexploitation. Restricted habitats include North America's Great Lakes, the Valley of Mexico, the cenotes (sinkholes) of southern Mexico, and East Africa's Rift Lakes—including Malawi, Victoria, and Tanganyika. Enclosed basins are also often rich in endemic species, especially in isolated environments such as desert pools.

The cichlids and some pupfishes are examples of fishes that have adapted to limited environments. Like Darwin's famous finches in the Galápagos Islands, they have evolved a remarkable range of adaptations during a short passage of geological time, including the development of specialized feeding strategies.

The Devil's Hole pupfish is one of the most extreme examples of a species with a restricted habitat. The entire population is found on a limestone shelf, measuring just 10 by 18 feet (3 by 5.5 m), that overhangs the Devil's Hole pool in the United States.

In Africa's Lake Victoria, haplochromine cichlid species can occupy small, distinctive niches despite the great size of the lake.

The asprete *Romanichthys valsanicola,* found only in the upper tributaries of the River Arges (Danube Basin), is believed to be the most threatened fish in Europe.

FOREST FISHES

Deforestation is a practice that is usually highlighted in relation to large-scale losses of terrestrial vertebrate and invertebrate species. But, in the tropical rain forests of the Amazon, Malaysia, and Indonesia, there are fishes that eat fruits, seeds, and leaves. Because of this, they are particularly vulnerable to the extensive clearing of forests—by logging industries and for both urban and agricultural development —underway in these nations. Between 1970 and 1975, for example, the fish catch in the rivers of the Amazon alone declined by a massive 25 percent. This decline was a direct result of deforestation around fish breeding grounds. Already, several commercial species that are found in the Amazon Basin are at risk from overexploitation and habitat destruction.

Disappearing shark The appearance of the sand tiger shark (*Carcharias taurus*) (left) belies a gentle nature but has seen it hunted almost to extinction by humans. Females produce only two pups per pregnancy which makes the species' road back from the brink particularly difficult.

Fish loss The desert pupfish (*Cyprinodon macularius*) (below left), found in streams in Mexico and Colorado, United States, was abundant during the first half of last century. Since the 1960s, predation by introduced fishes has decimated its numbers so that it is now endangered.

Vulnerable distributions Most cichlids, such as these (below right), gathering to gulp air in a disappearing dry-season pond in the Pantanal wetlands, Brazil, have narrow distributions. This makes them susceptible to habitat destruction, pollution, and overharvesting.

Overexploited species The dusky grouper (*Epinephelus marginatus*) (above) is a marine species found around reefs in African, European, and South American waters. Overfishing across its range has led to such a decline in its numbers that it is now endangered.

HABITAT CHANGE

Although natural environmental changes can lead to extinctions or significant declines of fish species, habitat change wrought by humans is now threatening an unprecedented number of species worldwide. In fact, habitat alteration has become one of the main causes of fish losses. It is believed that virtually all fish habitats, even those in remote locations, have been affected by one or more of the following impacts: urban development, pollution, water extraction or diversion, dam construction (which blocks fish migration paths), canalization of rivers and streams, international trade (which includes cyanide fishing and dynamiting of coral reefs for the aquarium trade), and overexploitation.

Pollution, in particular, is affecting a rising number of habitats. The Great Lakes of North America, which comprise one of the world's largest freshwater systems, illustrate the terrible impacts of industrial, agricultural, and urban pollution. Together with urban development and habitat alteration, this pollution has had a drastic effect on the water quality and productivity of the lakes. Resident fishes such as the lake sturgeon and the shortjaw cisco are just two of many species that have been adversely affected.

Rivers that flow through several countries are often subjected to serious impacts along their courses. Europe's Danube, for example, passes through 12 countries with a combined population of more than 70 million. It has been polluted by more than 1,700 industries, and subjected to overfishing, water extraction, and damming. Pollution has been worsened by the low water levels and it is the area of its delta, in Romania, where the effects are most dramatic. Similarly, pollution and water extraction in the Rio Colorado, which flows through the United States and Mexico, are critically endangering the totoaba (*Totoaba macdonaldi*).

INTRODUCED FISHES

Many fishes worldwide are facing serious threats from introduced species. The impacts can be devastating, particularly in enclosed or specialized habitats. Introduced species compete with native fishes for food and living space, as well as preying on them. They can even breed with native fishes, and place them at further risk by changing their genetic make-up.

Gambusia, known commonly as the mosquitofish, has been among the most destructive of introduced species. They are native to the southern and eastern United States, but have been introduced to so many countries around the world, mainly in an attempt to control mosquitoes, that they now have one of the widest distributions of all freshwater fishes. As it turns out, these tiny, highly aggressive fishes are not particularly efficient at consuming mosquito larvae. They are considered to be serious pests in many countries.

Environmental change Scenes such as this dried riverbed (above) are normal for Death Valley, in California, United States, one of the driest and hottest places on Earth. But it is predicted that such scenes could become commonplace across the globe due to the long-term impact of climate change and global warming. High levels of water extraction from rivers for urban, industrial, and agricultural uses intensify such problems.

Riverine death Flowing east to west through the French capital, the River Seine has contributed to the life and soul of Paris for centuries, its beauty captured in great paintings and fine novels. Today, (above right), it is more often a metaphor for environmental vandalism.

Devastating impact In a rare case of what is often referred to as explosive evolution and speciation, more than 400 unique cichlid fish species evolved in less than 200,000 years in Africa's Lake Victoria. About five decades ago the Nile perch (right) was introduced to the lake. Today, little more than a handful of Lake Victoria's hundreds of endemic species survive due to a range of damaging environmental impacts wreaked by the perch.

INTERNATIONAL TRADE

Humans have been exploiting fishes for millennia, but never with the same sort of effectiveness as we do now. Many fishes are commercially exploited for food, for either animal or human consumption. Sturgeons and paddlefishes are heavily exploited for caviar.

Although commercial fisheries certainly dominate the exploitation of wild fish stocks, the growing trade in tropical aquarium fishes has become an important source of income for local populations in many parts of the developing world. As many as 800 species are now listed as "commonly available" in the aquarium trade. Although a large part of the market is already supplied by farm-bred freshwater species, with 90 percent said to be captive-bred, a considerable portion is still supplied by wild-caught specimens from Africa and South America. Some uncommonly attractive varieties of fishes can command huge prices. An individual Asian bonytongue, for example, can fetch more than $US18,000.

In contrast, roughly 90 percent of the marine species in the trade are believed to be taken directly from the wild in countries such as the Philippines, Singapore, and Indonesia. In the Philippines alone, at least 386 species of coral reef fishes, belonging to 79 families, are used in the aquarium trade. They supply up to 80 percent of the market.

Trade adversely affects wild populations in two ways. Non-native escapees from fish farms can compete with or prey on native species, while introducing parasites and disease at the same time. The international trade in marine fishes also has a deleterious impact by directly reducing wild stocks of native species.

Traditional Chinese medicine is another market that has placed an increased pressure on certain fishes. Demand for seahorses and pipefishes, in particular, has resulted in the listing of 37 species in threatened categories.

Legal slaughter Although the southern blue fin tuna (right) is endangered, it is legally fished by several countries. Demand comes particularly from Japan and the high prices paid for fish in good condition ensure the continuation of tuna fishing.

Destructive practice One of the biggest threats to shark populations has been finning, where fins are removed to supply a market for shark-fin soup and other culinary delicacies. The trade is largely unregulated, illegal, and widely condemned, but Asia's marketplaces, such as this one in Singapore (above) continue to sell shark fins.

Ocean dumping Habitat loss and degradation are major threats to endangered fishes. Discarded plastic items, such as these dumped at the bottom of the Mediterranean Sea (top right), pollute and damage marine environments. Such garbage will take many centuries to break down, ensuring that its impact continues beyond current generations.

Useful rubbish Artificial reefs (bottom right) are a positive use for large machinery and other garbage that would otherwise be hard to dispose of. Most importantly, they increase habitat for fishes. They also help protect fish stocks and the seabed from trawling and dredging. Artificial reefs can be made from natural rocks, concrete blocks, old ships, and even aircraft.

FISH CONSERVATION

At least 93 species from 11 countries have gone extinct in modern times and the number threatened increases annually. Long-term public awareness programs, combined with genuine commitment to conserve species, are needed to reverse this trend.

Many countries already provide protective legislation for fishes but few enforce them. Unique environments, such as Europe's Danube delta and the Amazon Basin are the focus of international conservation efforts. But such programs may be too late for many species inhabiting systems such as the Mekong River Basin.

Conservation needs often differ between species. A combination of habitat preservation and management, pollution control, elimination of introduced species, bans on poaching and overfishing, and stricter trade controls, would help ensure the survival of species at risk.

KINDS
OF FISHES

JAWLESS FISHES

SUPERCLASS Agnatha
CLASSES 2
ORDERS 2
FAMILIES 2
SPECIES 105

These were the first fishes and most became extinct by about 360 million years ago. The two surviving groups—hagfishes and lampreys—are probably only distantly related to each other. They comprise 105 species. All lack scales and jaws and have cartilaginous skeletons. True fins are either absent or poorly developed. Hagfishes are eel-like in appearance and produce copious quantities of mucus from slime glands along the length of the body, possibly for defensive reasons. These scavengers of dead and dying fishes and invertebrates have photoreceptors but do not have true eyes or a larval phase. Lampreys have functional eyes and a long larval phase. Larval lampreys are filter feeders but most adults are external parasites on other fishes.

Widespread curiosities Hagfishes and lampreys are found in temperate waters of the Northern and Southern hemispheres, and in cool, deep waters in parts of the tropics. Although lampreys are found in both fresh and saltwater, hagfishes are exclusively marine. Larval lampreys burrow into soft stream and river substrates where they feed by filtering algae, detritus, and microorganisms from the water.

Serious suckers Lampreys parasitize other fishes by attaching to their bodies with a toothed oral disk (right). They mainly live on their host's body fluids but sometimes also consume pieces of flesh and even internal body organs. They often cause the death of their hosts.

Mouth and gills To function as a sucker, the mouth is separated from the gills (below) and is not normally used to draw water into the gills. Instead, lampreys use their mouths to cling to large stones and rocks in fast-flowing streams.

CONSERVATION WATCH

Lamprey losses The IUCN Red List records that the Lombardy brook lamprey (*Lethenteron zanandreai*) is endangered and the Greek brook lamprey (*Eudontomyzon hellenicus*) and non-parasitic lamprey (*Mordacia praecox*) are vulnerable. Habitat destruction is a major threat.

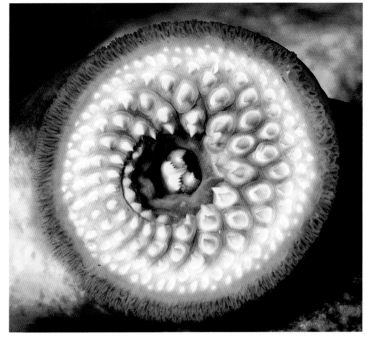

REPRODUCTION

Hagfish reproduction remains largely a mystery. These fishes begin life as hermaphrodites, later becoming either female or male. They are thought to spawn repeatedly during their lives, each time producing a small number of large eggs—about 1 inch (2.5 cm) long—in toughened cases. They do not have a free-living larval phase. The young within the egg cases have sufficient nourishment from the yolk to emerge as miniature adults.

Lampreys only spawn once, producing large numbers of much smaller eggs before dying. The eggs are laid in a nest pit excavated in streambeds. They spend their early years as filter-feeding larvae called ammocoetes. Metamorphosis into young adults usually occurs when they are 3–6½ inches (7.5–16.5 cm) long and takes 3–6 months.

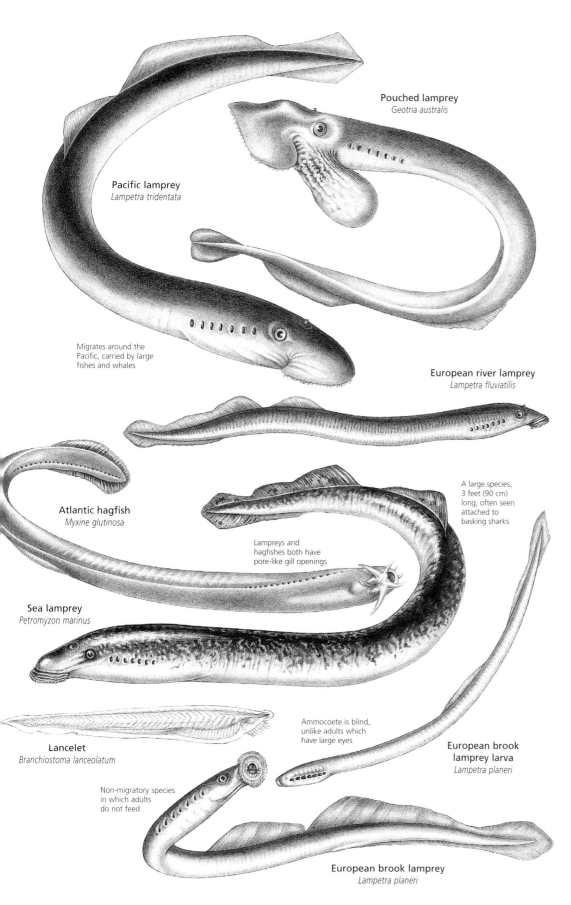

Pouched lamprey
Geotria australis

Pacific lamprey
Lampetra tridentata

Migrates around the
Pacific, carried by large
fishes and whales

European river lamprey
Lampetra fluviatilis

Atlantic hagfish
Myxine glutinosa

A large species,
3 feet (90 cm)
long, often seen
attached to
basking sharks

Lampreys and
hagfishes both have
pore-like gill openings

Sea lamprey
Petromyzon marinus

Lancelet
Branchiostoma lanceolatum

Ammocoete is blind,
unlike adults which
have large eyes

European brook
lamprey larva
Lampetra planeri

Non-migratory species
in which adults
do not feed

European brook lamprey
Lampetra planeri

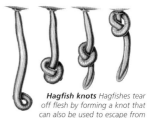

FACT FILE

Pacific lamprey This lamprey spawns
in freshwater and adults die shortly
afterward. The ammocoete larvae
remain buried in the stream bottom for
up to five or six years before changing
into the adult form and migrating to the
sea. Adults spend 12–20 months in the
sea before returning to rivers to spawn.

- Up to 30 in (76 cm)
- Up to 1¼ lb (500 g)
- Oviparous
- ♀♂ Male & female
- Common

Pacific coasts of North America & Asia

Pouched lamprey The adult pouched
lamprey lives in the sea where it is
parasitic on other fishes. It spawns in
gravel in shallow, fast-flowing streams
and rivers, and dies shortly after.

- Up to 24 in (61 cm)
- Up to 8 oz (225 g)
- Oviparous
- ♀♂ Male & female
- Locally common

South America; S. Australia & New Zealand

Atlantic hagfish The hagfish is mainly
a nocturnal predator of invertebrates,
but it is also a scavenger of animal
carcasses. It is well known for its ability
to produce vast amounts of mucus
hence its alternative names of slime
eel, slime hag, or snot eel.

- Up to 24 in (61 cm)
- Up to 8 oz (225 g)
- Oviparous
- ♀♂ Male & female
- Common

W. & E. North Atlantic & W. Mediterranean Sea

Hagfish knots Hagfishes tear
off flesh by forming a knot that
can also be used to escape from
predators or remove excess mucus.

SHARKS, RAYS, AND ALLIES

CLASS Chondrichthyes	
SUBCLASSES 2	
ORDERS 12	
FAMILIES 47	
SPECIES 999	

Having skeletons of cartilage, not bone, sharks and rays are known collectively as cartilaginous fishes. Shark evolutionary history extends back some 400 million years, while rays probably first appeared 200 million years ago. All feed on other animals and most are marine. Teeth are embedded in connective tissue and replaced throughout life; they usually have five, but sometimes six or seven, external gill slits on each side of the pharynx; and all have internal fertilization. Together with skates (a type of ray) and chimaeras (a mainly deepwater group, including spookfishes, ghost sharks, and elephant-fishes), sharks and rays today comprise about 1,000 species.

Shark napping Caribbean reef sharks (above) occur on reefs around islands in the Caribbean Sea. They are known for the way they rest motionlessly in caves and on the ocean bottom as if sleeping.

Gentle giant The largest living fish, the whale shark (left) is about 25 years old and 30 feet (9 m) long before it reaches sexual maturity. It roams the Indian, Pacific, and Atlantic oceans, mouth agape, filtering mainly plankton from surface waters.

ANCIENT FEATURES

Unlike jawless fishes (which also have skeletons of cartilage), sharks, rays, and their close relatives have well-developed jaws, paired nostrils, and paired pectoral and pelvic fins. In addition to their cartilaginous skeletons, they differ from the bony fishes in having dermal denticles and teeth that are replaced throughout their lives or which are fused into continuously growing bony plates.

The class Chondrichthyes, to which the cartilaginous fishes belong, is usually divided into two subclasses. Elasmobranchii is a large group that includes the wide-ranging sharks, skates, and rays. The smaller Holocephali group contains the relatively "primitive" chimaeras. These bizarre-looking and mostly bottom-dwelling fishes differ from the elasmobranchs in having only a single gill cleft and four gills on each side of the head, mainly naked skin, teeth fused into plates, and the upper jaw fused to the skull.

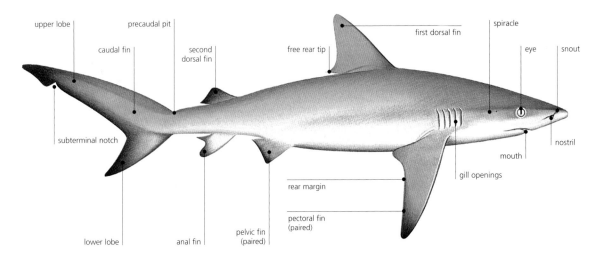

upper lobe · precaudal pit · first dorsal fin · spiracle · caudal fin · second dorsal fin · free rear tip · eye · snout · subterminal notch · mouth · nostril · gill openings · rear margin · pectoral fin (paired) · lower lobe · anal fin · pelvic fin (paired)

Shark anatomy Basic shark attributes (left) have changed little since the group's early evolution. Body shape is designed for hydrodynamic efficiency and to suit a predatory lifestyle. Fins are thick, stiff, and usually lack spines. All sharks have paired pelvic and pectoral fins and between two and four unpaired anal, caudal, and dorsal fins. Gill openings are visible externally.

Excellent eyesight Large eyes on short stalks provide this reef-dwelling ray with excellent vision to the front and sides.

Upperside view

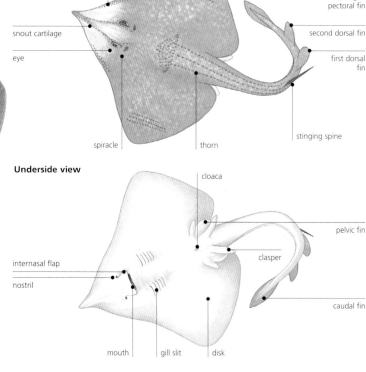

- malar thorn patch
- enlarged pectoral fin
- second dorsal fin
- first dorsal fin
- snout cartilage
- eye
- spiracle
- thorn
- stinging spine

Underside view

- cloaca
- pelvic fin
- clasper
- internasal flap
- nostril
- caudal fin
- mouth
- gill slit
- disk

REPRODUCTION

All of the cartilaginous fishes have internal fertilization, and elaborate courtship rituals are believed to be widespread in the group. Males do not possess a penis but have claspers instead. These stiffened, fin-like rods, which extend parallel to the body from behind the pelvic fins, are inserted into the female's cloaca to guide sperm. Pup numbers range from 2 to 300 per pregnancy, depending on the species.

Most fishes adopt a strength-in-numbers approach to reproduction, dispersing sometimes millions of tiny eggs at a time so that at least some reach adulthood. In contrast, sharks and rays produce very few offspring but invest far more energy in their early development.

Some sharks and rays lay large yolky eggs that nourish embryos for months before hatching. In most sharks and rays, however, mothers retain young internally to give birth after a lengthy gestation. Either way, baby sharks and rays are born as miniature versions of their parents.

Parental devotion almost always ends with birth. In fact, the pups of many shark species probably separate quickly from their mothers to avoid ending up as prey.

Powerful swimmers Spotted eagle rays (*Aetobatus narinari*) are highly social fish that frequently frolic in groups near the ocean's surface. They move through the water with great strength and grace and have been reported to escape predators by leaping clear of the water.

Feeding migrations The blue-spotted ribbontail ray (*Taeniura lymma*) (above) moves in small groups on the rising tide to graze on invertebrates living on reefs. It returns with the falling tide to deeper water to hide under ledges and in caves.

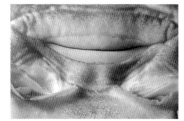

Ray anatomy Rays have flattened, disk-like bodies with eyes on the dorsal surface and a ventrally located mouth (left). They also have five or six pairs of gill slits located on the underside of the body, just behind the mouth. Rays take in water for respiration through large openings on the upper surface of the head called spiracles, as well as or instead of through the mouth. The long slender tail is often equipped with sharp spines to deter predators and is not used for swimming. Instead, rays propel themselves using their greatly enlarged wing-like pectoral fins. The caudal and dorsal fins are often reduced or lacking.

SHARKS

| CLASS Chondrichthyes |
| SUBCLASS Elasmobranchii |
| ORDERS 8 |
| FAMILIES 31 |
| SPECIES 415 |

Although less than 2 percent of living fish species are sharks, they are of crucial ecological importance in marine ecosystems because they are apex predators. As a result they occur at naturally low levels of abundance compared with most bony fishes. This, combined with low reproductive rates, makes sharks particularly vulnerable to overexploitation. Most only reach sexual maturity after 6 years, and some not until 18 years or more. They produce few young and embryos undergo long periods of development before birth. Chimaeras are related to the sharks but belong to the subclass Holocephali, which contains a single order with 3 families and 37 species.

Widespread distribution Sharks are found throughout the world's oceans, although very few species can tolerate polar waters. Most prefer shallow marine habitats but a small number of species, such as dogfish sharks, dwell at great depths.

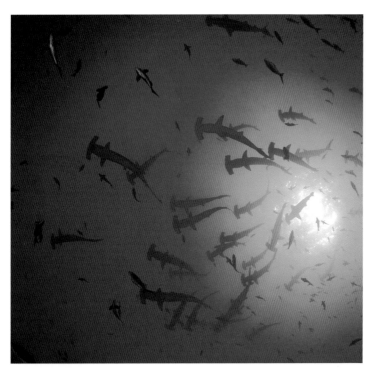

"Mermaid purses" Shark eggs are large and yolky. The purse-like outer layer is made of a tough keratinoid (horny) protein and can be up to 6¾ inches (17 cm) long. Each contains a single embryo that can take up to 15 months to mature.

Gatherings Sharks do not school in the same highly coordinated way that bony fishes often do. But many species form aggregations. In the Sea of Cortez, large day-time groups of mainly juvenile female hammerheads form regularly in areas of high productivity (left). Reasons for this remain unclear.

PREDATORY LIVES

Because most sharks are highly active predators, they tend to be strong, agile swimmers, and some species make long migrations covering many hundreds of miles (km) in search of food. As they have slower metabolisms than most fishes, sharks do not need to feed as frequently and only hunt when necessary. Prey typically includes small fishes and invertebrates but larger sharks also hunt sea turtles and marine mammals.

They have no internal swim bladder but other adaptations help to increase buoyancy and enhance their swimming capabilities. The cartilaginous skeleton, which is lighter than true bone, contributes. And large livers with high levels of oil also help keep many afloat. They do need, however, to keep swimming to avoid dropping to the ocean floor.

Sharks reduce water loss by retaining urea in their tissues.

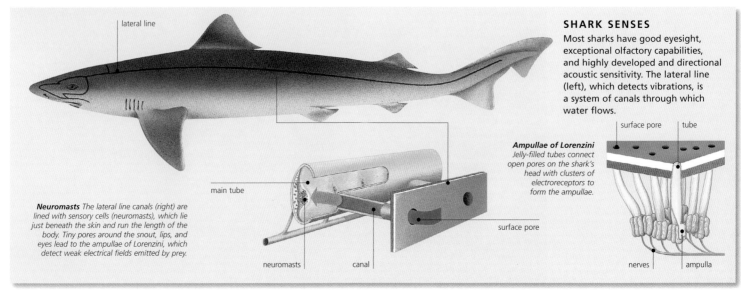

lateral line

SHARK SENSES

Most sharks have good eyesight, exceptional olfactory capabilities, and highly developed and directional acoustic sensitivity. The lateral line (left), which detects vibrations, is a system of canals through which water flows.

Ampullae of Lorenzini Jelly-filled tubes connect open pores on the shark's head with clusters of electroreceptors to form the ampullae.

surface pore   tube

Neuromasts The lateral line canals (right) are lined with sensory cells (neuromasts), which lie just beneath the skin and run the length of the body. Tiny pores around the snout, lips, and eyes lead to the ampullae of Lorenzini, which detect weak electrical fields emitted by prey.

main tube

surface pore

neuromasts   canal

nerves   ampulla

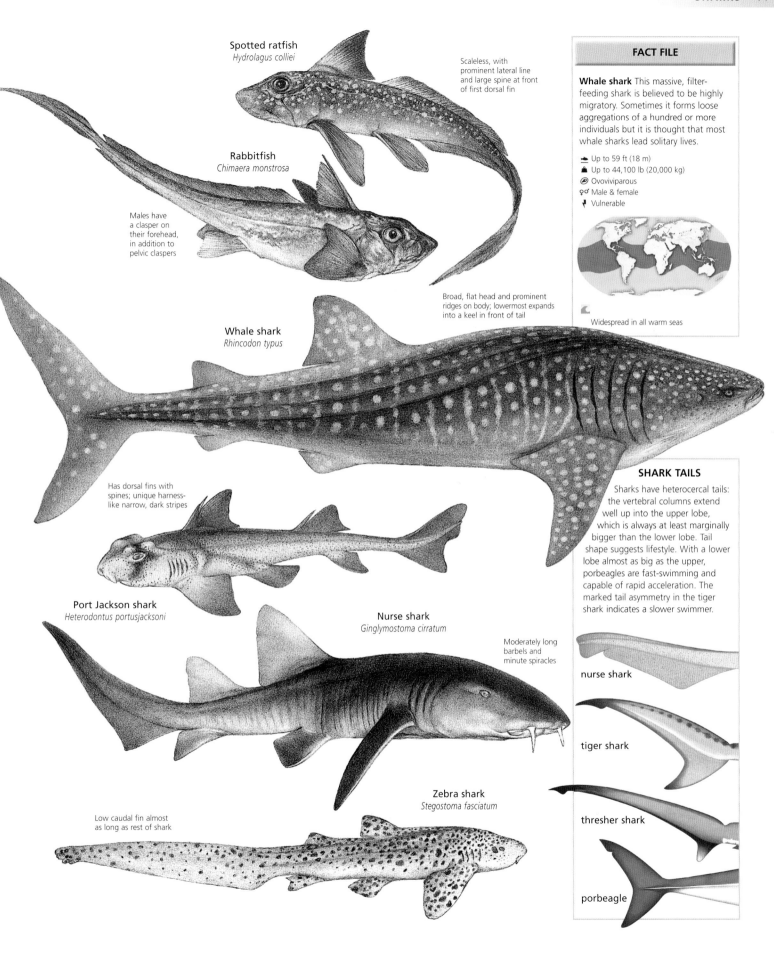

Spotted ratfish
Hydrolagus colliei

Scaleless, with prominent lateral line and large spine at front of first dorsal fin

Rabbitfish
Chimaera monstrosa

Males have a clasper on their forehead, in addition to pelvic claspers

Broad, flat head and prominent ridges on body; lowermost expands into a keel in front of tail

Whale shark
Rhincodon typus

Has dorsal fins with spines; unique harness-like narrow, dark stripes

Port Jackson shark
Heterodontus portusjacksoni

Nurse shark
Ginglymostoma cirratum

Moderately long barbels and minute spiracles

Zebra shark
Stegostoma fasciatum

Low caudal fin almost as long as rest of shark

FACT FILE

Whale shark This massive, filter-feeding shark is believed to be highly migratory. Sometimes it forms loose aggregations of a hundred or more individuals but it is thought that most whale sharks lead solitary lives.

- Up to 59 ft (18 m)
- Up to 44,100 lb (20,000 kg)
- Ovoviviparous
- Male & female
- Vulnerable

Widespread in all warm seas

SHARK TAILS

Sharks have heterocercal tails: the vertebral columns extend well up into the upper lobe, which is always at least marginally bigger than the lower lobe. Tail shape suggests lifestyle. With a lower lobe almost as big as the upper, porbeagles are fast-swimming and capable of rapid acceleration. The marked tail asymmetry in the tiger shark indicates a slower swimmer.

nurse shark

tiger shark

thresher shark

porbeagle

SPECIALIZED SENSES

Sharks have been able to survive and flourish in the world's oceans for more than 200 million years because of the variety and sensitivity of their sensory systems. These have enabled sharks to find food, mating partners, and avoid predation with exceptional efficiency. All sharks rely on their senses to survive, whether they are active hunters locating and ambushing prey, bottom feeders nosing through sediments, or large, sluggish filter feeders. In addition to touch, taste, and smell, many sharks are able to detect low frequency vibrations using a specialized sensory system that complements their hearing. Many sharks also have an electromagnetic sense that detects the very weak electric fields generated by nerve impulses and muscle activity in other animals. Vision is usually extremely sharp at close range.

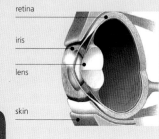

Sight Sharks' eyes are adapted to low-light conditions. Light is regulated by the iris and the retina provides color vision. Most sharks have eyes that are rimmed with immovable eyelids. Some, however, have the lower lid folded into a nictitating membrane (left), which closes over the eye during feeding and protects it from damage.

retina

iris

lens

skin

Thresher shark This shark detects vibrations from schools of small fishes and hunts cooperatively, stunning or killing prey with its long tail.

eye

mouth

gills

THE SHARK BRAIN

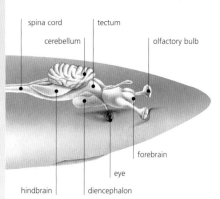

spina cord

tectum

cerebellum

olfactory bulb

forebrain

eye

hindbrain

diencephalon

Brain power Sharks are not mindless killing machines; they are capable of highly complex behavior. Their midbrain and optic lobes process the large amounts of information constantly supplied by their senses. In general, the fast-moving mid-water sharks have larger and more complex brains than slower, bottom-dwelling species. Sharks are intelligent enough to be capable of learning.

The shark's hindbrain processes information from many sensory systems, controls movements of the head and jaw, and interacts between the higher brain centers and the spinal cord. The cerebellum coordinates body movements. The tectum receives and integrates visual and other sensory information, while the diencephalon regulates hormone production and output. The forebrain receives information from the olfactory, electrosensory, and lateral line systems.

Sound Although sharks lack any external evidence of well-developed ears, their hearing is actually acute. In most species, sound-pressure waves traveling through the water, such as those produced by the movements of fishes or unusual acoustic disturbances on a reef, are channeled down tiny cartilaginous tubes in the top of the skull where they enter the inner ear to stimulate the macula neglecta. The semi-circular canal system gives the shark information on the speed and direction of its movements, while the sacculus and macula neglecta detect the orientation of the shark's body in the water.

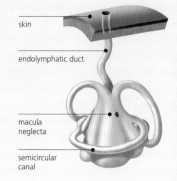

skin

endolymphatic duct

macula neglecta

semicircular canal

Touch Sharks have mechanical touch receptors—a network of nerve fibers enclosed in a capsule. They are only found on the fins. Many sharks can detect small changes in water temperature and remain at the same point on the temperature gradient in moving water masses. Specialized scales (right) reduce drag as the shark swims.

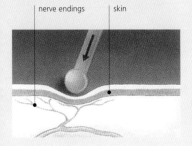

nerve endings | skin

Taste Found on the roof and floor of the mouth and throat, taste receptors (below) enable a shark, such as this tiger shark (right) feeding on a young albatross, to test the palatability of food before it is swallowed. Apart from its role in food selection, taste may also be involved in detecting differences in salinity.

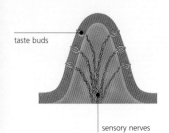

taste buds

sensory nerves

Smell Sharks can detect one part blood in a million parts seawater (above). Water is forced through the nostrils into nasal sacs when swimming, or pumped through them when resting. A flap across the center of each sac (below) directs the flow on to rows of receptor-bearing olfactory tissue.

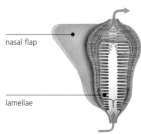

nasal flap

lamellae

FACT FILE

Bull shark The only wide-ranging shark to penetrate far into freshwater, it has been found 2,610 miles (4,200 km) up the Amazon River and 746 miles (1,200 km) up the Mississippi River.

- Up to 11½ ft (3.5 m)
- Up to 697 lb (316 kg)
- Viviparous
- Male & female
- Lower risk, near threatened

Widespread in tropical & subtropical seas, some rivers & lakes

Smooth hammerhead This mostly temperate species feeds on bony fishes, small sharks and rays, crustaceans, and squid. Groups migrate to lower latitudes.

- Up to 16½ ft (5 m)
- Up to 880 lb (400 kg)
- Viviparous
- Male & female
- Near threatened

Widespread in temperate & tropical seas

PLACENTAL VIVIPARITY

Developing young in some sharks—including blue and hammerhead sharks—are nourished, like mammals, by maternal nutrients. Embryos hatch in the oviducts and live initially off egg sac yolk after which empty sacs develop into placentae that interweave with the uterine walls. Yolk stalks become "umbilical cords" extending from between the embryos' pectoral fins. Sharks with placental viviparity can produce up to a hundred offspring with every pregnancy, depending on the species.

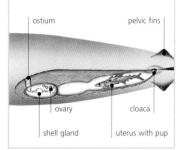

ostium

pelvic fins

ovary

cloaca

shell gland

uterus with pup

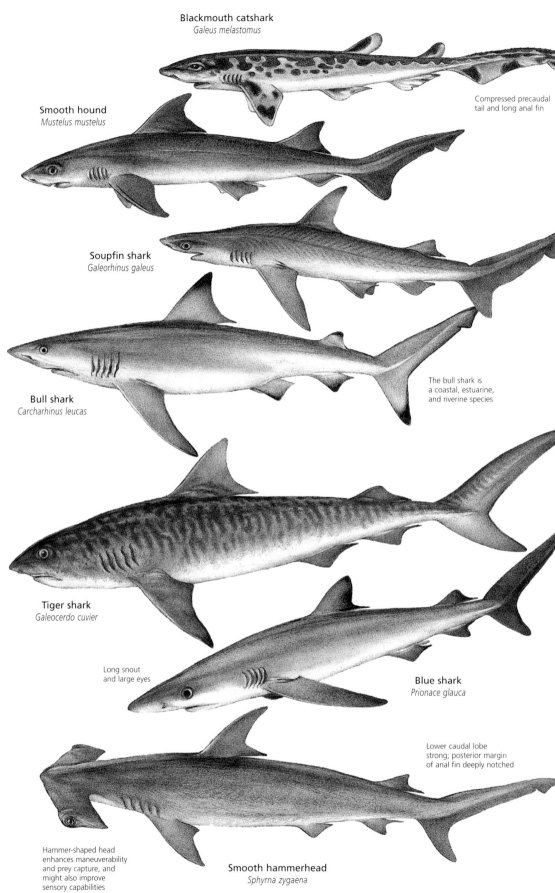

Blackmouth catshark
Galeus melastomus

Compressed precaudal tail and long anal fin

Smooth hound
Mustelus mustelus

Soupfin shark
Galeorhinus galeus

The bull shark is a coastal, estuarine, and riverine species

Bull shark
Carcharhinus leucas

Tiger shark
Galeocerdo cuvier

Long snout and large eyes

Blue shark
Prionace glauca

Lower caudal lobe strong; posterior margin of anal fin deeply notched

Hammer-shaped head enhances maneuverability and prey capture, and might also improve sensory capabilities

Smooth hammerhead
Sphyrna zygaena

MIGRATION

Most sharks migrate annually, often in response to seasonal fluctuations in water temperature and in search of transient food sources, such as breeding groups of prey. This can be coupled with sharks' own reproductive strategies. The distance that sharks travel depends essentially on their swimming ability. While some species, such as the epaulette and gray carpetshark, may not migrate at all, powerful and active species, such as the mako shark and blue shark (featured here), have the ability to cross entire oceans.

Tagging There are many organizations dedicated to shark research and conservation, especially as it is now recognized that sharks are a sustainable natural resource for tourism industries, particularly in developing countries. Tags have been used for many decades to follow migratory species and such programs have mapped a number of shark migrations. Recent tagging technologies include archival tags, which store the animal's location each day, and satellite tags, which transmit its location to a satellite whenever the shark breaks the surface.

Extra research Tagging studies also provide an opportunity to make other measurements, such as length and weight, that can be used to gauge the state of a population. Today, DNA sampling is also often routine and provides valuable information on migrations and breeding groups.

Predator and prey Among the most abundant and widely distributed pelagic species, the blue shark is also the most heavily fished shark in the world. There is concern over the removal of such large numbers of this keystone predator from the oceanic ecosystem.

Mapping migration The blue shark moves around the Atlantic Ocean, venturing as far as Brazil, west Africa, and the Mediterranean Sea. The mako shark migrates individually from the northeast coast of the United States where it spends summer, to wintering grounds in warmer waters from the South Atlantic to the Sargasso Sea.

Long-distance swimmer
The blue shark can migrate over great distances with incredible accuracy. Tracking suggests sharks may use anomalies in Earth's magnetic field to gain their bearings.

■ Mako shark migration
■ Blue shark migration

SHOWCASE OF SHARKS

When sharks are mentioned, most people immediately think of large, dangerous predators with sleek bodies and razor-sharp teeth, cruising in tropical coastal waters. Although some of the most abundant shark species in the seas today conform to this stereotype, sharks are found in many marine habitats and some have even moved into freshwater. Sharks also vary enormously in both shape and size. As well as the torpedo-like, active predators there are tiny, deep-sea forms; flattened, ray-like bottom dwellers; and the biggest fish in the sea—the filter-feeding whale shark. Male sharks tend to be smaller than females of the same species, although a number of catsharks reverse this rule.

White shark This highly active, torpedo-shaped mackerel shark is a powerful and efficient predator that is probably responsible for the majority of attacks on humans in many areas.

Bonnethead This small hammerhead is an active coastal shark. The flattened, bi-lobed head acts as a bow plane and increases sensory capacity.

Tasseled Wobbegong This small, flattened, bottom-dwelling carpetshark has fleshy tassels on its chin and jaw, which resemble weeds. It is the most frequently observed wobbegong, and is often seen by divers on the Great Barrier Reef, Australia.

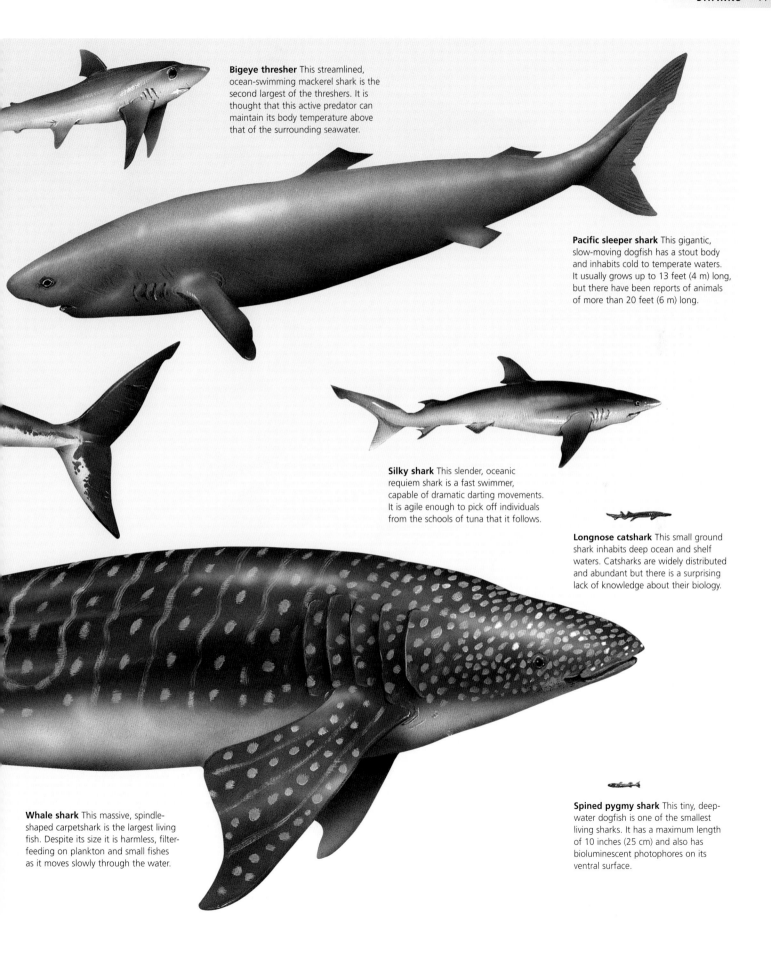

Bigeye thresher This streamlined, ocean-swimming mackerel shark is the second largest of the threshers. It is thought that this active predator can maintain its body temperature above that of the surrounding seawater.

Pacific sleeper shark This gigantic, slow-moving dogfish has a stout body and inhabits cold to temperate waters. It usually grows up to 13 feet (4 m) long, but there have been reports of animals of more than 20 feet (6 m) long.

Silky shark This slender, oceanic requiem shark is a fast swimmer, capable of dramatic darting movements. It is agile enough to pick off individuals from the schools of tuna that it follows.

Longnose catshark This small ground shark inhabits deep ocean and shelf waters. Catsharks are widely distributed and abundant but there is a surprising lack of knowledge about their biology.

Whale shark This massive, spindle-shaped carpetshark is the largest living fish. Despite its size it is harmless, filter-feeding on plankton and small fishes as it moves slowly through the water.

Spined pygmy shark This tiny, deep-water dogfish is one of the smallest living sharks. It has a maximum length of 10 inches (25 cm) and also has bioluminescent photophores on its ventral surface.

FACT FILE

Sand tiger shark The embryos of sand tiger sharks cannibalize each other until only one in each uterus survives. As a result, these sharks can only ever produce two pups per pregnancy.

- Up to 10½ ft (3.2 m)
- Up to 348 lb (158 kg)
- Viviparous
- Male & female
- Vulnerable

Widespread in warm seas except E. Pacific

Basking shark These huge sharks filter tiny animals from surface waters and can process a body of water equivalent in size to an Olympic pool every hour.

- Up to 32 ft (9.8 m)
- Up to 8,820 lb (4,000 kg)
- Ovoviviparous
- Male & female
- Vulnerable

Widespread in temperate & tropical seas

AGONISTIC DISPLAY

When threatened, gray reef sharks indicate their readiness to attack by raising the snout, dropping the pectoral fins, and holding the tail sideways as the back is arched and flexed. They swim like this in a figure-of-eight pattern with increasing intensity until they make either a rapid attack or retreat.

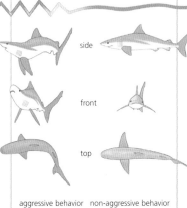

side

front

top

aggressive behavior   non-aggressive behavior

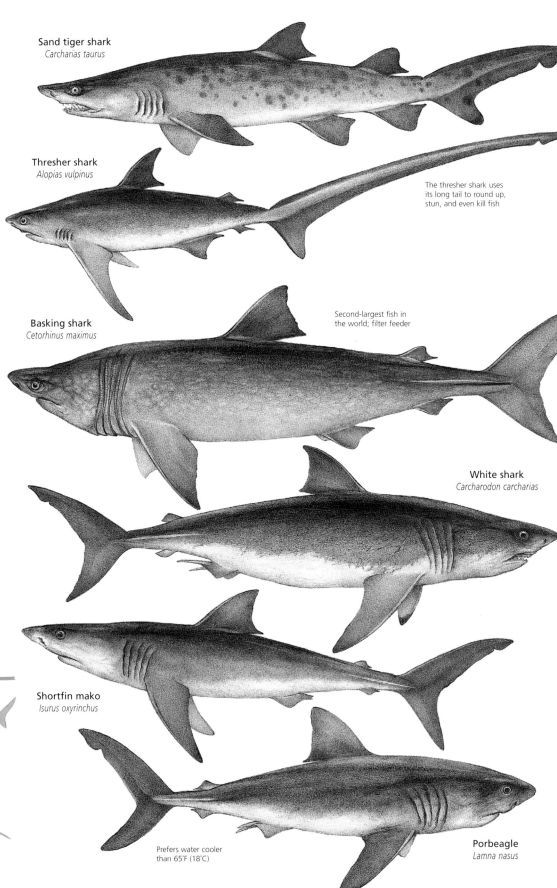

Sand tiger shark
Carcharias taurus

Thresher shark
Alopias vulpinus

The thresher shark uses its long tail to round up, stun, and even kill fish

Basking shark
Cetorhinus maximus

Second-largest fish in the world; filter feeder

White shark
Carcharodon carcharias

Shortfin mako
Isurus oxyrinchus

Prefers water cooler than 65°F (18°C)

Porbeagle
Lamna nasus

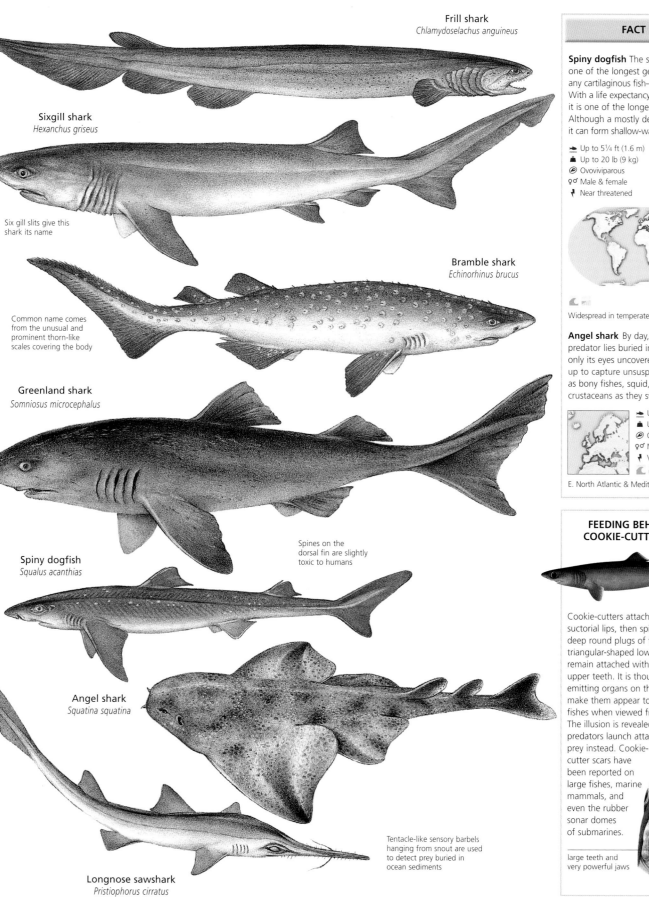

Frill shark
Chlamydoselachus anguineus

Sixgill shark
Hexanchus griseus

Six gill slits give this
shark its name

Bramble shark
Echinorhinus brucus

Common name comes
from the unusual and
prominent thorn-like
scales covering the body

Greenland shark
Somniosus microcephalus

Spines on the
dorsal fin are slightly
toxic to humans

Spiny dogfish
Squalus acanthias

Angel shark
Squatina squatina

Tentacle-like sensory barbels
hanging from snout are used
to detect prey buried in
ocean sediments

Longnose sawshark
Pristiophorus cirratus

FACT FILE

Spiny dogfish The spiny dogfish has one of the longest gestation periods of any cartilaginous fish—up to 24 months. With a life expectancy of about 70 years, it is one of the longest-lived sharks. Although a mostly deepwater species, it can form shallow-water coastal groups.

- Up to 5¼ ft (1.6 m)
- Up to 20 lb (9 kg)
- Ovoviviparous
- Male & female
- Near threatened

Widespread in temperate seas

Angel shark By day, this ambush predator lies buried in sediment with only its eyes uncovered. It bursts rapidly up to capture unsuspecting prey such as bony fishes, squid, skates, and crustaceans as they swim overhead.

- Up to 8 ft (2.4 m)
- Up to 175 lb (80 kg)
- Ovoviviparous
- Male & female
- Vulnerable

E. North Atlantic & Mediterranean Sea

FEEDING BEHAVIOR OF COOKIE-CUTTER SHARKS

Cookie-cutters attach to prey with their suctorial lips, then spin around to carve deep round plugs of flesh using large triangular-shaped lower teeth. They remain attached with small hook-like upper teeth. It is thought that light-emitting organs on their undersides make them appear to be much smaller fishes when viewed from beneath. The illusion is revealed when would-be predators launch attacks and become prey instead. Cookie-cutter scars have been reported on large fishes, marine mammals, and even the rubber sonar domes of submarines.

large teeth and
very powerful jaws

RESPIRATION

Sharks extract oxygen from the water that passes over their gills, which is then transferred to the blood. The circulatory system then delivers oxygenated blood to the tissues and organs. At the same time, metabolic wastes such as carbon dioxide are discharged into the water. The gills receive carbon dioxide-rich, oxygen-depleted blood directly from the heart, which lies in a separate chamber beneath the gills. Blood is pumped through thin-walled capillary beds in the gill arches which are arranged in such a way that the blood flows in the opposite direction to the inflowing water. In fast-swimming species, water is forced into the open mouth and directed to the gills as the shark swims. In bottom-dwelling species, there are well-developed spiracles that serve as auxiliary water inlets when the animal is resting or using the mouth to feed.

GILLS IN ACTION

As water flows into a shark's mouth and through the internal gill openings, it ventilates the gill filaments, which are richly supplied with blood vessels. The flow of water and blood in opposite directions (right) allows oxygen to be extracted from the water at the same time as carbon dioxide is extracted from the blood.

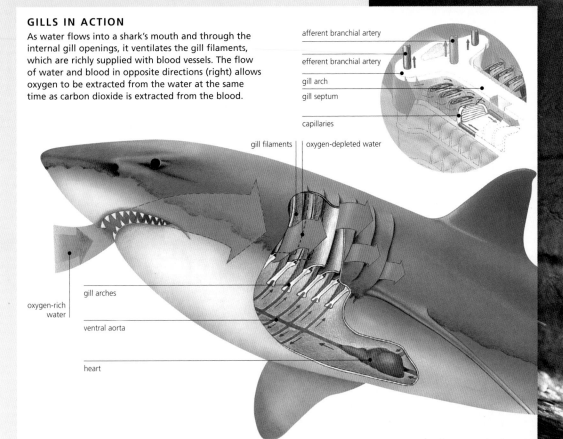

afferent branchial artery

efferent branchial artery

gill arch

gill septum

capillaries

gill filaments | oxygen-depleted water

gill arches

oxygen-rich water

ventral aorta

heart

Ram ventilation In order to absorb enough oxygen, sharks need to maintain a good flow of water over their gills. Some sharks generate much of this flow through constant forward movement—known as ram ventilation. Great white sharks (right) barely stop moving from the time they are born. Although they can hover motionless for brief periods, they must soon start moving again in order to breathe.

FOOD AND FEEDING

As predators at the top of the food chain, sharks are highly proficient at detecting and tracking prey. Each species of shark occupies a specific feeding niche within its habitat, and provides an important link in the flow of energy through Earth's oceans. A predator of fishes, squid, stingrays, turtles, and marine mammals, the white shark is believed to have exceptional eyesight and to see in color. This huge carnivore has evolved to consume large meals infrequently and is thought to undertake long migrations to favored hunting grounds. The white shark is one of just 27 shark species that is known to have attacked either people or boats. A single, massive bite can inflict major, often fatal, injury.

Filter feeder Sharks are carnivores and consume a wide variety of food, ranging from microscopic zooplankton to whales. Despite its enormous size, the basking shark (right) is a filter feeder, using its gill rakers derived from its dermal denticles to sieve approximately 330,000 gallons (1.3 million liters) of water an hour. It cruises near the surface at around 2 knots, with its mouth open wide, filtering food.

Breaching behavior White sharks around seal colonies off South Africa have been observed making sudden, powerful, and spectacular leaps, sometimes clear of the water, to snatch unsuspecting prey.

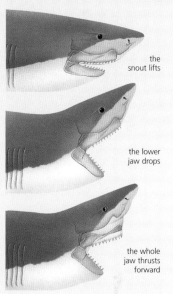

the snout lifts

the lower jaw drops

the whole jaw thrusts forward

Protrusible jaws During the evolution of white sharks, as in other sharks, the upper jaw has become separated from the cranium. This allows the upper jaw to move more freely and makes it possible for both jaws to protrude. The jaws are connected to each other at their outer corners but hang loosely beneath the skull. As the snout lifts at the start of a bite, the lower jaw drops and, as the mouth opens, the whole jaw arrangement is thrust forward, providing extra reach.

SHARK TEETH

Teeth reveal much about shark prey preferences: white sharks have large, triangular-shaped teeth with serrated edges for tearing flesh; the flattened hind teeth of the horn shark crush hard-shelled invertebrates; blue shark teeth are finely serrated for catching fishes and squid; and the needle-like mako teeth are adept at grasping large, slippery prey.

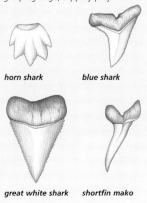

horn shark   *blue shark*

great white shark   *shortfin mako*

Menacing mouth The mouth of the white shark (left) can readily gouge flesh from large animals and sever the bodies of smaller ones. The ferocity of the bite comes from a combination of powerful jaw muscles acting on a mechanically efficient jaw system, and the sharpness of the teeth. The multiple rows of razor-sharp, dagger shaped teeth are serrated like stake knives. They emerge continuously on the jaws from a whorl of developing teeth below the gum line, replacing blunt and broken teeth.

Garbage guts The tiger shark (*Galeocerdo cuvier*) (right) is omnivorous, eating fishes including other sharks, sea turtles, mollusks, seabirds, carrion, and garbage. It has unique teeth that are flat, triangular, highly serrated, and with a large notch on the outer margin. These teeth are particularly effective in cutting through hard turtle shells and biting lumps from big prey items. Tiger sharks will attempt to eat coal, tin cans, and even clothing.

RAYS AND ALLIES

Body shape is the principal difference between these fishes and other cartilaginous fishes. Known as batoids, skates and rays are dorsoventrally flattened, an adaptation for a bottom-dwelling lifestyle. Their greatly enlarged pectoral fins extend from near the snout to the base of the tail. Together with the body, and often the head, they form the "disk," which can be triangular, round, or diamond-shaped. Most batoids take in water for gill ventilation through spiracles, openings located on the tops of their heads that are often mistaken for the eyes. Teeth are often plate-like and used for crushing prey, which ranges from bottom-dwelling invertebrates to pelagic fishes.

CLASS	Chondrichthyes
SUBCLASS	Elasmobranchii
ORDERS	3
FAMILIES	13
SPECIES	547

Mostly benthic Skates and rays are found in most benthic marine communities. A small number of ray families live in the open ocean and a few stingray and sawfish species survive in brackish estuaries and freshwater rivers and lakes, ranging from the tropics to polar waters. The guitarfishes, too—found in the temperate and tropical waters of the Atlantic, Pacific, and Indian oceans—are mostly marine.

BATOID DIVERSITY

Almost half the living batoid species are skates, all of which are bottom-dwelling egg-layers with large flat disks and small tails. The dorsal surface usually bears "thorns" for defense against predators and these are also used by males to grip females during mating. Although some species can attain lengths over 8 feet (2.4 m), most are less than 3¼ feet (1 m). Most skates prefer shallow water but some are found to depths of 9,000 feet (2,750 m).

The rays are often categorized into four major groups: the electric rays, sawfishes, stingrays and their allies, and guitarfishes.

Sawfishes have distinctive flat elongated snouts with conspicuous "teeth" along their edges. These can account for as much as a third of the body length in adults. They are thrashed about in schools of fishes to stun and kill prey. Some of the seven known living species attain lengths of over 23 feet (7 m).

Electric rays stun prey using electric organs located behind the eyes. There are more than 40 species worldwide, all of which tend to be rather lethargic bottom dwellers.

Many of the 150-plus species of stingrays and their allies have slender tails armed with serrated spines and are powerful swimmers. They tend to be bottom dwellers but three families have adopted an open ocean lifestyle. The largest, the manta, attains widths in excess of 21 feet (6.4 m).

Guitarfishes comprise about 50 species and have well-developed tails and either a poorly developed or absent disk. They are all ovo-viviparous and tend to have more shark-like features than the other batoids, including well-developed tails bearing two dorsal fins.

claspers (modified pelvic fins); the male copulatory organ

pectoral fin or wing

fleshy fins supported by horny fin rays

Typical skate Most skates have slender tails bearing two small dorsal fins. The nose is often pointed and spiny thorns on the dorsal surface are common. The disk of most species is diamond-shaped.

Clever fishes Rays are inquisitive, often sociable animals with complex behaviors. Although they are usually seen alone, many species will aggregate into loosely formed groups, particularly for the purposes of mating or migration.

Out of sight Taking water through spiracles located just behind the eyes enables batoids, such as the thornback ray (above), to breathe when their mouths are buried. Most batoids have good vision.

DANGEROUS TAIL

The tail of the thorntail stingray (*Dasyatis thetidis*) can be twice as long as its body and makes a formidable weapon against would-be predators. Thick at its base, but whip-like toward the end, it is spiked with small, sharp thorns and armed with one or two sharp, serrated, and venomous barbs. The venom is dangerous to humans.

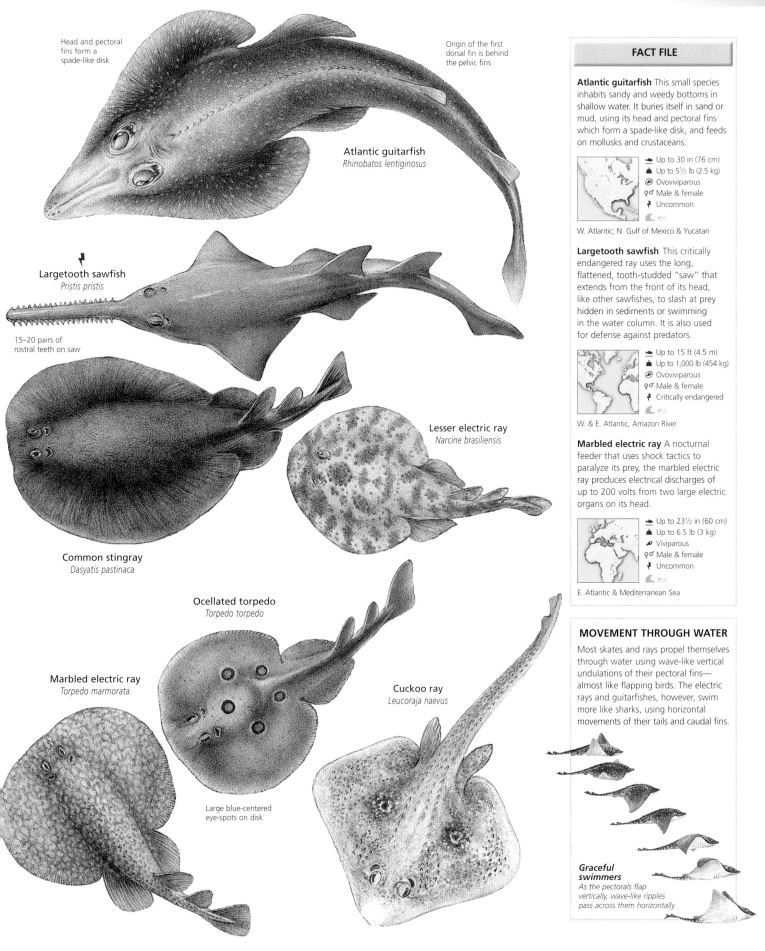

Head and pectoral fins form a spade-like disk

Origin of the first dorsal fin is behind the pelvic fins

Atlantic guitarfish
Rhinobatos lentiginosus

Largetooth sawfish
Pristis pristis

15–20 pairs of rostral teeth on saw

Common stingray
Dasyatis pastinaca

Lesser electric ray
Narcine brasiliensis

Ocellated torpedo
Torpedo torpedo

Marbled electric ray
Torpedo marmorata

Large blue-centered eye-spots on disk

Cuckoo ray
Leucoraja naevus

FACT FILE

Atlantic guitarfish This small species inhabits sandy and weedy bottoms in shallow water. It buries itself in sand or mud, using its head and pectoral fins which form a spade-like disk, and feeds on mollusks and crustaceans.

- Up to 30 in (76 cm)
- Up to 5½ lb (2.5 kg)
- Ovoviviparous
- Male & female
- Uncommon

W. Atlantic; N. Gulf of Mexico & Yucatan

Largetooth sawfish This critically endangered ray uses the long, flattened, tooth-studded "saw" that extends from the front of its head, like other sawfishes, to slash at prey hidden in sediments or swimming in the water column. It is also used for defense against predators.

- Up to 15 ft (4.5 m)
- Up to 1,000 lb (454 kg)
- Ovoviviparous
- Male & female
- Critically endangered

W. & E. Atlantic, Amazon River

Marbled electric ray A nocturnal feeder that uses shock tactics to paralyze its prey, the marbled electric ray produces electrical discharges of up to 200 volts from two large electric organs on its head.

- Up to 23½ in (60 cm)
- Up to 6.5 lb (3 kg)
- Viviparous
- Male & female
- Uncommon

E. Atlantic & Mediterranean Sea

MOVEMENT THROUGH WATER

Most skates and rays propel themselves through water using wave-like vertical undulations of their pectoral fins—almost like flapping birds. The electric rays and guitarfishes, however, swim more like sharks, using horizontal movements of their tails and caudal fins.

Graceful swimmers
As the pectorals flap vertically, wave-like ripples pass across them horizontally.

FACT FILE

Blue skate The eggs of the blue skate, like those of other skate species, are encased in rectangular capsules of collagen, toughened with keratin and containing antibacterial agents. At each corner are tendrils to attach the capsules to weeds, rocks, or other fixed objects.

- Up to 9¼ ft (2.85 m)
- Up to 250 lb (113 kg)
- ○ Oviparous
- ♀♂ Male & female
- ⚑ Endangered

E. North Atlantic & W. Mediterranean Sea

Atlantic stingray Very few sharks, skates, or rays can tolerate freshwater but the Atlantic stingray can be found in marine, estuarine, and riverine environments. Some populations even breed in freshwater lakes. Freshwater rays do not accumulate urea in their blood, excreting it via the kidneys.

- Up to 24 in (61 cm)
- Up to 10½ lb (4.7 kg)
- Ovoviviparous
- ♀♂ Male & female
- ⚑ Locally common

W. Atlantic & Gulf of Mexico

Common stingray The poisonous barb on the tail of the common stingray can grow to a length of 14 inches (36 cm). Occasionally it is shed, but a new one grows to replace it. Like most rays, this fish is not aggressive, preferring to flee rather than confront aggressors.

- Up to 4½ ft (1.4 m)
- Up to 56 lb (25.4 kg)
- Ovoviviparous
- ♀♂ Male & female
- ⚑ Locally common

E. Atlantic & Mediterranean Sea

STINGRAY TAIL

Stingrays are the largest fishes with venom. Many have tails equipped with at least one, and often two, cartilaginous barbs or spines. These are usually notched with sharp, backward-facing teeth and encased in a thin sheath of tissue that keeps them bathed in a layer of mucus laced with venom (secreted from glands at the base of each spine). The sheath ruptures and releases the poison when the spine is driven into an attacker.

Fierce weapon As well as being toxic, the sting of a ray can cause savage lacerations.

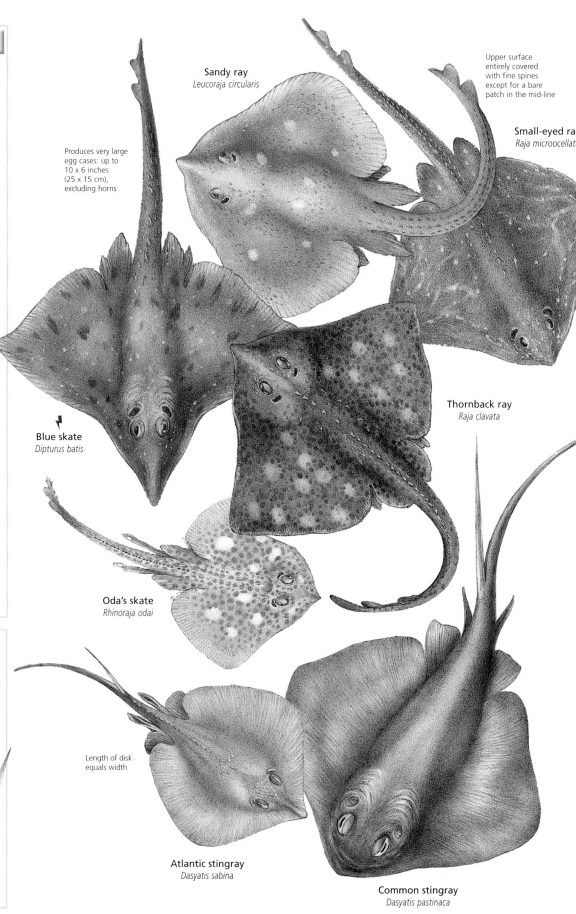

Sandy ray
Leucoraja circularis

Produces very large egg cases: up to 10 x 6 inches (25 x 15 cm), excluding horns

Upper surface entirely covered with fine spines except for a bare patch in the mid-line

Small-eyed ra
Raja microocellat

Blue skate
Dipturus batis

Thornback ray
Raja clavata

Oda's skate
Rhinoraja odai

Length of disk equals width

Atlantic stingray
Dasyatis sabina

Common stingray
Dasyatis pastinaca

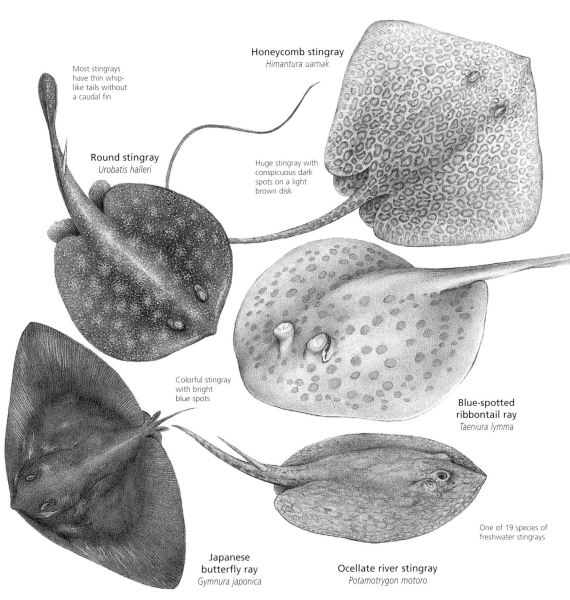

Most stingrays have thin whip-like tails without a caudal fin

Honeycomb stingray
Himantura uarnak

Huge stingray with conspicuous dark spots on a light brown disk

Round stingray
Urobatis halleri

Colorful stingray with bright blue spots

Blue-spotted ribbontail ray
Taeniura lymma

Japanese butterfly ray
Gymnura japonica

Ocellate river stingray
Potamotrygon motoro

One of 19 species of freshwater stingrays

FACT FILE

Blue-spotted ribbontail ray A colorful stingray, this species has bright blue spots and lateral blue stripes along the tail. It rarely buries itself in sand, preferring to take refuge in caves and under ledges. The sting on the tail is further behind the base than in most stingrays.

- Up to 28 in (71 cm)
- Up to 11 lb (4.9 kg)
- Ovoviviparous
- Male & female
- Near threatened

Indo-Pacific & Red Sea

Ocellate river stingray
Little is known of the life history of this live bearing stingray. It can be extremely dangerous, the sting causing severe pain.

- Up to 39 in (99 cm)
- Up to 33 lb (15 kg)
- Ovoviviparous
- Male & female
- Data deficient

South America

⚡ CONSERVATION WATCH

Vanishing sawfishes All seven sawfish species (family Pristidae) are on the IUCN Red List: five are endangered and two are critically endangered. They are a particularly vulnerable bycatch in commercial coastal and estuarine net fisheries. Habitat destruction and pollution have contributed to their decline. They mature late, are long-lived, and have few pups, which means populations recover slowly.

POWERFUL WINGS

The spotted eagle ray (*Aetobatus narinari*) is the most common and most widely distributed of the eagle rays. Its dramatic pattern of white spots or rings on its greenish to pinkish back makes it easily recognizable. It is extremely active, swimming for long periods both in the water column and near the bottom. With its graceful action, it appears to fly and glide along, slowly moving its pectoral fins like the wings of a bird. This ray is powerfully built and can accelerate rapidly, swerving and twisting away from hungry hammerheads or tiger sharks at extraordinary speeds to find safety in shallows. Females are said to leap clear out of the water when giving birth, in spectacular display.

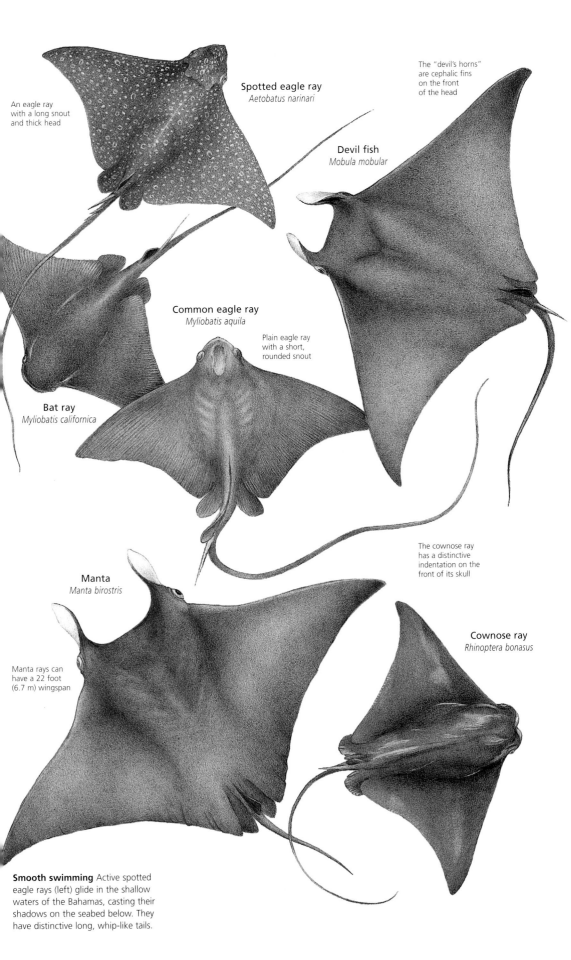

An eagle ray with a long snout and thick head

Spotted eagle ray
Aetobatus narinari

The "devil's horns" are cephalic fins on the front of the head

Devil fish
Mobula mobular

Common eagle ray
Myliobatis aquila

Plain eagle ray with a short, rounded snout

Bat ray
Myliobatis californica

Manta
Manta birostris

Manta rays can have a 22 foot (6.7 m) wingspan

The cownose ray has a distinctive indentation on the front of its skull

Cownose ray
Rhinoptera bonasus

Smooth swimming Active spotted eagle rays (left) glide in the shallow waters of the Bahamas, casting their shadows on the seabed below. They have distinctive long, whip-like tails.

FACT FILE

Bat ray During mating, the male bat ray pokes thorns around his eyes into the underbelly of his mate. This helps the pair remain together in mid-water as the male maneuvers around to insert a clasper into the female.

- Up to 5 ft (1.5 m)
- Up to 180 lb (82 kg)
- Ovoviviparous
- Male & female
- Common

E. Pacific: Oregon to Gulf of California

Manta These huge rays return repeatedly to "cleaning stations," often near reefs, where small fishes known as wrasses dutifully remove their external parasites. Mantas have been observed to "queue" at such locations, patiently awaiting their turn.

- Up to 22 ft (6.7 m)
- Up to 6,600 lb (3,000 kg)
- Ovoviviparous
- Male & female
- Data deficient

Widespread in tropical seas

FILTER FEEDING

Feeding mantas are often seen swimming in large loops in surface waters. These vertical flips may concentrate the tiny animals filtered from the plankton.

Feeding aids Cephalic fins at the front of the manta's head "herd" plankton through the mouth during feeding.

BONY FISHES

SUPERCLASS Gnathostomata
CLASSES 2
ORDERS 48
FAMILIES 455
SPECIES 24,673

In terms of both species and total numbers, this is by far the most successful living vertebrate group. Bony fishes first appeared about 395 million years ago, the fossil record indicating that the earliest forms inhabited freshwater. There are two distinct evolutionary lineages. The lobe-finned fishes (the sarcopterygians) are now represented by only a small number of living species. They are critically important in evolutionary terms because their ancestors gave rise to the earliest tetrapods—four-limbed land vertebrates—which, in turn, ultimately led to all other vertebrates. The overwhelming majority of living bony fishes, however, are the ray-finned fishes—the actinopterygians.

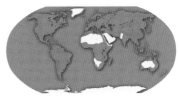

Successful radiation The bony fishes are found in virtually every available marine, freshwater, and brackish habitat throughout the world, and occasionally even desiccated environments. Species diversity increases nearer to the tropics and decreases toward the poles. Diversity tends to be highest close to coastlines and lowest in the open ocean.

Safety in numbers Blue-and-gold fusiliers (*Caesio teres*) (above) have elongated bullet-shaped bodies and iridescent coloring. Like all members of the family Caesionidae, these fish form huge, fast-moving, mid-water schools that feed on zooplankton by day but shelter by night on the outer slopes of reefs. Their aggregations sometimes incorporate other fusilier species.

Sit and wait The northern pike (*Esox lucius*) (right) is an ambush predator par excellence. It is able to finely control its fin movements so that it hangs motionless in the water, often hidden among vegetation. As its intended prey draws closer, the pike approaches it extremely slowly. Once in range it uses its powerful tail to produce an explosive lunge forward, so that it can clamp its jaws onto its victim, which is swallowed whole.

EFFECTIVE EVOLUTION

Bony fishes are distinguished, as the name suggests, by a lightweight internal skeleton that is strengthened entirely or partially by true bone.

The fins of bony fishes are supported by more complex skeletal and muscle arrangements than those of cartilaginous fishes, giving bony fishes much finer control of swimming movements. As a result, many can move backward and even hover mid-water.

Maneuverability is also enhanced by the capacity to precisely and immediately adjust their buoyancy. This is achieved with a gas-filled sac known as a swim bladder. In some species, this is connected to the gullet and emptied and filled via the mouth, requiring fishes to gulp air at the water's surface. Mostly, however, there is no external connection and the swim bladder's content is controlled by the transfer of gases between adjacent blood vessels.

As they have a flap covering the gills (an operculum) and additional bony supports in the gill chamber known as branchiostegal rays, bony fishes can pump water over their gills and do not need to move forward to breathe.

About 90 percent of all bony fishes expel their reproductive cells from the body, making use of the watery environments in which they live for fertilization and the distribution of young.

Although cartilaginous fishes sometimes form aggregations, they do not school in the same highly coordinated way as many bony fishes, behavior made possible by a well-developed lateral line system and exceptional hearing and vision. Schools confuse predators by making lone targets difficult to select.

Fish lure The heads of anglerfishes (below) are equipped with a bony rod complete with a fleshy "bait" at the tip to attract prey. This is often waved around to enhance the ruse but the strategy doesn't always work as planned. Anglerfishes have been found with missing lures, suggesting their prey sometimes escapes with the bait.

SUCCESSFUL MOVEMENTS

Migration has been another significant behavioral adaptation among bony fishes that has helped underpin the group's success. Mass, predictable movements are undertaken by many species to exploit changing food resources, avoid predators, or for the purposes of mating and spawning.

Such movements can be vertical, from deep to shallower waters and back, and measured in just meters. Horizontal migrations, however, can cover many hundreds, and even thousands, of miles (kilometers). When this involves migration from freshwater to ocean and back, and most of a species' life is spent at sea, it is termed anadromy. This is typical of the salmon family. The reverse—ocean to freshwater and back—is termed catadromy and is typical of freshwater eels.

Spawning migrations are common among the bony fishes because they allow adults and young to exploit different niches or even habitats.

Bony fish anatomy The gills of nearly all adult bony fishes are covered by an operculum. Most species have thin, flexible scales covered by a thin mucus-secreting skin layer. Teeth are fixed to the upper jaw. The upper and lower lobes of the tail are usually symmetrical and the vertebral column stops before the fin. Most bony fishes have at least one dorsal fin, one anal fin, and paired pectoral fins. Except for a number of viviparous species, males do not have external organs to aid reproduction.

Deadly stalker Venom glands at the base of the fin spines of red lionfish (*Pterois volitans*) (above) deliver a poison that is potentially fatal to humans. This highly aggressive and mostly solitary fish tends to hide by day and hunt by night, stalking prey such as small fishes and crustaceans, which it corners by stretching out and expanding its fan-like pectoral fins.

Arduous journeys Like most tuna species, the northern bluefin (*Thunnus thynnus*) is highly migratory. It forms large schools of like-sized fish to make seasonal movements thought to be influenced by spawning, water temperature, and prey aggregations. One study found that northern bluefins migrated across the Atlantic at an average of 40 miles (65 km) per day, covering 4,800 miles (7,700 km) in just 119 days.

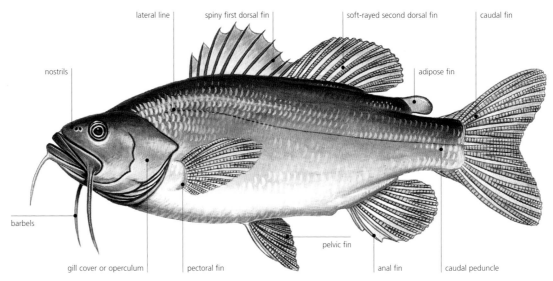

lateral line | spiny first dorsal fin | soft-rayed second dorsal fin | caudal fin

nostrils | adipose fin

barbels | gill cover or operculum | pectoral fin | pelvic fin | anal fin | caudal peduncle

LUNGFISHES AND ALLIES

CLASS Sarcopterygii
SUBCLASSES 2
ORDERS 3
FAMILIES 4
SPECIES 11

Long-extinct ancestors of this relict group, known as the Sarcopterygii or "lobe-finned fishes," gave rise to the earliest land animals. Today, just nine lungfish and two coelacanth species survive. All have fleshy fins with skeletal structures and musculature more reminiscent of tetrapod limbs than they are of the fan-like fins of most other living fishes. In fact, 19th-century scientists mistakenly classified lungfishes as both reptiles and amphibians before realizing that they were fishes. Larval lungfishes breathe through gills but, in all but one species, adults rely on lungs to survive, allowing them to exist in waters with low oxygen levels. They occur in tropical freshwater rivers, lakes, and flood-plains, while the gill-breathing coelacanths are exclusively marine.

Restricted distribution Lungfishes survive only in Africa, South America, and Australia. One of the two coelacanth species (*Latimeria chalumnae*) is known from a small number of specimens caught off coastlines in the Indian Ocean around the Comoros Islands. The other (*L. menadoensis*) was discovered off Sulawesi in Indonesian waters in 1999. These are the only two known sites that support living coelacanth populations.

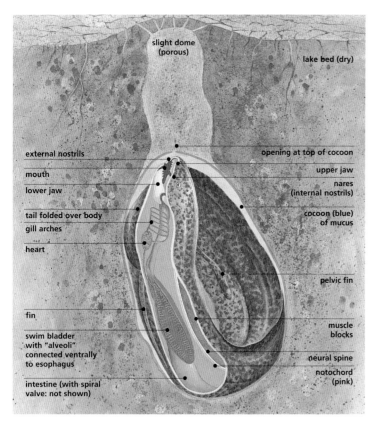

slight dome (porous)

lake bed (dry)

external nostrils

mouth

lower jaw

tail folded over body

gill arches

heart

fin

swim bladder with "alveoli" connected ventrally to esophagus

intestine (with spiral valve: not shown)

opening at top of cocoon

upper jaw

nares (internal nostrils)

cocoon (blue) of mucus

pelvic fin

muscle blocks

neural spine

notochord (pink)

Surviving desiccation The African lungfish (*Protopterus annectens*) (below) estivates during the dry season in a vertical burrow (left). It excavates the burrow by chewing its way into soft mud that it ejects through its gill openings. The lungfish makes a chamber below the surface where it is protected by a cocoon formed from dried mucus. It breathes air through a tube that connects with the surface and can exist in this dormant state for over a year.

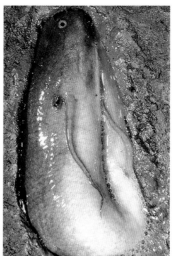

AIR-BREATHERS

Lungfish swim bladders have a unique structure with internal subdivisions (alveoli), so that they are fully functional lungs. There are four species and three sub-species of African lungfishes, belonging to the genus *Protopterus*, and one South American species, *Lepidosiren paradoxa*.

The African and South American lungfishes are more closely related to one another than to the Australian lungfish. They both have two lungs and thread-like paired pectoral and pelvic fins. Spawning occurs at the onset of the rainy season to aid survival of the gill-breathing larvae. Adults are able to survive protracted dry spells by estivating in burrows, extracting oxygen from air via their lungs.

The Australian lungfish (*Neoceratodus forsteri*) has a single lung and paddle-shaped fins. Although it can breathe air, it retains functional gills and cannot survive complete desiccation—it does not burrow into mud or form a cocoon. This lungfish can, however, survive for several months in a dried-up pool, provided that moist leaves and mud are present. Many biologists believe that the Australian lungfish is closest to the ancestral form.

Swim or crawl African lungfishes use two methods of movement: anguilliform (eel-like) swimming, and crawling with the paired fins. They swim when scavenging in mid-water or moving to the surface to breathe air. They crawl when in very shallow water or when scavenging along the bottom. When the African lungfish is crawling (left), the buoyant body is raised and the thin paired fins are used alternately to propel the body forward.

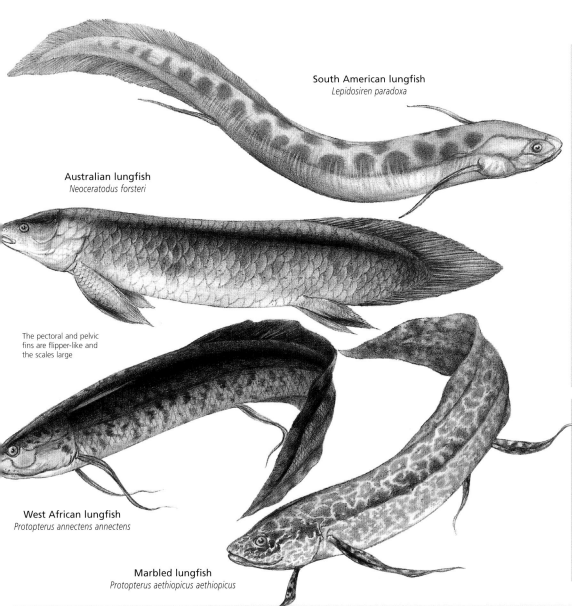

South American lungfish
Lepidosiren paradoxa

Australian lungfish
Neoceratodus forsteri

The pectoral and pelvic
fins are flipper-like and
the scales large

West African lungfish
Protopterus annectens annectens

Marbled lungfish
Protopterus aethiopicus aethiopicus

FACT FILE

Australian lungfish This lungfish
inhabits still or slow-flowing waters.
It can tolerate stagnant conditions by
breathing air, however, it lacks the ability
to survive dry spells by estivation.

- Up to 5½ ft (1.7 m)
- Up to 88 lb (40 kg)
- ○ Oviparous
- ♀♂ Male & female
- Locally common

Queensland, Australia

Marbled lungfish To survive in
streams and swamps which completely
dry up, this species estivates in a
cocoon until the rains fall again.

- Up to 6½ ft (2 m)
- Up to 37 lb (17 kg)
- ○ Oviparous
- ♀♂ Male & female
- Locally common

Africa: River Nile & Rift Valley lakes

⚡ CONSERVATION WATCH

Facing extinction Listed on the IUCN
Red List as critically endangered,
the coelacanth *Latimeria chalumnae*
is known mainly from the Indian
Ocean's Comoro Islands, where
the world's largest population of
this fish is thought to comprise just
several hundred adults. Growing
to 6 feet (1.8 m) in length, it is late
to mature and long-lived. Females
have a long gestation period of
13 months and bear live young.

LIVING FOSSIL

Coelacanths were believed to have
been extinct since the end of the
Cretaceous, 60 million years ago.
They were known only from fossils
until a specimen of *Latimeria
chalumnae* was trawled up near
South Africa's Chaluma River in
1938 and spotted in the catch by
Margaret Courtney-Latimer. For
60 years it was thought that all
modern coelacanths belonged to
this single species found around the
Comoro Islands. However, in 1998
a coelacanth-like fish was seen in
a fisherman's catch 6,215 miles
(10,000 km) away in North Sulawesi,
Indonesia. DNA tests confirmed that
it was a separate species, *Latimeria
menadoensis*. Both species inhabit
deep lava caves and submarine
caverns, where their white speckling
serves as camouflage against the
dark, oyster-shell-encrusted reefs.

BICHIRS AND ALLIES

During the Permian period (285–245 million years ago) the direct ancestors of fishes such as the bichirs, reedfish, sturgeons, and paddlefishes—known collectively as chondostreans—were widespread and numerous both in species and total numbers. Today, these most primitive of the living ray-finned fishes have restricted distributions and are largely considered relics with archaic features. Most have rhombic-shaped scales hardened with a coating of an enamel-like substance called ganoine, not seen in modern species. Spiracles and intestinal spiral valves, characteristics more typical of cartilaginous fishes, are other common features. Most also have a single dorsal fin and a swim bladder, used for breathing air, connected to the gut.

CLASS Actinopterygii
SUBCLASS Chondrostei
ORDERS 2
FAMILIES 3
SPECIES 47

Relict distribution Although fossil records reveal this group once occurred worldwide, its distribution is now restricted to Europe, Asia, Africa, and North America. One paddlefish species occurs in the eastern United States, the other in China. Fossils of the freshwater bichir and reedfish family (Polypteridae) have been uncovered in North Africa but it is now confined to tropical Africa and the Nile River system.

Fish delicacy Caviar (unfertilized sturgeon eggs) has become a symbol of opulence and indulgence. When the ripe females are stripped of their roe and released alive, it is a renewable resource. Too often, however, these fishes are killed for their roe.

Sensitive snouts The elongated snouts of paddlefishes, which account for as much as half their adult length, have a sensory function and are richly endowed with electroreceptors. These fishes are largely freshwater and feed by filtering zooplankton from the water. Although once thought mistakenly to be sharks, their closest living relatives are sturgeons.

STURGEON FEATURES

Sturgeons have been better studied than the other chondostreans, because of their high economic value. Found in both fresh and coastal marine waters, they are very large, long-lived fishes that take many years to reach sexual maturity. Females only spawn every few years.

Like the paddlefishes, sturgeons have several shark-like features, such as partly cartilaginous skeletons and heterocercal tails, where the vertebral column extends well into the tail's upper lobe.

They are unique among the living actinopterygians in having five rows of bony plates running along the body. They also have long flattened snouts and several tentacle-like barbels surrounding a ventrally located protractile mouth.

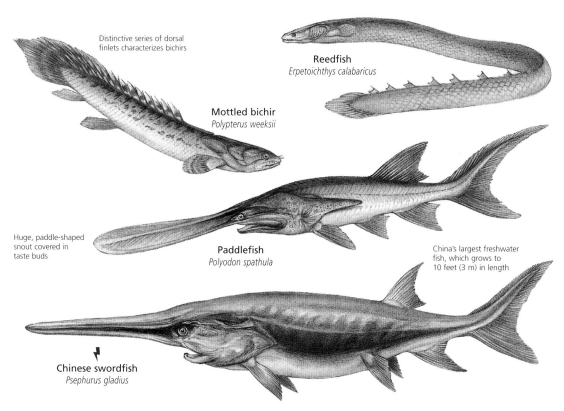

Distinctive series of dorsal finlets characterizes bichirs

Reedfish
Erpetoichthys calabaricus

Mottled bichir
Polypterus weeksii

Huge, paddle-shaped snout covered in taste buds

Paddlefish
Polyodon spathula

China's largest freshwater fish, which grows to 10 feet (3 m) in length

Chinese swordfish
Psephurus gladius

⚡ CONSERVATION WATCH

Sturgeon losses Overharvesting of caviar, habitat degradation, and overfishing have decimated sturgeon populations since the late 20th century. Most species are included on the IUCN Red List, including five that are classified as critically endangered. As part of efforts to halt the decline, sturgeon products were placed under the Convention on International Trade in Endangered Species of Wild Fauna and Flora in 1998.

Atlantic sturgeon
Acipenser oxyrinchus

Snout is long and
sharply V-shaped

Pelvic fins are
set well back

Stellate sturgeon
Acipenser stellatus

European sturgeon
Acipenser sturio

Mouth is small
and tubular

Five rows of bony
scutes or plates
on the body

White sturgeon
Acipenser transmontanus

Beluga
Huso huso

Probably the largest fish
to enter freshwater

FACT FILE

Stellate sturgeon This fish has all
the characteristic sturgeon features:
five rows of bony plates on the dorsal
surface of its body, a flattened snout,
a protractile, ventrally located toothless
mouth, and sensitive, fleshy, tentacle-
like projections known as barbels in
front of the mouth below the snout.
Sturgeons drag these over bottom
sediments in search of prey such as
small fishes and invertebrates.

- Up to 7¼ ft (2.2 m)
- Up to 175 lb (80 kg)
- ○ Oviparous
- ♀♂ Male & female
- Endangered

Basins of Black, Azov, Caspian seas; Adriatic Sea

White sturgeon The largest of the
freshwater fishes in North America, the
white sturgeon grows to 20 feet (6 m)
in length and attains weights in excess
of 1,500 pounds (680 kg). Sturgeons
are typically very long-lived and this
species is thought to have a life
expectancy of at least a century.

- Up to 20 ft (6 m)
- Up to 1,800 lb (820 kg)
- ○ Oviparous
- ♀♂ Male & female
- Near threatened

N.W. North America

Beluga Often described as the "most
expensive fish in the world," the beluga
is the most sought-after of the caviar
sturgeons because of both the quality
and quantity of its roe. A 13 foot (4 m)
female can yield 400 pounds (180 kg).

- Up to 13 ft (4 m)
- Up to 1,760 lb (800 kg)
- ○ Oviparous
- ♀♂ Male & female
- Endangered

Basins of Black & Caspian seas; Adriatic Sea

STERLET

The sterlet (*Acipenser ruthenus*), a caviar
sturgeon, is designated as vulnerable on
the IUCN Red List. Endemic to freshwater
tributaries feeding the Black and Caspian
seas, it survives cold winter months like
other sturgeons in a type of "suspended
animation," resting at depth without
eating. Adults rise in spring to migrate
upriver and spawn.

rows of bony plates are
characteristic of all
sturgeons

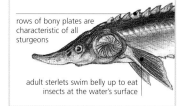

adult sterlets swim belly up to eat
insects at the water's surface

PRIMITIVE NEOPTERYGII

CLASS	Actinopterygii
SUBCLASS	Neopterygii
ORDERS	2
FAMILIES	2
SPECIES	8

The Neopterygii are the second of the two living ray-finned fish groups. They arose from primitive fishes—probably early chondrosteans—some 250 million years ago and, compared with their predecessors, had more mobile mouth parts, more symmetrical compact tails, and a simpler fin structure. Such advances enhanced feeding and swimming capabilities and the group ultimately gave rise to the extraordinarily successful teleosts, which comprise the majority of living fish species. Features of the earliest Neopterygii can still be seen today in a few surviving primitive representatives of the group: the bowfin and the seven species of gars, all of which are agile and voracious predators.

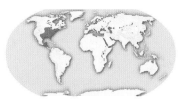

Northern Hemisphere inhabitants The bowfin is mostly restricted to still bodies of freshwater in temperate eastern North America. Five gar species are found in eastern North America. The remaining two species occur in Central America.

ANCIENT FISHES
Gars and the bowfin have elongated body shapes, abbreviated shark-like heterocercal tails, and numerous sharp teeth. They inhabit mostly still-water swamps and backwaters where they can survive low levels of dissolved oxygen by using lung-like gas bladders to breathe air. Gars have primitive, interlocking ganoid scales, while the bowfin has cycloid scales, the type common in more modern fishes.

Bayou dweller Like other semionotiforms, the alligator gar (*Atractosteus spatula*) (above) is an aggressive carnivore with lightning reflexes that prefers slow-moving, poorly oxygenated, swampy backwaters. Growing to almost 10 feet (3 m) in length, it is the largest of the seven gar species.

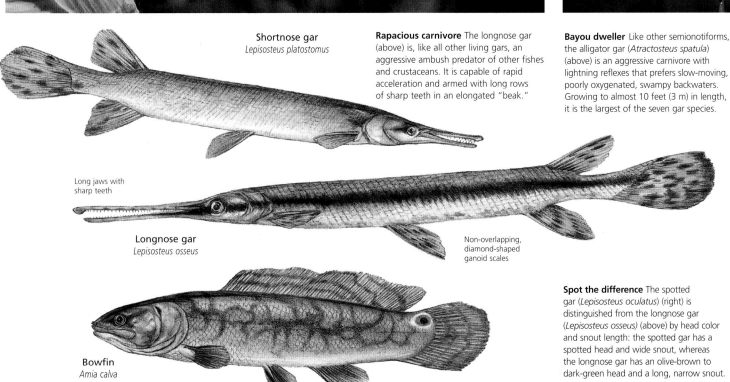

Shortnose gar
Lepisosteus platostomus

Rapacious carnivore The longnose gar (above) is, like all other living gars, an aggressive ambush predator of other fishes and crustaceans. It is capable of rapid acceleration and armed with long rows of sharp teeth in an elongated "beak."

Long jaws with sharp teeth

Longnose gar
Lepisosteus osseus

Non-overlapping, diamond-shaped ganoid scales

Bowfin
Amia calva

Spot the difference The spotted gar (*Lepisosteus oculatus*) (right) is distinguished from the longnose gar (*Lepisosteus osseus*) (above) by head color and snout length: the spotted gar has a spotted head and wide snout, whereas the longnose gar has an olive-brown to dark-green head and a long, narrow snout.

BONYTONGUES AND ALLIES

CLASS	Actinopterygii
SUBDIVISION	Osteoglossomorpha
ORDER	Osteoglossiformes
FAMILIES	6
SPECIES	221

These fishes, the osteoglossomorphs, are considered the most primitive of the modern teleosts. The term bonytongue describes a trait shared by all members of the group: well-developed, tooth-like tongue bones that bite against teeth on the roof of the mouth. Beyond this unifying trait—and the fact that all are exclusively freshwater, even though the fossil record indicates that some past forms may have endured brackish water—these fishes exhibit an extraordinary diversity of form and behaviors. They are found on all continents except Europe and Antarctica, with most species occurring in Africa and just one family containing two species in North America.

Tropical endemics True bonytongues occur in South America, Africa, Australia, Malaysia, Borneo, Sumatra, Thailand, and New Guinea. Featherbacks are restricted to Asia and Africa. All elephantfish species are found only in Africa.

Odd-shaped head The arawana (right) has a distinctive appearance. It has two forward-pointing sensory barbels on the chin and a large trap-like mouth in which the lower jaw edge opens almost vertically.

Skillful swimmer With rippling movements of its very long anal fin, the African knifefish (*Xenomystus nigri*) (above) can swim backward with as much ease as it moves forward.

FRESHWATER CURIOSITIES

There are three main groups in the osteoglossomorph subdivision. True bonytongues range from a small butterflyfish that seemingly glides in air using its well-developed pectoral fins, to the arapaima, one of the largest freshwater fishes.

Featherbacks have almost no tail fin but their anal fin runs two-thirds of their body length.

The elephantfishes, the third main group, includes species with elongated snouts that look like elephant trunks. Anal fin shape differs between the sexes in these bizarre-looking fishes. It is thought these fins are brought together in spawning pairs to form a cup into which eggs and sperm are ejected and mixed.

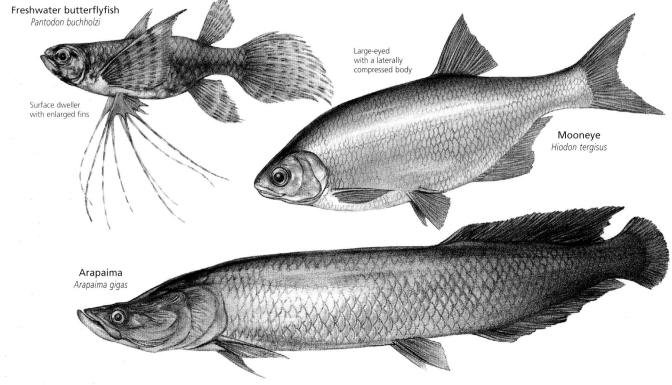

Freshwater butterflyfish
Pantodon buchholzi

Surface dweller with enlarged fins

Large-eyed with a laterally compressed body

Mooneye
Hiodon tergisus

Arapaima
Arapaima gigas

Aba
Gymnarchus niloticus

Dorsal fin set
well back on body

Bulldog
*Marcusenius
macrolepidotus*

Dolphin whale
Brienomyrus longianalis

Homocercal tail

Dorsal-band whale
Petrocephalus simus

Long dorsal fin

Eastern bottlenose mormyrid
Mormyrus longirostris

Anal fin continuous
with caudal fin

Clown knifefish
Chitala chitala

Discharges weak
electric currents

Blunt-jaw elephantnose
Campylomormyrus elephas

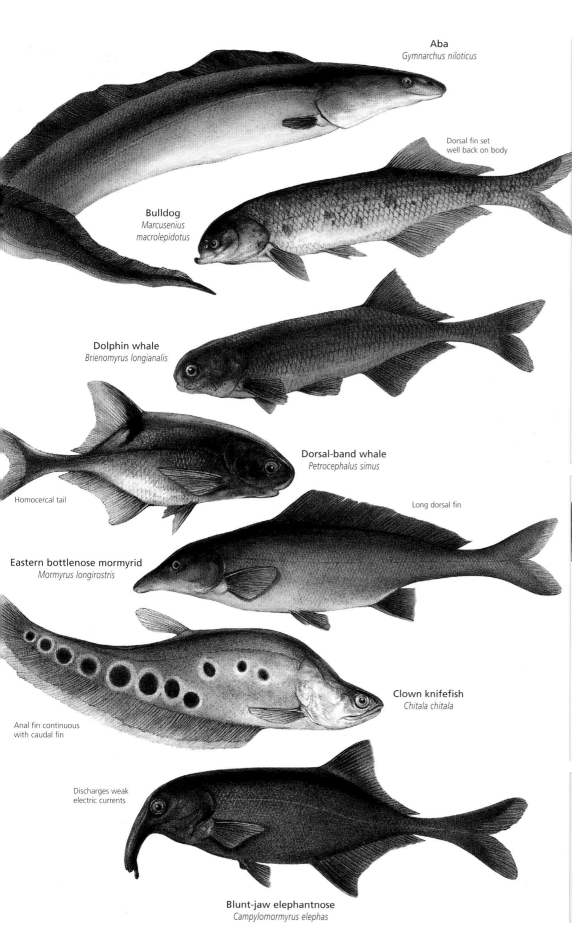

FACT FILE

Aba This species is in the same super-family as the elephantfishes, but differs from all other members of that group in that it has no caudal, anal, or pelvic fins. It does, however, have a very long dorsal fin that runs the length of its body and can be over 5 feet (1.5 m).

⚓ Up to 5½ ft (1.7 m)
⚖ Up to 40 lb (18 kg)
○ Oviparous, guarders
♀♂ Male & female
⚐ Common

N. & N.W. Central Africa

Clown knifefish The female clown knifefish lays eggs on hard substrates, usually a stump of wood. The male guards the eggs against small catfishes and other predators. He also fans the eggs with his tail to aerate and remove silt. The anal fin is continuous with the caudal fin. This species does not produce electric currents.

⚓ Up to 4 ft (1.2 m)
⚖ Up to 7¾ lb (3.5 kg)
○ Oviparous
♀♂ Male & female
⚐ Common

South Asia

BIG BRAINS

enlarged "chin" used to probe
muddy substrates for food

Elephantfishes have a very large brain, proportionately as big as a human brain when body sizes are compared, and are said to have strong capabilities for learning. They have a particularly well-developed cerebellum. This processes the sensory information they gather by electroreception, their most important sense. They can detect and produce weak electric currents, and can create an electrical field around the body, which they use in murky river waters and for night navigation.

⚡ CONSERVATION WATCH

Of the 221 species contained in the Osteoglossiformes order (i.e. bony tongues and their allies), four are included on the IUCN Red List, as follows:

    1 Endangered
    2 Near threatened
    1 Data deficient

EELS AND ALLIES

CLASS Actinopterygii	
SUBDIVISION Elopomorpha	
ORDERS 5	
FAMILIES 24	
SPECIES 911	

Many of the more than 900 species grouped together among these fishes, the elopomorphs, appear at first to have little to do with the elongated snake-like creatures most people know as eels. All, however, are linked because they invariably begin life as leptocephalus larvae. These translucent ribbon-shaped organisms drift in ocean currents for up to three years before metamorphosing into juvenile versions of their adult forms. This diverse assemblage of mainly marine and estuarine species includes three major groups: "true eels," such as moray, conger, and freshwater eels; the tarpons, ladyfishes, bonefishes, halosaurs, and spiny eels; and the bizarre deep-sea gulper eels.

Widespread distribution Most true eels are found in tropical and subtropical seas and oceans, although members of the family Anguillidae spend most of their lives in temperate freshwater. Tarpons and their closest relatives occur mainly in warm coastal and estuarine waters. Spiny eels are found throughout the world's oceans down to depths of 16,000 feet (4,900 m). All four families of deep-sea gulper eels also occur worldwide in deep ocean waters.

VARIED FORMS

With more than 700 species, the true eels are by far the largest group of elopomorphs. These have an elongated shape and almost all lack pelvic and pectoral fins. This streamlined body design suits a burrowing lifestyle and allows ease of movement into and out of holes around coral reefs.

Adult tarpons, bonefishes, and ladyfishes have large metallic scales, forked tails, and a typical fish shape. The former two groups are highly regarded as sportfish.

The spiny eels have deep-sea habits, are long, scaled, and feed on slow-moving, bottom-dwelling invertebrates. Deep-sea gulper eels have elongate, scaleless bodies. Enormous mouths and highly distensible stomachs take advantage of infrequent large meals.

Cryptic but common
Work by Hawaiian scientists has identified that morays can account for almost half the carnivorous biomass on tropical reefs.

Fierce faces Many morays, such as the dragon moray (*Enchelycore pardalis*) (above), have wide jaws filled with large sharp teeth. This species also has unusually prominent nose-tubes. Bold color patterns are also common among the morays; these help to camouflage them on the tropical reefs where they live. There are more than 200 species of this largely nocturnal family of carnivores. They have relatively small eyes and poor vision and locate prey using their keen sense of smell.

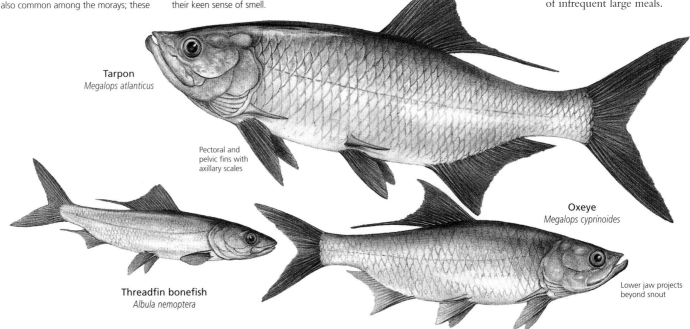

Tarpon
Megalops atlanticus

Pectoral and pelvic fins with axillary scales

Threadfin bonefish
Albula nemoptera

Oxeye
Megalops cyprinoides

Lower jaw projects beyond snout

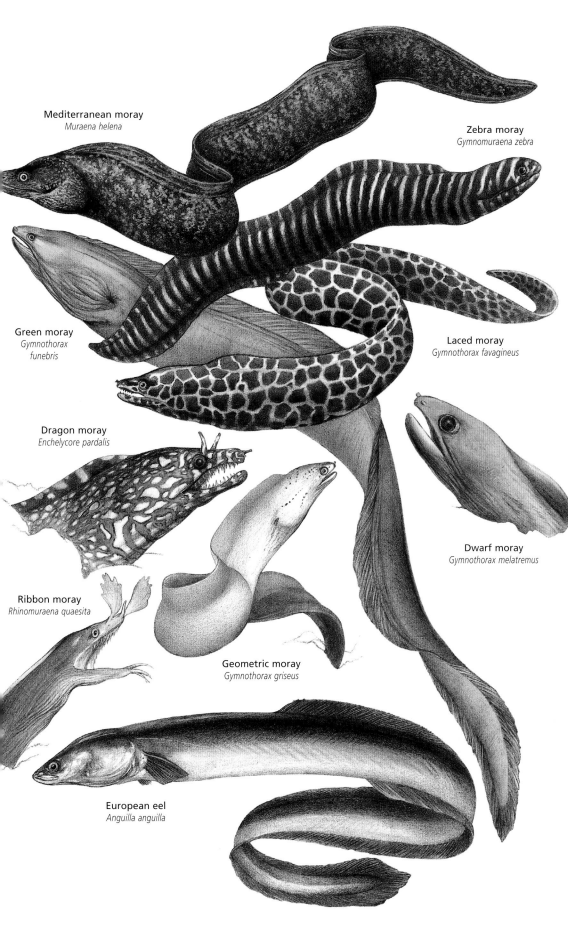

Mediterranean moray
Muraena helena

Zebra moray
Gymnomuraena zebra

Green moray
Gymnothorax funebris

Laced moray
Gymnothorax favagineus

Dragon moray
Enchelycore pardalis

Dwarf moray
Gymnothorax melatremus

Ribbon moray
Rhinomuraena quaesita

Geometric moray
Gymnothorax griseus

European eel
Anguilla anguilla

FACT FILE

Laced moray One of the largest Indo-Pacific morays, the laced moray inhabits reef flats and crevices within the reef, often in the company of cleaner wrasses or shrimps. It has a bold, spotted pattern that acts as camouflage by resembling the reflections of light in the water. It feeds on fishes and cephalopods. Larger adults may be aggressive.

➡ Up to 10 ft (3 m)
⚖ Up to 88 lb (40 kg)
○ Oviparous
♀♂ Not known
🐟 Common

Indo-West Pacific

Green moray Adult morays in this species are uniformly greenish or dark greenish-gray, hence their common name. The largest of the Atlantic morays, it is a solitary species found along rocky shorelines, reefs, and mangroves. It feeds mainly at night on fishes and crustaceans. It is an aggressive species of moray; this behavioral trait combined with its large size, makes its bite particularly dangerous.

➡ Up to 8 ft (2.4 m)
⚖ Up to 64 lb (29 kg)
○ Oviparous
♀♂ Not known
🐟 Common

W. Atlantic

Dragon moray A predator of other fishes, the dragon moray inhabits crevices in rocky and coral reefs. Long extensions of the rear nostrils give the impression of horns and an ornate pattern of spots and bars make this an impressive beast. It is much sought after by the aquarium trade but is difficult to find in the wild and its aggressive and predatory behavior make it difficult to keep with other fishes.

➡ Up to 35 in (89 cm)
⚖ Up to 2¼ lb (1 kg)
○ Oviparous
♀♂ Not known
🐟 Common

Indo-Central Pacific

TOOTHED TURKEY

Like other morays, the turkey moray (*Gymnothorax meleagris*) has large canine teeth and powerful jaws. Morays have been known to bite divers when scared or threatened but usually reserve their aggression for hunting prey.

morays have small eyes and poor vision

FACT FILE

European conger An elongated, scaleless, and nocturnal marine predator, the European conger can attain huge proportions. Juveniles occur around rocks and on sandy substrates near coastlines but adults live in deeper offshore waters. Like other congers, reproduction is a once-in-a-lifetime event, during which a female can produce up to 8 million eggs.

⇔ Up to 9 ft (2.8 m)
⚖ Up to 143 lb (65 kg)
○ Oviparous, semelparous
♀♂ Male & female
⚑ Common

E. Atlantic, Mediterranean Sea, Black Sea

Pelican eel A typical gulper eel, this fish has an enormously enlarged mouth, distensible buccal cavity, and a stomach that can expand to two-thirds its total size: all adaptations to irregular feeding of large meals of invertebrates and other fishes. It dwells at depths of 1,650–24,500 feet (500–7,500 m) and bears a luminous tail organ.

⇔ Up to 3¼ ft (1 m)
⚖ Up to 2 lb (900 g)
○ Oviparous
♀♂ Male & female
⚑ Common

Widespread in temperate & tropical seas

EEL GARDENS

At least 20 conger eel species spend their entire juvenile and adult lives in colonies—sometimes comprising thousands of individuals—permanently embedded in substrate. With tails down and heads waving, they feed on plankton. Known as garden eels, they occur at depths of up to 1,000 feet (300 m), retreating into their mucus-lined burrows when threatened.

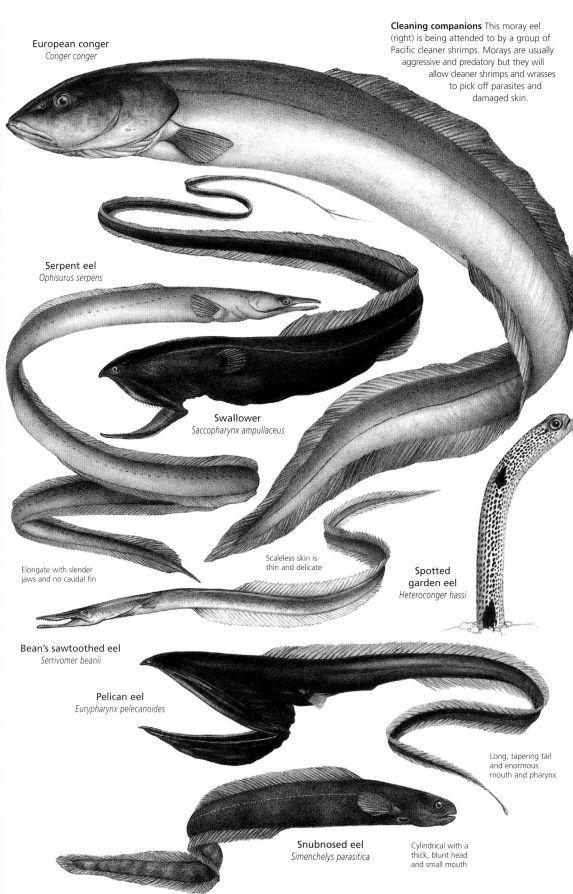

European conger
Conger conger

Cleaning companions This moray eel (right) is being attended to by a group of Pacific cleaner shrimps. Morays are usually aggressive and predatory but they will allow cleaner shrimps and wrasses to pick off parasites and damaged skin.

Serpent eel
Ophisurus serpens

Swallower
Saccopharynx ampullaceus

Scaleless skin is thin and delicate

Spotted garden eel
Heteroconger hassi

Elongate with slender jaws and no caudal fin

Bean's sawtoothed eel
Serrivomer beanii

Pelican eel
Eurypharynx pelecanoides

Long, tapering tail and enormous mouth and pharynx

Snubnosed eel
Simenchelys parasitica

Cylindrical with a thick, blunt head and small mouth

THE MYSTERIOUS LIVES OF FRESHWATER EELS

It was not until late in the 19th century that scientists began uncovering the truth about the life-cycles of the European eel (*Anguilla anguilla*) and its relative the American eel (*Anguilla rostrata*). Both species, it is now known, spawn in the Sargasso Sea, but precisely where remains a mystery. Their lives take decades and up to 7,000 miles (11,250 km) to complete. European eels head east, their American cousins west, both spending most of their lives in freshwater before returning to the Sargasso Sea to spawn once and die.

Small beginnings European eels are just 2–4 inches (5–10 cm) long when, after several years of oceanic drifting, they finally reach the estuaries that will take them to their freshwater adult habitats.

Parallel lives Adult European eels dwell in freshwater throughout Europe and parts of northern Africa. Their life history (below) mirrors that of the American species, in which adults occupy freshwater along North America's east coast. Research has shown that both species have suffered massive declines since the 1970s. Some investigations indicate adult European eel numbers may have fallen by 90 percent or more as a result of overfishing, pollution, disease, and habitat destruction.

Silver fishes Adult European eels occupy freshwater that feeds the North Atlantic Ocean and Baltic and Mediterranean seas. Females mature between 9 and 20 years; males between 6 and 12 years.

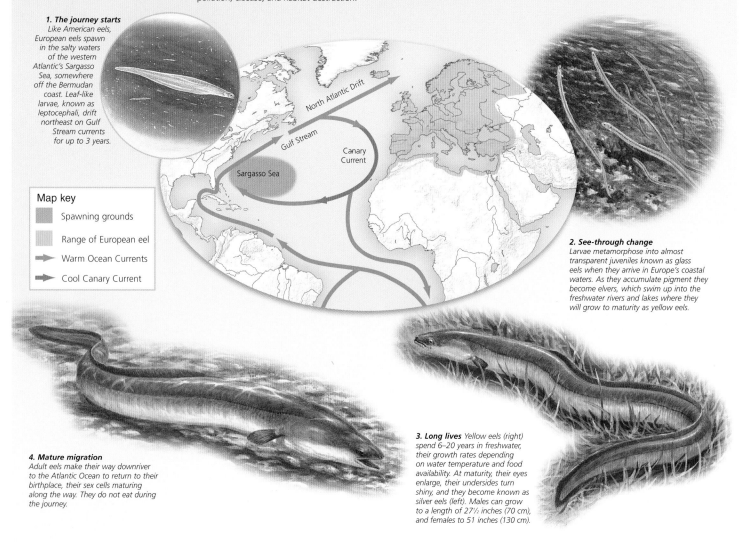

1. The journey starts
Like American eels, European eels spawn in the salty waters of the western Atlantic's Sargasso Sea, somewhere off the Bermudan coast. Leaf-like larvae, known as leptocephali, drift northeast on Gulf Stream currents for up to 3 years.

North Atlantic Drift

Gulf Stream

Canary Current

Sargasso Sea

Map key

Spawning grounds

Range of European eel

Warm Ocean Currents

Cool Canary Current

2. See-through change
Larvae metamorphose into almost transparent juveniles known as glass eels when they arrive in Europe's coastal waters. As they accumulate pigment they become elvers, which swim up into the freshwater rivers and lakes where they will grow to maturity as yellow eels.

4. Mature migration
Adult eels make their way downriver to the Atlantic Ocean to return to their birthplace, their sex cells maturing along the way. They do not eat during the journey.

3. Long lives *Yellow eels (right) spend 6–20 years in freshwater, their growth rates depending on water temperature and food availability. At maturity, their eyes enlarge, their undersides turn shiny, and they become known as silver eels (left). Males can grow to a length of 27½ inches (70 cm), and females to 51 inches (130 cm).*

SARDINES AND ALLIES

SION Teleostei

DIVISION peomorpha

ER Clupeiformes

ILIES 5

CIES 378

Known as the clupeoids, this group of 378 species comprises some of the world's most commercially important fishes, including herrings, sardines, anchovies, shads, and pilchards. Most are marine filter feeders of zooplankton that form large schools and lead pelagic lifestyles, although their distributions tend to be more coastal than open water. Spawning is frequently in near-shore surface waters and usually seasonal. Females mostly produce large numbers of small eggs which develop into larvae that can drift in surface currents for many months before metamorphosing into juveniles. Some species undertake extraordinary migrations as adults, covering thousands of miles and several years.

Coastal preferences The clupeoids are largely a Northern Hemisphere group. The adults of most species feed along the coasts of tropical and temperate seas, but more than 70 species inhabit freshwater rivers and lakes. Very few species occur far from shore in the open ocean and none are found in polar seas or at oceanic depths. Seasonal migrations to spawning grounds are common in the group.

Staying in school The gas bladder of all clupeoids extends into the inner ear. Known as an otophysic condition, this is thought to increase their abilities to detect low-frequency sounds such as those produced by beating tail fins, and may aid in schooling. Larvae old enough to have a swim bladder are thought to only inflate it, and rise in the water column, at night.

BOOM-BUST POPULATIONS

Renowned for natural boom-bust population cycles, clupeoids suffer from extremely high mortality rates—frequently up to 99 percent—partly because they fall victim to a wide range of predators at all stages of their life-cycle. They are also highly vulnerable as adults to variations in food availability, a result of increasingly fluctuating environmental conditions.

Most species, however, have very high reproductive rates and reach sexual maturity at early ages (rarely later than three years of age). As a consequence, populations tend to bounce back quickly when good conditions prevail.

The clupeoid group contributes enormously to the total biomass of the world's aquatic environments and is a crucial lower link in many aquatic food chains.

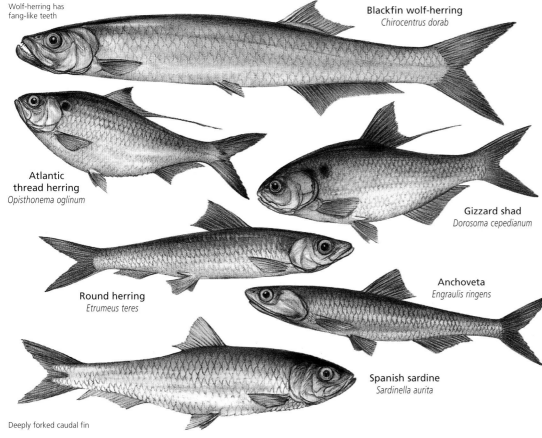

Wolf-herring has fang-like teeth

Blackfin wolf-herring
Chirocentrus dorab

Atlantic thread herring
Opisthonema oglinum

Gizzard shad
Dorosoma cepedianum

Round herring
Etrumeus teres

Anchoveta
Engraulis ringens

Spanish sardine
Sardinella aurita

Deeply forked caudal fin

Archetypal fish Clupeoids, such as these herrings, are what most people visualize when they think of fishes: small—most attaining lengths less than 12 inches (30 cm)—streamlined, and schooling, with large silver scales and forked tails.

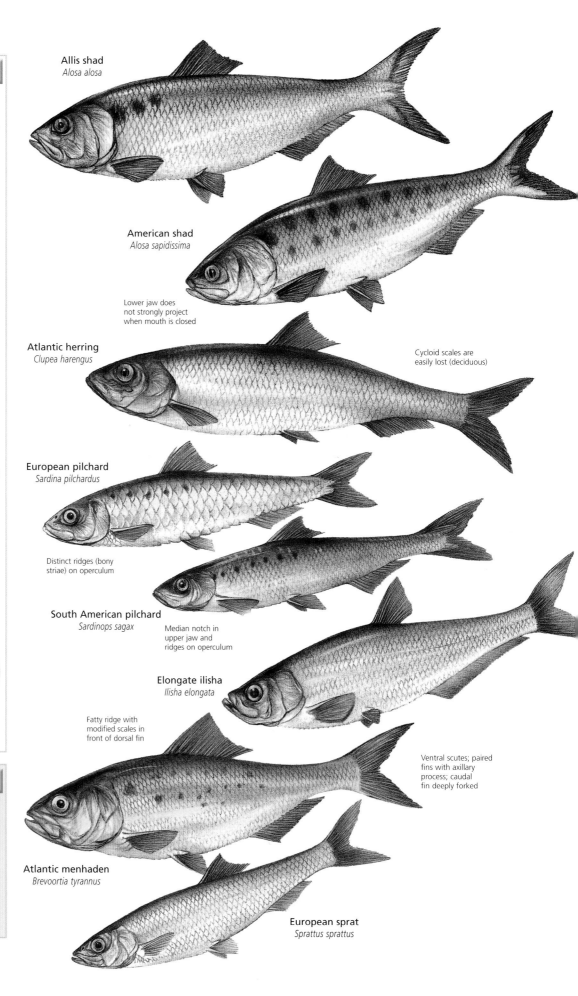

Allis shad
Alosa alosa

American shad
Alosa sapidissima

Lower jaw does
not strongly project
when mouth is closed

Atlantic herring
Clupea harengus

Cycloid scales are
easily lost (deciduous)

European pilchard
Sardina pilchardus

Distinct ridges (bony
striae) on operculum

South American pilchard
Sardinops sagax

Median notch in
upper jaw and
ridges on operculum

Elongate ilisha
Ilisha elongata

Ventral scutes; paired
fins with axillary
process; caudal
fin deeply forked

Fatty ridge with
modified scales in
front of dorsal fin

Atlantic menhaden
Brevoortia tyrannus

European sprat
Sprattus sprattus

FACT FILE

American shad Adult American shad spend most of their lives in coastal marine and brackish waters but migrate, without feeding, to freshwater streams and rivers in eastern North America to spawn. Each female releases up to 600,000 eggs during one evening.

🗣 Up to 30 in (76 cm)
⚖ Up to 12 lb (5.4 kg)
○ Oviparous
♀♂ Male & female
🏃 Common

North America

Atlantic herring This herring has been observed running in 17 mile (27 km) long schools containing millions of individuals. Schools of this species undertake daily vertical migrations. During daylight hours they typically drop to the ocean floor. By night they rise to feed, mostly on zooplankton.

🗣 Up to 17 in (43 cm)
⚖ Up to 24 oz (680 g)
○ Oviparous
♀♂ Male & female
🏃 Common

North Atlantic

South American pilchard This pilchard was once believed to be five different species. Recent research has shown that there are three lineages of the same species: southern Africa (*ocellatus*) and Australia (*neopilchardus*); Chile (*sagax*) and California (*caeruleus*); and Japan (*melanostictus*).

🗣 Up to 16 in (40 cm)
⚖ Up to 17 oz (480 g)
○ Oviparous
♀♂ Male & female
🏃 Common

Indo-Pacific

⚡ CONSERVATION WATCH

Shad shortages The 12 clupeoids on the IUCN Red List include the endangered Alabama shad (*Alosa alabamae*) and the Laotian shad (*Tenualosa thibaudeaui*). The former has declined dramatically due to dam constructions that have impeded spawning migrations into large freshwater rivers. Declining numbers of the Laotian shad may be due to overfishing and dams.

HERMAPHRODITISM

Most fishes are dioecious; they are either male or female from an early age and remain that way throughout life. Hermaphroditism (where individuals possess both male and female sex organs during their lives) is, however, widespread in the group, much more so than among other vertebrates. In some species, individuals are sequential hermaphrodites, changing gender once they reach a certain size or when there is a shortfall of one sex or the other. Less common are simultaneous hermaphrodites, which can perform as either sex at the same time. Hermaphroditism tends to be more prevalent among fishes of lower latitudes. The fish life on tropical coral reefs, in particular, is noted for the phenomenon.

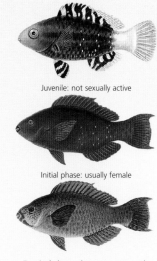

Juvenile: not sexually active

Initial phase: usually female

Terminal phase: always a mature male

Sex-changing eel Ribbon morays (*Rhinomuraena quaesita*) are protandrous hermaphrodites: males become females. This male will turn bright yellow as it matures into a female.

Dominance changeover Among spotbreast angelfish (*Genicanthus melanospilos*), which are protogynous hermaphrodites, a single dominant male is associated with a small harem of females. In response to the death or removal of the male, the largest female grows larger and then changes color before becoming the dominant male.

Replaceable males Hermaphroditism is common in parrotfishes. A dominant male often maintains a harem of females but, if he disappears, the largest and most aggressive female undergoes a sex change accompanied by a dramatic color change, all in a matter of weeks.

4. Quick change The sexual transformation is completed within about 14 days and the new male begins spawning with the members of his harem.

1. Harem life Female spotbreast angelfish are yellow on their upper surface and pale blue below, with strong black lines defining their tails. Harems usually contain between three and five females.

3. Girl power As her sexual transformation continues, her body reabsorbs its eggs and begins sperm production. She begins behaving more aggressively and displays courtship behavior toward the harem's remaining females.

2. Changing colors When the dominant male disappears, the harem's largest female begins to grow and develop the distinctive coloration of a male: a pale blue body with black stripes.

CATFISHES AND ALLIES

CLASS Actinopterygii	
SUPERORDER Ostariophysi	
ORDERS 5	
FAMILIES 62	
SPECIES 7,023	

These fishes, the ostariophysans, dominate the world's freshwater habitats. They form a massive group of over 7,000 species united by two key characteristics. A unique set of bones, the Weberian apparatus, connects the gas bladder and inner ear in an arrangement that enhances hearing. The second trait is an alarm response involving the release of distress chemicals from special skin cells. Many ostariophysans not only produce these substances but can also perceive and respond to them by fleeing. Some species that eat other ostariophysans, however, are not capable of the latter as most of their prey produce these alarm chemicals and reacting would thus inhibit feeding.

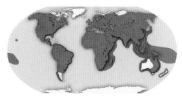

Freshwater dominance Most characins are tropical. Cyprinids are naturally found in North America and Africa, but most are found in Eurasia. Catfishes are found on all continents and the electric knifefishes are restricted to Central and South America. Many ostariophysans, however, are now found well beyond their original range, partly as a result of the aquarium trade.

ENORMOUS DIVERSITY

The most primitive ostariophysans are a tropical group with incomplete Weberian apparatus. The milkfish, an important protein source for people in Southeast Asia, is in this group.

The largest ostariophysan group, the cyprinids, includes the carps, minnows, and many of the world's most popular aquarium fishes, from goldfish to rasboras. These lack jaw teeth but grind food between a pharyngeal tooth-bearing bone and a hard keratinized pad at the base of the skull.

The mostly South American characins include species as diverse and well known as the piranhas and the aquarium favorites, the tetras.

There are well over 2,000 catfish species, all have barbels around the mouth and are substrate feeders.

The electric knifefishes make up a small and poorly studied group that includes the legendary electric eel.

Defensive schooling Striped catfish (*Plotosus lineatus*) (left) school into a ball when threatened by predators.

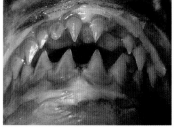

Efficient feeders In some but not all piranha species, short powerful jaws and sharp, interlocking teeth (above) enable flesh removal from prey in clean bites.

Popular fish Originally from the upper reaches of the Amazon River, neon tetras (left) have become a mainstay of the aquarium trade worldwide.

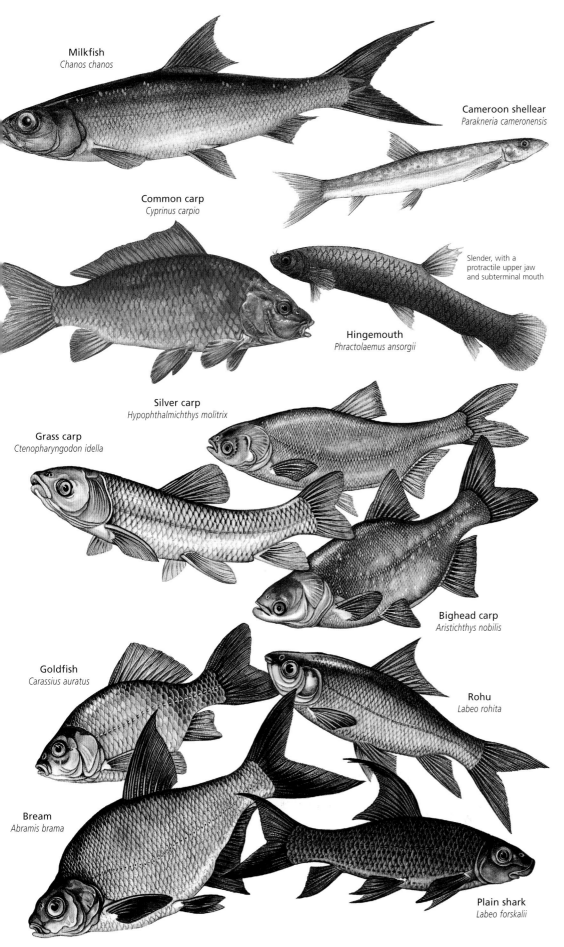

Milkfish
Chanos chanos

Cameroon shellear
Parakneria cameronensis

Common carp
Cyprinus carpio

Slender, with a protractile upper jaw and subterminal mouth

Hingemouth
Phractolaemus ansorgii

Silver carp
Hypophthalmichthys molitrix

Grass carp
Ctenopharyngodon idella

Bighead carp
Aristichthys nobilis

Goldfish
Carassius auratus

Rohu
Labeo rohita

Bream
Abramis brama

Plain shark
Labeo forskalii

FACT FILE

Milkfish Larval milkfish develop in brackish coastal wetlands. They do occasionally enter freshwater but return to the sea to breed. This species is an important protein source for human populations throughout the Indo-Pacific, where it is sometimes farmed in ponds.

🐟 Up to 6 ft (1.8 m)
⚖ Up to 30 lb (14.5 kg)
○ Oviparous
♀♂ Male & female
🔱 Common

E. Africa, S.E. Asia, Oceania & E. Pacific

Hingemouth This species is able to survive in deoxygenated water by taking air from the surface with its mouth that can be projected like a small trunk. It also extracts oxygen in its swim bladder which acts as a lung.

🐟 Up to 7 in (18 cm)
⚖ Up to 3 oz (85 g)
○ Oviparous
♀♂ Male & female
🔱 Common

W. Africa

Grass carp The grass carp prefers large, still or slow-moving water bodies with plenty of vegetation. It feeds on aquatic plants and submerged grasses but will also eat insects and other invertebrates. It has been widely introduced for weed control, sometimes with adverse effects.

🐟 Up to 5 ft (1.5 m)
⚖ Up to 99 lb (44 kg)
○ Oviparous
♀♂ Male & female
🔱 Common

E. Asia

🔱 CONSERVATION WATCH

Barely there In Southern Africa's Twee River and tributaries, the Twee redfin (*Barbus erubescens*) leads a precarious existence, facing threats such as agricultural pollution and excessive water extraction. Introduced fish species, too, have taken a toll. It is among 49 critically endangered ostariophysans worldwide. A further 45 species are endangered and 18 have already gone extinct.

FACT FILE

Putitor mahseer The most common mahseer of the Himalaya, the putitor is also known as the golden or yellow-finned mahseer. It ascends streams to breed over gravel and stones then returns to perennial pools and lakes after spawning.

- Up to 9 ft (2.8 m)
- Up to 119 lb (54 kg)
- ○ Oviparous
- ♀♂ Male & female
- Locally common

Asia

Fallfish This species is the largest minnow native to North America. It inhabits gravel or rubble-bottomed pools, runs of small and medium sized rivers, and also lake margins. The breeding males develop fairly large tubercles on the head.

- Up to 20 in (51 cm)
- Up to 3½ lb (1.6 kg)
- ○ Oviparous
- ♀♂ Male & female
- Common

North America

Zebra danio The zebra danio prefers slow-moving to still bodies of water, particularly rice fields. It feeds on worms, small crustaceans, and insect larvae. Its bright colors and liveliness have made it one of the most popular aquarium fishes.

- Up to 2½ in (6.6 cm)
- Up to 0.18 oz (5 g)
- ○ Oviparous
- ♀♂ Male & female
- Common

Asia

BITTERLING

To breed, the female bitterling develops a long ovipositor down which she passes eggs into the gill chamber of a freshwater mussel. Eggs are fertilized when sperm, released by a male near the bivalve's inhalant aperture, is drawn in and mixes with the eggs. Bitterling larvae develop inside the mussel for up to a month.

Fish pregnancy tests
Female bitterlings were once used to test for pregnancy in women. Urine carrying traces of pregnancy hormones encourages ovipositor development when injected into these fish.

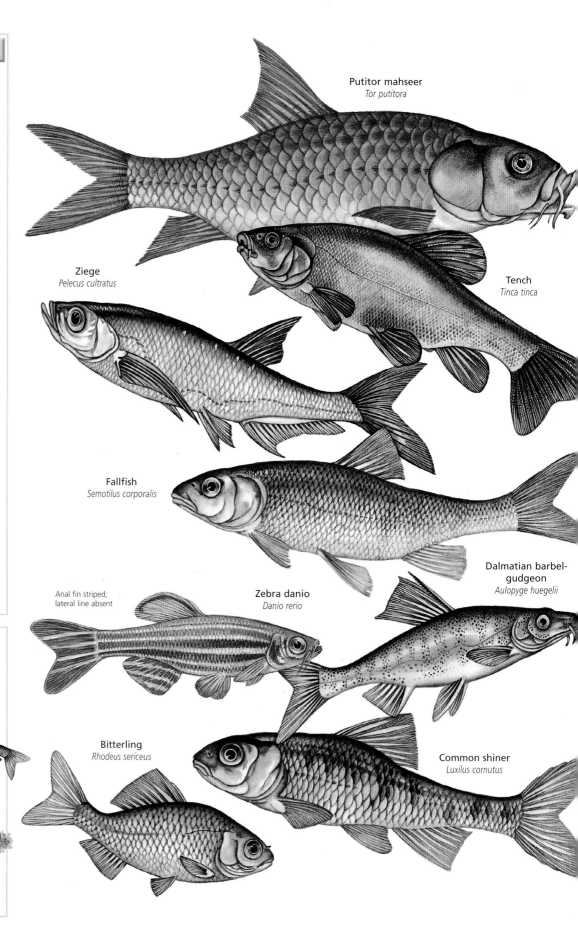

Putitor mahseer
Tor putitora

Ziege
Pelecus cultratus

Tench
Tinca tinca

Fallfish
Semotilus corporalis

Dalmatian barbel-gudgeon
Aulopyge huegelii

Anal fin striped; lateral line absent

Zebra danio
Danio rerio

Bitterling
Rhodeus sericeus

Common shiner
Luxilus cornutus

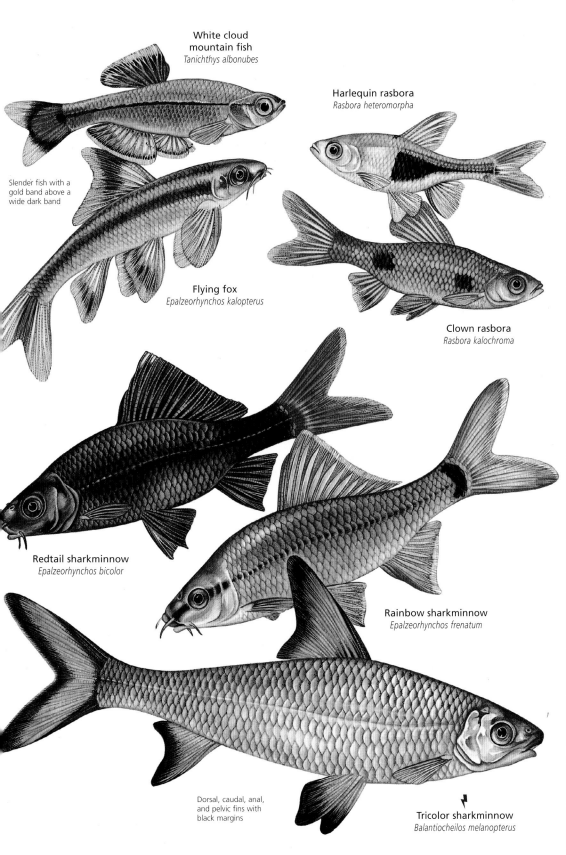

White cloud
mountain fish
Tanichthys albonubes

Slender fish with a
gold band above a
wide dark band

Harlequin rasbora
Rasbora heteromorpha

Flying fox
Epalzeorhynchos kalopterus

Clown rasbora
Rasbora kalochroma

Redtail sharkminnow
Epalzeorhynchos bicolor

Rainbow sharkminnow
Epalzeorhynchos frenatum

Dorsal, caudal, anal,
and pelvic fins with
black margins

Tricolor sharkminnow
Balantiocheilos melanopterus

FACT FILE

White cloud mountain fish Popular in the aquarium trade, this species is native to China and Vietnam. It lives in clear, slow-moving mountain brooks where it feeds on zooplankton and detritus. It can survive temperatures as low as 41°F (5°C).

↦ Up to 1½ in (4 cm)
⚖ Up to ½ oz (15 g)
○ Oviparous
♀♂ Male & female
⚡ Common

S.E. Asia

Clown rasbora This species is native to the Malay Peninsula, Borneo, and Sumatra. It is found in still and sluggish waters that are acidic and rich in humus. The basic coloration is salmon pink with two darker lateral patches.

↦ Up to 4 in (10 cm)
⚖ Up to 3½ oz (100 g)
○ Oviparous
♀♂ Male & female
⚡ Locally common

S.E. Asia

Redtail sharkminnow Endemic to Thailand, this sharkminnow is now thought to be extinct in the wild. Many thousands are now bred in captivity every year and exported from Thailand for the aquarium trade.

↦ Up to 5 in (13 cm)
⚖ Up to 6 oz (170 g)
○ Oviparous
♀♂ Male & female
⚡ Extinct in the wild

S.E. Asia

Tricolor sharkminnow Another popular aquarium fish, this species has become rare or even extinct in many river basins. A mid-water swimmer of medium to large rivers and lakes, it feeds mainly on small crustaceans and insects.

↦ Up to 14 in (36 cm)
⚖ Up to 16 oz (455 g)
○ Oviparous
♀♂ Male & female
⚡ Endangered

S.E. Asia

⚡ CONSERVATION WATCH

Barely there Once presumed extinct, the smoky madtom (*Noturus baileyi*) was rediscovered in a Tennessee stream in the eastern United States in 1980. Fewer than 1,000 adults of this tiny catfish, which grows to 2½ inches (6.6 cm), survive.

Tinfoil barb Found in still and flowing waters where it feeds mainly on aquatic vegetation, this species will also eat invertebrates and small fishes. A silvery, deep-bodied fish with black tipped red fins, it is popular in large aquaria.

- Up to 14 in (36 cm)
- Up to 24 oz (680 g)
- Oviparous
- Male & female
- Common

S.E. Asia

Rosy barb Due to its popularity in the aquarium trade, this colorful barb has been widely introduced outside of its natural range. Found in fast-flowing hill streams as well as in lakes, it feeds on crustaceans, insects, worms, and plants.

- Up to 5½ in (14 cm)
- Up to 5 oz (140 g)
- Oviparous
- Male & female
- Common

S. Asia

Spanner barb Many of the barbs are popular within the aquarium trade, but the spanner barb grows a little too large to be a highly sought-after species.

- Up to 7 in (18 cm)
- Up to 8 oz (225 g)
- Oviparous
- Male & female
- Common

Malay Peninsula to Borneo

Tiger barb Native to Malaysia, Sumatra, and Borneo, the tiger barb has been widely introduced for the aquarium trade. In the wild, it is found in nearly all running and still waters including mountain streams where it feeds on small invertebrates and plant matter.

- Up to 3 in (7.5 cm)
- Up to 2 oz (60 g)
- Oviparous
- Male & female
- Common

S.E. Asia

Chinese sucker Native to the Yangtze River basin, this species is named for its thickened lips, which are used to suck up food, such as invertebrates and algae, from sediments and around river rocks and plants. In some suckers, the dorsal fin can be almost as tall as the body is long.

- Up to 23½ in (60 cm)
- Up to 8 lb (3.6 kg)
- Oviparous
- Male & female
- Locally common

China (Yangtze River basin)

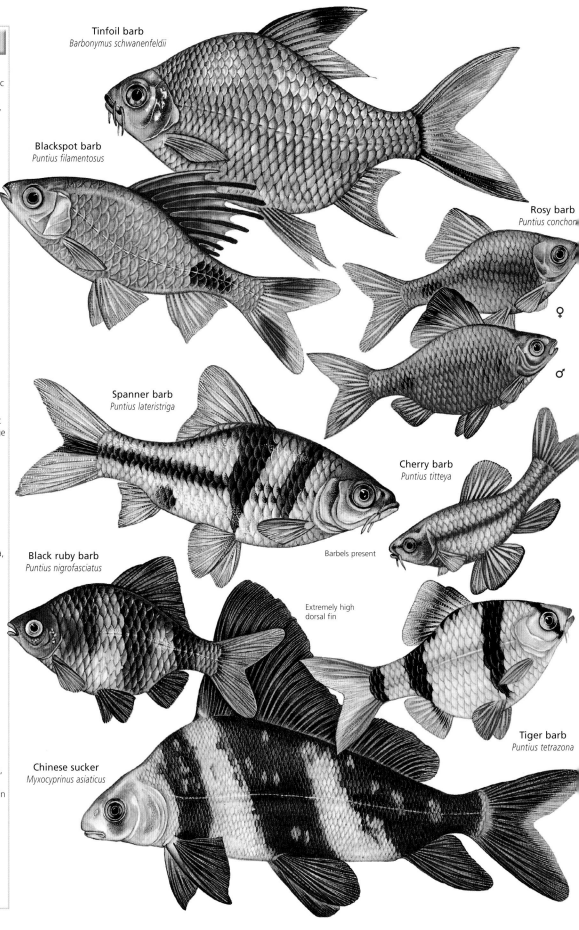

Tinfoil barb
Barbonymus schwanenfeldii

Blackspot barb
Puntius filamentosus

Rosy barb
Puntius conchon

♀

♂

Spanner barb
Puntius lateristriga

Cherry barb
Puntius titteya

Barbels present

Black ruby barb
Puntius nigrofasciatus

Extremely high dorsal fin

Tiger barb
Puntius tetrazona

Chinese sucker
Myxocyprinus asiaticus

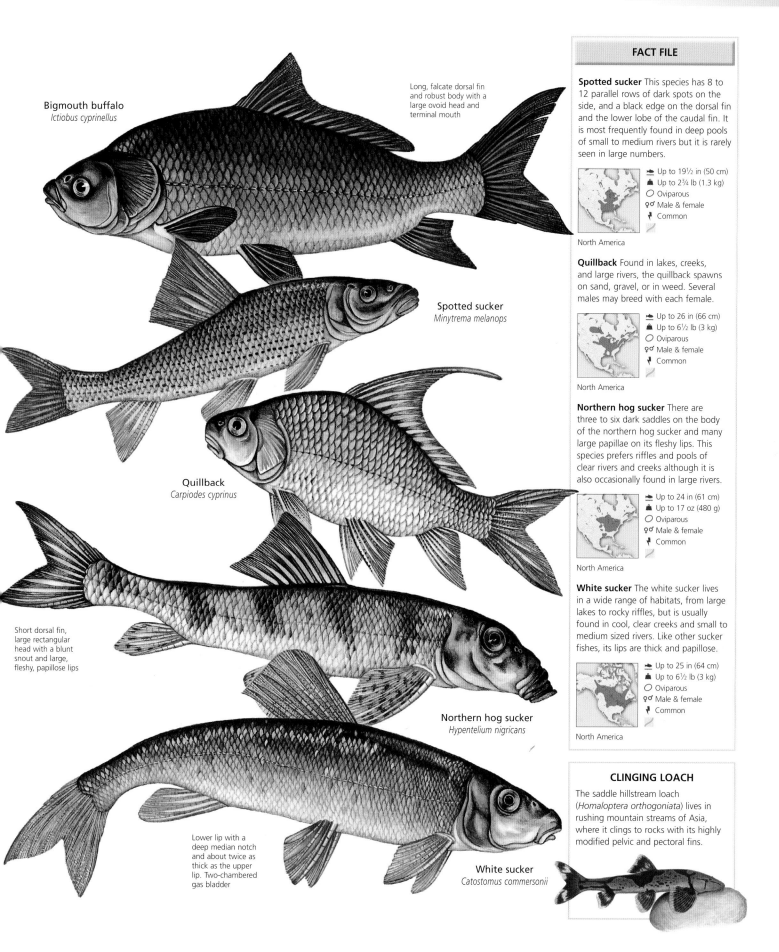

Bigmouth buffalo
Ictiobus cyprinellus

Long, falcate dorsal fin and robust body with a large ovoid head and terminal mouth

Spotted sucker
Minytrema melanops

Quillback
Carpiodes cyprinus

Short dorsal fin, large rectangular head with a blunt snout and large, fleshy, papillose lips

Northern hog sucker
Hypentelium nigricans

Lower lip with a deep median notch and about twice as thick as the upper lip. Two-chambered gas bladder

White sucker
Catostomus commersonii

FACT FILE

Spotted sucker This species has 8 to 12 parallel rows of dark spots on the side, and a black edge on the dorsal fin and the lower lobe of the caudal fin. It is most frequently found in deep pools of small to medium rivers but it is rarely seen in large numbers.

- Up to 19½ in (50 cm)
- Up to 2¾ lb (1.3 kg)
- Oviparous
- Male & female
- Common

North America

Quillback Found in lakes, creeks, and large rivers, the quillback spawns on sand, gravel, or in weed. Several males may breed with each female.

- Up to 26 in (66 cm)
- Up to 6½ lb (3 kg)
- Oviparous
- Male & female
- Common

North America

Northern hog sucker There are three to six dark saddles on the body of the northern hog sucker and many large papillae on its fleshy lips. This species prefers riffles and pools of clear rivers and creeks although it is also occasionally found in large rivers.

- Up to 24 in (61 cm)
- Up to 17 oz (480 g)
- Oviparous
- Male & female
- Common

North America

White sucker The white sucker lives in a wide range of habitats, from large lakes to rocky riffles, but is usually found in cool, clear creeks and small to medium sized rivers. Like other sucker fishes, its lips are thick and papillose.

- Up to 25 in (64 cm)
- Up to 6½ lb (3 kg)
- Oviparous
- Male & female
- Common

North America

CLINGING LOACH

The saddle hillstream loach (*Homaloptera orthogoniata*) lives in rushing mountain streams of Asia, where it clings to rocks with its highly modified pelvic and pectoral fins.

BARBELS

Catfishes are most readily recognized by the thread-like "whiskers," named barbels, that are around their mouths. At least one pair of barbels, called the maxillary barbels, is invariably present at the two corners of the mouth. Usually two additional pairs are found on the lower jaw and sometimes a fourth pair on the snout, associated with the nostrils. When more than one pair of barbels is present, the maxillary barbels are usually largest, sometimes exceeding the length of the entire fish. The barbels are used in a number of ways, but are best known as sense organs. They are covered with taste buds that allow a catfish to detect food in front, below, and alongside it, and are more sensitive than a bloodhound's nose. When visibility is low, the barbels can also act as guides, feeling around by sensing the electrical fields generated by living things.

Extra taste buds This catfish (above) is commonly known as the black bullhead in reference to its barbels which were thought to resemble the horns of a bull. The barbels are covered in taste buds that allow the black bullhead to actually taste a food item without even touching it. This is particulary important when searching for food in muddy waters.

Sensing The Indo-Pacific's striped eel-catfish (*Plotosus lineatus*) is one of the few marine catfish species. The young are often found in schools (right) while adults are more solitary. This species has four pairs of mouth barbels to feel and taste food.

FACT FILE

Siamese algae-eater This fish is mainly herbivorous but occasionally eats insect larvae and zooplankton. It has a sucker-like mouth which it uses to hold onto solid surfaces. Water is pumped into the gill chamber through a small spiracle.

- Up to 11½ in (29 cm)
- Up to 10 oz (285 g)
- Oviparous
- Male & female
- Common

S.E. Asia

Reticulate loach A tropical Asian freshwater species, this fish is commonly known as the Pakistani loach. It is a nocturnal feeder with an omnivorous diet consisting of mainly bottom-dwelling invertebrates, such as snails and worms, as well as algae. When threatened, it will rapidly bury the front end of its body in sediment leaving only its tail exposed.

- Up to 4¾ in (12 cm)
- Up to 4 oz (115 g)
- Oviparous, hiders
- Male & female
- Common

Pakistan, India, Bangladesh, Nepal

Weatherfish This species lives in waters with a low oxygen content in which few other fishes could survive. It is a facultative air-breather and gulps air at the water surface, absorbing the oxygen through the lining of the gut. It is sensitive to barometric pressure and becomes agitated before thunderstorms.

- Up to 14 in (36 cm)
- Up to 8 oz (225 g)
- Oviparous
- Male & female
- Near threatened

Europe

Stone loach A nocturnal bottom dweller with three pairs of barbels, the stone loach feeds on benthic invertebrates. Because of its sensitivity to pollution and low levels of dissolved oxygen, it is regarded as a good biological indicator of water quality.

- Up to 8½ in (21 cm)
- Up to 7 oz (200 g)
- Oviparous
- Male & female
- Common

Eurasia

Siamese algae-eater
Gyrinocheilus aymonieri

Erectile spine below each eye

Reticulate loach
Botia lohachata

Clown loach
Botia macracanthus

Coolie loach
Pangio kuhlii

Skunk botia
Botia morleti

Flat loach
Gastromyzon sp.

Halfbanded loach
Pangio semicincta

Weatherfish
Misgurnus fossilis

Stone loach
Barbatula barbatula

Three pairs of mouth barbels; no erectile spine below eye

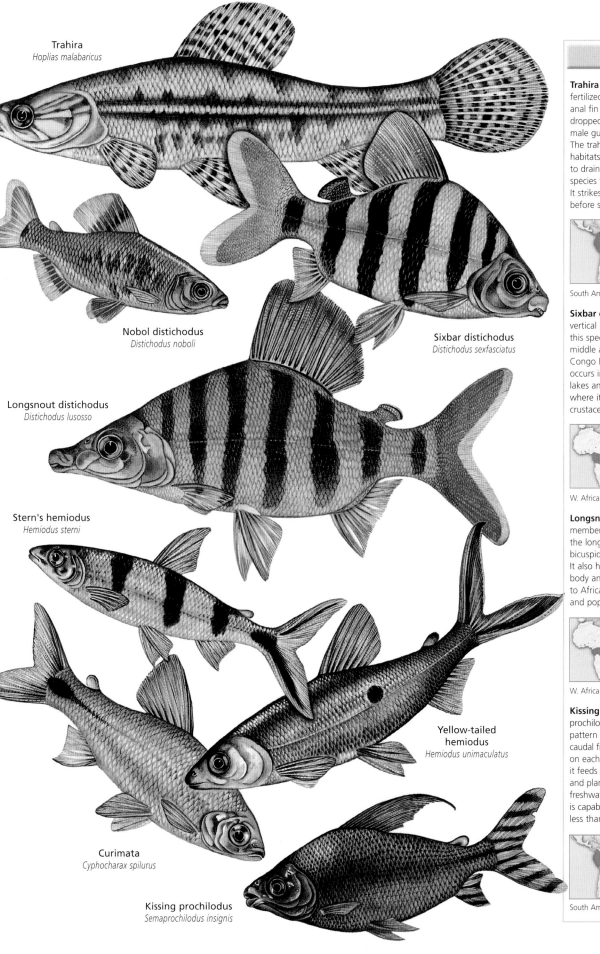

Trahira
Hoplias malabaricus

Nobol distichodus
Distichodus noboli

Sixbar distichodus
Distichodus sexfasciatus

Longsnout distichodus
Distichodus lusosso

Stern's hemiodus
Hemiodus sterni

Yellow-tailed hemiodus
Hemiodus unimaculatus

Curimata
Cyphocharax spilurus

Kissing prochilodus
Semaprochilodus insignis

FACT FILE

Trahira The eggs of this fish are fertilized while held in the cupped anal fin of the female. They are then dropped into a simple pit nest and the male guards the eggs until they hatch. The trahira occurs in a wide range of habitats, from fast-flowing streams to drainage ditches and ponds. This species feeds on crustaceans and fishes. It strikes prey and shakes it violently before swallowing it head first.

- Up to 19½ in (50 cm)
- Up to 3½ lb (1.6 kg)
- ○ Oviparous
- ♀♂ Male & female
- Common

South America

Sixbar distichodus Six prominent vertical bars on the body distinguish this species which is found in the middle and lower reaches of the Congo River and Lake Tanganyika. It occurs in shoals near the shores of lakes and near the bottom of rivers, where it feeds on worms, insects, crustaceans, and plant matter.

- Up to 31½ in (80 cm)
- Up to 19½ lb (8.9 kg)
- ○ Oviparous
- ♀♂ Male & female
- Common

W. Africa

Longsnout distichodus Like other members of the species *Distichodus*, the longsnout distichodus has bicuspidate teeth and ctenoid scales. It also has seven vertical bars on its body and a prominent snout. Native to Africa, this species is herbivorous and popular with the aquarium trade.

- Up to 15 in (38 cm)
- Up to 2½ lb (1.1 kg)
- ○ Oviparous
- ♀♂ Male & female
- Common

W. Africa

Kissing prochilodus The kissing prochilodus is characterized by the color pattern of its anal and caudal fins. The caudal fin has four to seven oblique bars on each lobe. Found near the riverbed, it feeds on detritus, small invertebrates, and plant matter. A highly resilient freshwater fish, it is a rapid breeder and is capable of doubling its population in less than 15 months.

- Up to 10½ in (27 cm)
- Up to 13 oz (370 g)
- ○ Oviparous
- ♀♂ Male & female
- Common

South America

FACT FILE

Gar characin Although quite small, the gar characin is a pelagic predator of smaller fishes in the rivers where it is found. It produces between 1,000 and 3,000 eggs per spawning that are scattered, not guarded. In total size, males are generally smaller and slimmer than females. The males do, however, have a large anal fin with a frayed edge, while in females the anal fin is smaller and has a straight edge.

- Up to 9½ in (24 cm)
- Up to 10 oz (285 g)
- ○ Oviparous
- ♀♂ Male & female
- Common

South America

Striped headstander This species is found in waters that lie within thickly wooded areas. It is omnivorous, eating both invertebrates and plant material. The striped headstander is often seen with its head inclined downward searching for food, hence the name.

- Up to 6 in (15 cm)
- Up to 4 oz (115 g)
- ○ Oviparous
- ♀♂ Male & female
- Common

South America

SPLASH TETRA

Splash tetras avoid aquatic egg-eaters by spawning out of water. Females leap into the air and, as their wet bodies stick to overhanging leaves, deposit up to eight eggs at a time before falling. Males follow quickly and the pair interlock fins to hang from the leaves as the male deposits his sperm. The procedure is repeated until several hundred fertilized eggs are laid. Tail flicks from males keep the eggs moist until fry hatch and fall into the water.

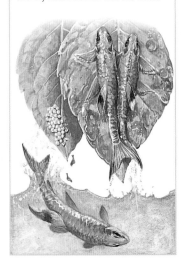

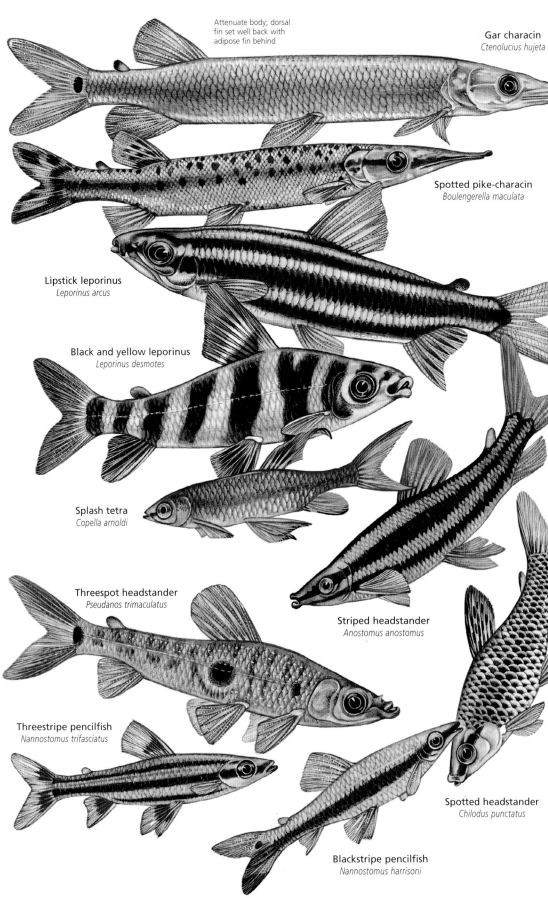

Attenuate body; dorsal fin set well back with adipose fin behind

Gar characin
Ctenolucius hujeta

Spotted pike-characin
Boulengerella maculata

Lipstick leporinus
Leporinus arcus

Black and yellow leporinus
Leporinus desmotes

Splash tetra
Copella arnoldi

Threespot headstander
Pseudanos trimaculatus

Striped headstander
Anostomus anostomus

Threestripe pencilfish
Nannostomus trifasciatus

Spotted headstander
Chilodus punctatus

Blackstripe pencilfish
Nannostomus harrisoni

Marbled hatchetfish
Carnegiella strigata

River hatchetfish
Gasteropelecus sternicla

Giant tigerfish
Hydrocynus goliath

Formidable jaws and
teeth used for grasping
fish prey

♂

Blackline penguinfish
Thayeria boehlkei

Congo tetra
*Phenacogrammus
interruptus*

♀

Females are smaller,
less vivid, and have
no tail fringe

A stout bodied
fish with powerful
dentition that can
inflict serious bites

The shape of the
swim bladder causes
this species to swim
at an angle, head up

Emperor tetra
Nematobrycon palmeri

Red piranha
Pygocentrus nattereri

Kafue pike
Hepsetus odoe

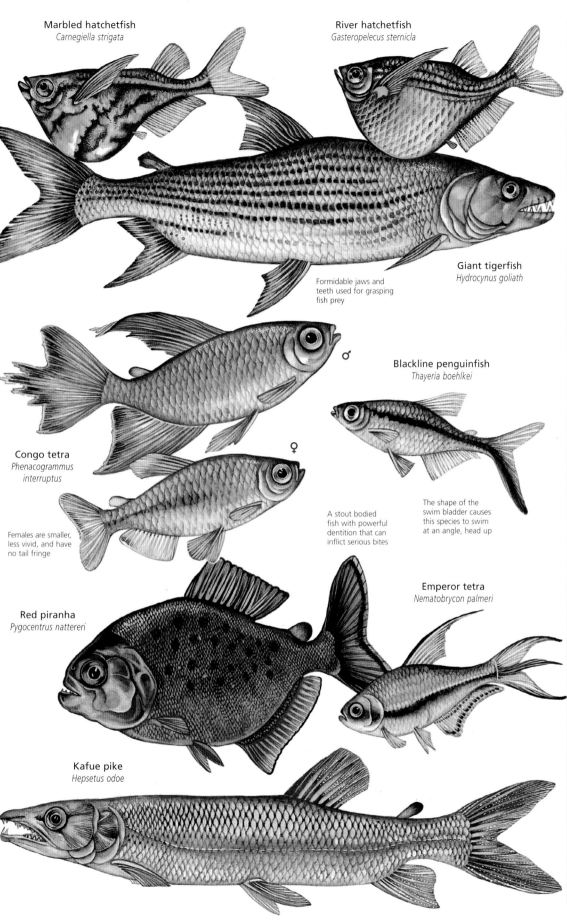

FACT FILE

Redhook myleus Non-aggressive and gregarious, the redhook myleus is found in slower areas of rivers—near the banks where vegetation overhangs the water. Although it has a powerful dentition, it feeds on the leaves of plants.

- Up to 15½ in (39 cm)
- Up to 5½ lb (2.5 kg)
- Oviparous
- Male & female
- Common

South America

Swordtail characin Found in the coastal rivers of Trinidad and in northern South America, this species has internal fertilization. The male deposits sperm capsules in the oviduct of the female and fertilization takes place when the female spawns in the absence of the male. The swordtail characin has a complex courtship ritual in which the male "dances" around potentially receptive females, extending his gill covers until they are at 90° to his body.

- Up to 2 in (5 cm)
- Up to 1 oz (30 g)
- Oviparous
- Male & female
- Common

South America

Wimple piranha This piranha has strong dentition and can inflict serious bites. The lower jaw is very prominent and armed with teeth with which it removes rows of scales from other fishes. It will also eat insects and algae. The common name "wimple" derives from the German word for the banner-like filaments that extend out from the dorsal fin.

- Up to 6 in (15 cm)
- Up to 6 oz (170 g)
- Oviparous
- Male & female
- Common

South America

Neon tetra This is one of the world's most popular aquarium fishes. Natural populations are found only in tributaries of the Solimtes River. In the wild, it feeds on small crustaceans, worms, insects, and plant material. A blue-green iridescent stripe runs back from the top of the eye to close to the adipose fin. Below this, there is a patch of red on the rear half of the body.

- Up to 1 in (2.5 cm)
- Up to 0.3 oz (10 g)
- Oviparous
- Male & female
- Common

South America

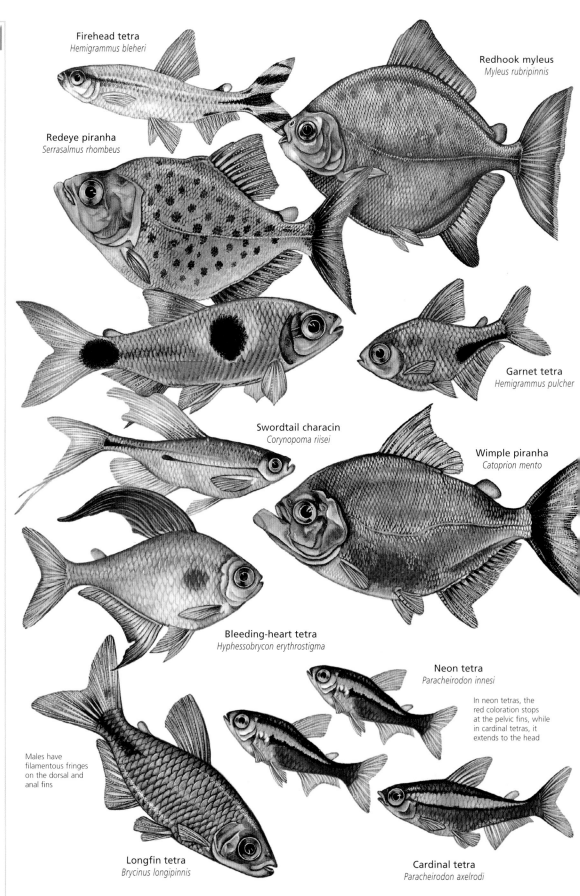

Firehead tetra
Hemigrammus bleheri

Redhook myleus
Myleus rubripinnis

Redeye piranha
Serrasalmus rhombeus

Garnet tetra
Hemigrammus pulcher

Swordtail characin
Corynopoma riisei

Wimple piranha
Catoprion mento

Bleeding-heart tetra
Hyphessobrycon erythrostigma

Neon tetra
Paracheirodon innesi

In neon tetras, the red coloration stops at the pelvic fins, while in cardinal tetras, it extends to the head

Males have filamentous fringes on the dorsal and anal fins

Longfin tetra
Brycinus longipinnis

Cardinal tetra
Paracheirodon axelrodi

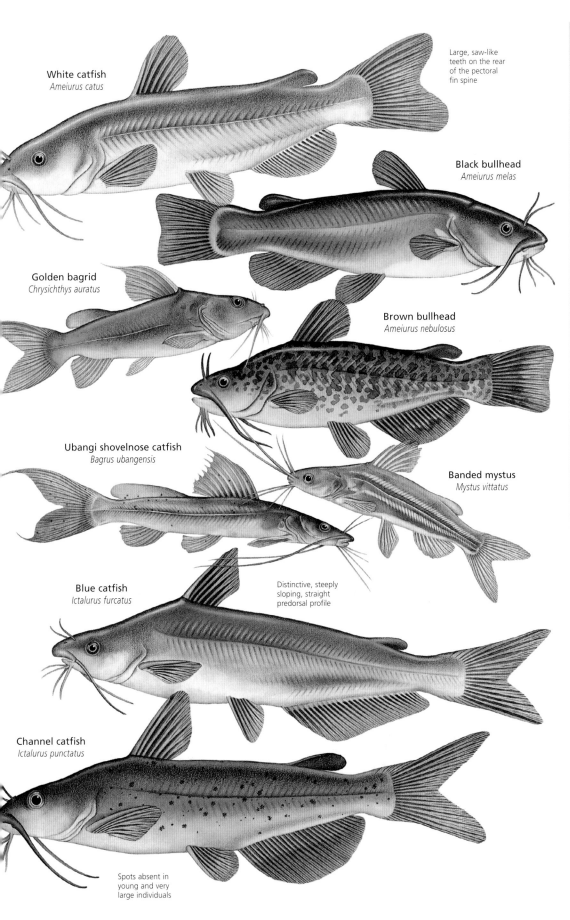

White catfish
Ameiurus catus

Large, saw-like
teeth on the rear
of the pectoral
fin spine

Black bullhead
Ameiurus melas

Golden bagrid
Chrysichthys auratus

Brown bullhead
Ameiurus nebulosus

Ubangi shovelnose catfish
Bagrus ubangensis

Banded mystus
Mystus vittatus

Blue catfish
Ictalurus furcatus

Distinctive, steeply
sloping, straight
predorsal profile

Channel catfish
Ictalurus punctatus

Spots absent in
young and very
large individuals

FACT FILE

Brown bullhead A nocturnal omnivore, the brown bullhead eats plant material, invertebrates, and fishes. It prefers soft substrates in sluggish rivers and ponds and is a nest builder. Either one or both sexes build the nest and the eggs are guarded by one or both parents.

⬌ Up to 21 in (53 cm)
⚖ Up to 6 lb (2.7 kg)
○ Oviparous
♀♂ Male & female
⚶ Common

North America

Ubangi shovelnose catfish This catfish is found in the Congo River system. The maxillary barbels are very long, extending to beyond the root of the pelvic fins. The head has well developed sensory canals.

⬌ Up to 12½ in (32 cm)
⚖ Up to 12 oz (340 g)
○ Oviparous
♀♂ Male & female
⚶ Common

Central W. Africa

Banded mystus The color of this species varies with age; changing from a pale silver-gray to a bright gold, with several pale blue or dark brown to black stripes on the flanks.

⬌ Up to 8¾ in (22 cm)
⚖ Up to 9½ oz (270 g)
○ Oviparous
♀♂ Male & female
⚶ Common

Southern Asia

Blue catfish The largest member of the genus, the blue catfish is found over mud, sand, and gravel in medium to large rivers. It is an important commercial species and is fished for using long lines and dead fish baits.

⬌ Up to 65 in (165 cm)
⚖ Up to 150 lb (68 kg)
○ Oviparous
♀♂ Male & female
⚶ Common

North America

Channel catfish Found over sand or rock in deep pools of lakes and rivers, the channel catfish makes a nest by creating a depression in the lake or riverbed. The egg mass, with as many as 20,000 eggs, is guarded by the male.

⬌ Up to 50 in (127 cm)
⚖ Up to 58 lb (26 kg)
○ Oviparous
♀♂ Male & female
⚶ Common

North America

Wels catfish
Silurus glanis

Elongate broad head with
a wide mouth surrounded
by three pairs of barbels,
the longest on the upper lip

Black walking catfish
Clarias angolensis

Butter catfish
Ompok bimaculatus

African butter catfish
Schilbe mystus

Glass catfish
Kryptopterus bicirrhis

African glass catfish
Pareutropius debauwi

Flatheaded eel catfish
Gymnallabes typus

The dark coloration
found in juveniles and
sub-adults is lost in
large, fully grown adults

Favorite pets One of the hardiest
fishes of all, the common carp
(*Cyprinus carpio*) (left) has been
domesticated for thousands of years.

Swai
Pangasius hypophthalmus

FACT FILE

Wels catfish One of the largest
fishes found in freshwater, it lives
in slow-flowing, deep lowland rivers
and lakes but is occasionally found in
the brackish waters of the Baltic and
Black seas, and has also been known
to spawn in the saltwater of the Aral
Sea. Some lakes in Russia may contain
1,000 pound (450 kg) monsters.

- Up to 16½ ft (5 m)
- Up to 675 lb (306 kg)
- ○ Oviparous
- ♀♂ Male & female
- Common

Europe & Asia

Glass catfish This species is a popular
aquarium fish because of its transparent
flesh, through which the skeleton and
internal organs are visible. It is a key
ingredient in the salty fish sauce that
is a flavoring staple in many Asian
cuisines. In the wild, the glass catfish
is a schooling species that lives in mid-
water. When kept in an aquarium, a
single fish will pine and die, unless there
are others of the same species with it.

- Up to 6 in (15 cm)
- Up to 2 oz (60 g)
- ○ Oviparous
- ♀♂ Male & female
- Common

S.E. Asia

PARASITIC BROODERS

Africa's cuckoo catfish is the only
fish species known to parasitize the
reproductive brooding of another fish.
Pairs of these catfish spawn near pairs
of mouth-brooding cichlids doing the
same, and consume most of the cichlid
eggs. As the female cichlid collects
what eggs she can into her mouth,
she also gathers up the catfish eggs.
The catfish fry hatch first, grow strong
on their yolk sacs, and often consume
the young cichlids as they hatch.

after hatching, catfish fry continue
to return to the safety of their
surrogate mother's mouth
for protection

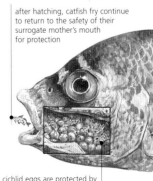

cichlid eggs are protected by
their tough skin, but larval
cichlids have no such protection

FACT FILE

Electric catfish With modified muscle around its body capable of discharging about 400 volts, this tropical African catfish generates electric shocks to stun prey and deter predators. Electrical discharge activity is most frequent around sunset.

- ➳ Up to 4 ft (1.2 m)
- ⚖ Up to 44 lb (20 kg)
- ○ Oviparous, guarders
- ♀♂ Male & female
- ⚑ Common

Nile River & Central Africa

Stinging catfish This catfish possesses a pair of long cavities on each side of the body extending backward from the gill cavity. These are accessory breathing organs and enable the stinging catfish to breathe atmospheric oxygen and survive in oxygen poor waters. It has poison glands on the pectoral fin spines.

- ➳ Up to 12 in (30 cm)
- ⚖ Up to 12 oz (340 g)
- ○ Oviparous
- ♀♂ Male & female
- ⚑ Common

Asia

Dewfish Endemic to Australia, the dewfish inhabits slow-flowing streams, lakes, and ponds. It is the male's duty to construct a nest with a central sandy depression using gravel and rocks. The male then guards up to 20,000 eggs deposited by the female.

- ➳ Up to 35½ in (90 cm)
- ⚖ Up to 13¼ lb (6.1 kg)
- ○ Oviparous
- ♀♂ Male & female
- ⚑ Common

Australia

Striped eel-catfish Juveniles of this marine species, the only catfish found on coral reefs, form tight schools to confuse predators, making it hard for them to focus in on one particular fish. The pectoral and dorsal fins are armed with venom that can cause death in humans.

- ➳ Up to 13 in (33 cm)
- ⚖ Up to 12 oz (340 g)
- ○ Oviparous, guarders
- ♀♂ Male & female
- ⚑ Common

Indo-Pacific

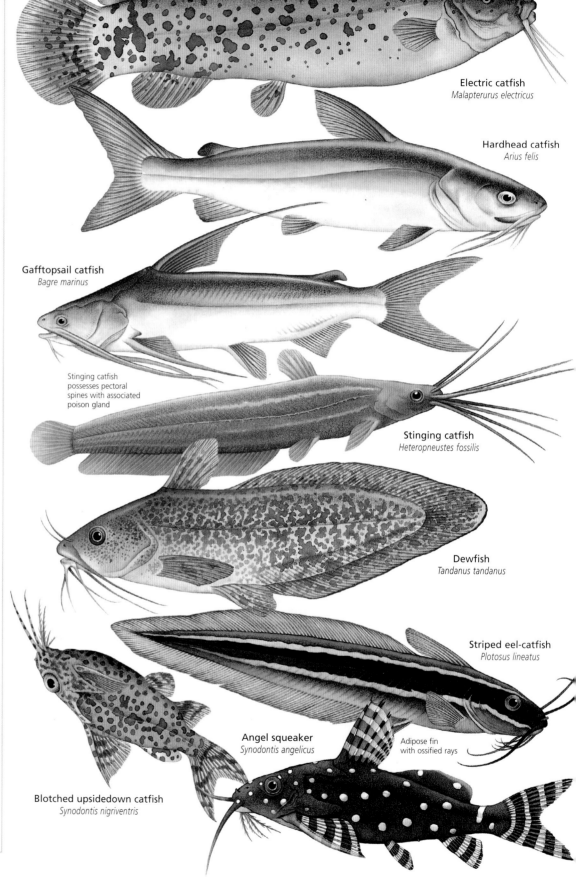

Electric catfish
Malapterurus electricus

Hardhead catfish
Arius felis

Gafftopsail catfish
Bagre marinus

Stinging catfish possesses pectoral spines with associated poison gland

Stinging catfish
Heteropneustes fossilis

Dewfish
Tandanus tandanus

Striped eel-catfish
Plotosus lineatus

Angel squeaker
Synodontis angelicus

Adipose fin with ossified rays

Blotched upsidedown catfish
Synodontis nigriventris

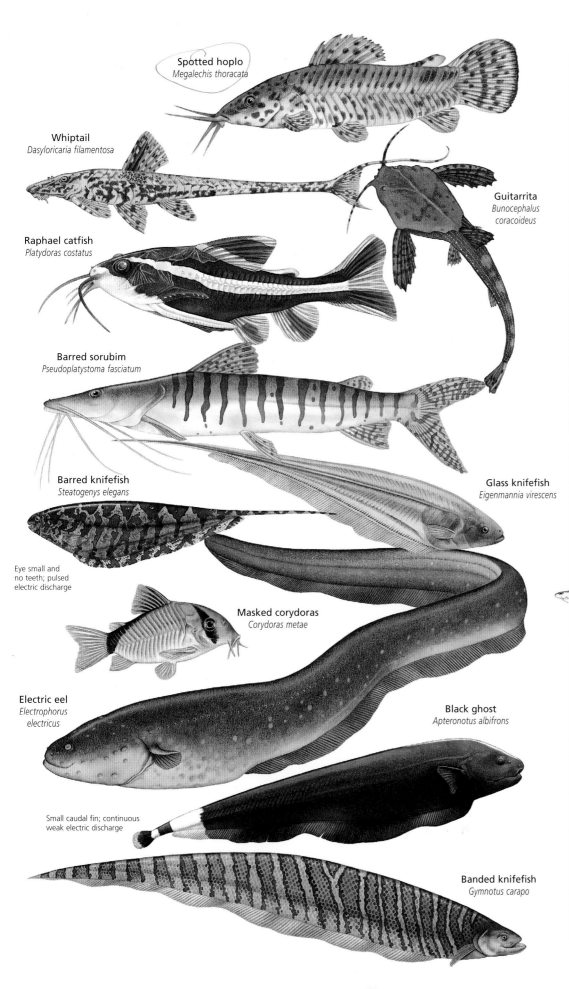

Spotted hoplo
Megalechis thoracata

Whiptail
Dasyloricaria filamentosa

Raphael catfish
Platydoras costatus

Guitarrita
Bunocephalus coracoideus

Barred sorubim
Pseudoplatystoma fasciatum

Barred knifefish
Steatogenys elegans

Glass knifefish
Eigenmannia virescens

Eye small and no teeth; pulsed electric discharge

Masked corydoras
Corydoras metae

Electric eel
Electrophorus electricus

Black ghost
Apteronotus albifrons

Small caudal fin; continuous weak electric discharge

Banded knifefish
Gymnotus carapo

SALMONS AND ALLIES

CLASS Actinopterygii	
SUPERORDER Protacanthopterygii	
ORDERS 3	
FAMILIES 15	
SPECIES 502	

Some of the world's most sought-after angling and table fishes are among this group, the protacanthopterygians, which has ancient origins stemming back to the Cretaceous (144–65 million years ago). It is usually divided into 15 families comprising more than 500 species arranged into three groups: esociforms, osmeriforms, and salmoniforms. These fishes are mostly carnivores equipped with large mouths and sharp teeth. Many are powerful and agile swimmers with elongate, streamlined bodies and well-developed tail fins. This swimming prowess is particularly evident in the salmons and trouts, many of which make extraordinarily long and arduous spawning migrations, journeys that have perplexed and fascinated scientists for centuries.

Expanding distribution Esociforms are found only in temperate North America, Europe, and Asia. Osmeriforms are also temperate fishes, with representatives in both hemispheres. The salmoniforms are Northern Hemisphere natives but many species have been introduced into suitable temperate-water ponds, streams, and rivers worldwide for the purposes of recreational angling and aquaculture.

Trout farming Several trout species, particularly rainbow trout (*Oncorhynchus mykiss*) (above), are farmed in temperate areas in both purpose-built ponds and netted enclosures within natural water courses. These are stocked with fry obtained by artificial fertilization from hatcheries and grown to marketable size on a diet of protein pellets derived as a by-product from the meat-packing industry.

Salty taste Rearing rainbow trout (above) in seawater improves their flavor and increases their value when they are marketed as salmon trout.

DIVERSE PREDATORS

The esociform group includes the pikes, muskellunge, pickerels, and mudminnows, all of which lead exclusively freshwater lives. Most are formidable ambush predators and the location of the median fins back toward the tail is an adaptation to this lifestyle.

There are more than 230 species of osmeriforms. Among the most bizarre are the barreleyes, which have upward-directed tubular eyes and other specialist adaptations for life in the high-pressure darkness of oceanic depths. Commercially important osmeriforms include the Northern Hemisphere's smelts— small, streamlined fishes that are particularly abundant in temperate coastal waters. In the Southern Hemisphere, the best-known osmeriforms are the galaxiids, a scaleless family with complex life-cycles in which juvenile stages move between fresh and saltwater.

The salmoniforms include the whitefishes, ciscoes, graylings, chars, salmons, and trouts. Most are commercially important but it is the homing and migratory capabilities of the salmons that attract particular attention.

The six species of Pacific salmon spend most of their lives at sea but all attempt to return to the fresh-water streams in which they were spawned when they reach sexual maturity. The sense of smell is believed to be critical to these fishes in locating their birthplaces.

Migratory marvels Each stream has a distinct odor created by the soil and vegetation in its drainage. It is believed that this may become imprinted on young salmon and help them to find their way home during spawning migrations (left).

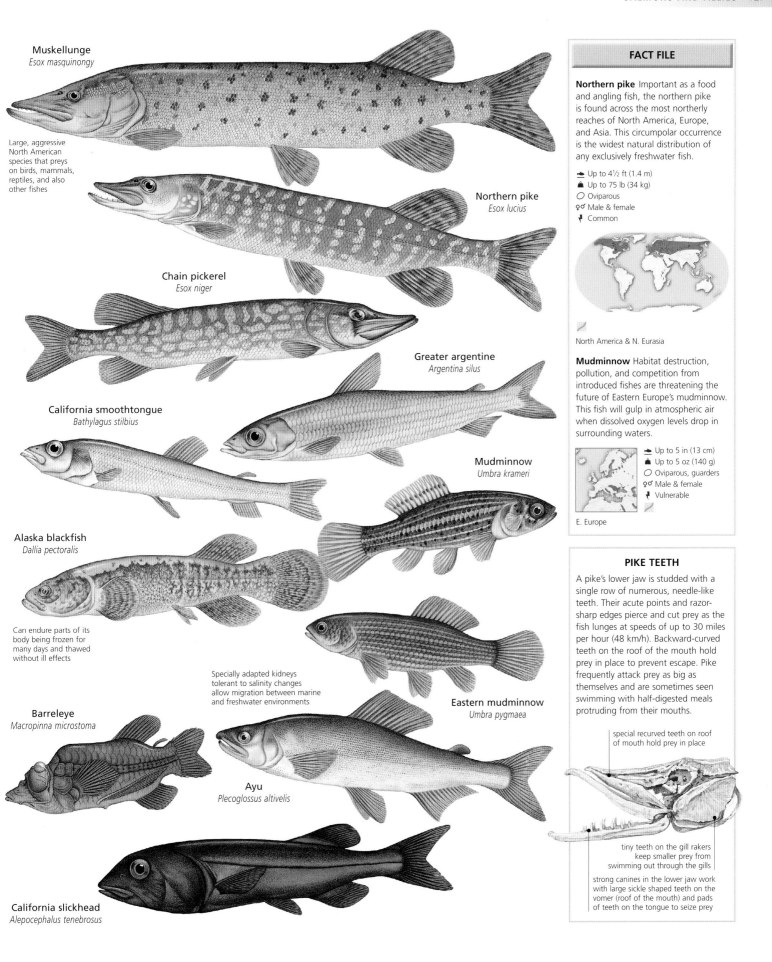

Muskellunge
Esox masquinongy

Large, aggressive North American species that preys on birds, mammals, reptiles, and also other fishes

Northern pike
Esox lucius

Chain pickerel
Esox niger

Greater argentine
Argentina silus

California smoothtongue
Bathylagus stilbius

Mudminnow
Umbra krameri

Alaska blackfish
Dallia pectoralis

Can endure parts of its body being frozen for many days and thawed without ill effects

Specially adapted kidneys tolerant to salinity changes allow migration between marine and freshwater environments

Eastern mudminnow
Umbra pygmaea

Barreleye
Macropinna microstoma

Ayu
Plecoglossus altivelis

California slickhead
Alepocephalus tenebrosus

FACT FILE

Northern pike Important as a food and angling fish, the northern pike is found across the most northerly reaches of North America, Europe, and Asia. This circumpolar occurrence is the widest natural distribution of any exclusively freshwater fish.

- ⬌ Up to 4½ ft (1.4 m)
- ⬍ Up to 75 lb (34 kg)
- ○ Oviparous
- ♀♂ Male & female
- ⚑ Common

North America & N. Eurasia

Mudminnow Habitat destruction, pollution, and competition from introduced fishes are threatening the future of Eastern Europe's mudminnow. This fish will gulp in atmospheric air when dissolved oxygen levels drop in surrounding waters.

- ⬌ Up to 5 in (13 cm)
- ⬍ Up to 5 oz (140 g)
- ○ Oviparous, guarders
- ♀♂ Male & female
- ⚑ Vulnerable

E. Europe

PIKE TEETH

A pike's lower jaw is studded with a single row of numerous, needle-like teeth. Their acute points and razor-sharp edges pierce and cut prey as the fish lunges at speeds of up to 30 miles per hour (48 km/h). Backward-curved teeth on the roof of the mouth hold prey in place to prevent escape. Pike frequently attack prey as big as themselves and are sometimes seen swimming with half-digested meals protruding from their mouths.

special recurved teeth on roof of mouth hold prey in place

tiny teeth on the gill rakers keep smaller prey from swimming out through the gills

strong canines in the lower jaw work with large sickle shaped teeth on the vomer (roof of the mouth) and pads of teeth on the tongue to seize prey

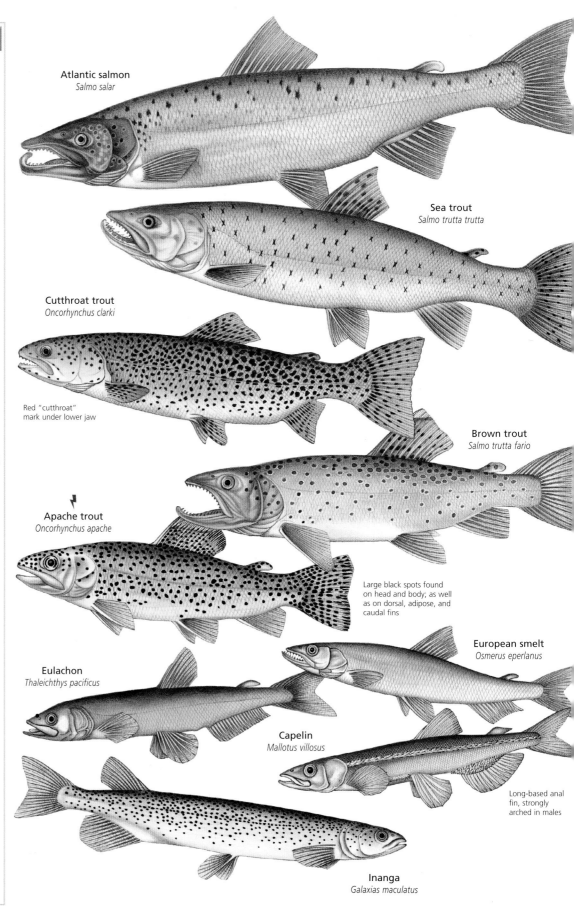

FACT FILE

Atlantic salmon Most young Atlantic salmon remain in freshwater for up to four years before migrating to the North Atlantic Ocean. Between one and four years later, they return to their birthplaces to spawn, often surviving to repeat the migration. Some landlocked populations migrate between deepwater feeding grounds and shallow shorelines.

- Up to 5 ft (1.5 m)
- Up to 79 lb (36 kg)
- ○ Oviparous, hiders
- ♀♂ Male & female
- ♪ Common

N. Atlantic, N.W. Europe, N.E. North America

Sea trout This species is also born in freshwater, migrates to live at sea, and then returns to freshwater to spawn. It is long-lived and thought capable of surviving for up to 20 years, during which time it makes repeated annual spawning migrations.

- Up to 4½ ft (1.4 m)
- Up to 33 lb (15 kg)
- ○ Oviparous, hiders
- ♀♂ Male & female
- ♪ Common

N.W. Europe; introd. widely

Brown trout A freshwater, non-migratory form of the sea trout, this fish is prized by anglers and gourmet alike. Originally from Europe, it has been introduced to many other areas worldwide. As in other salmonids, females create nests, known as "redds," with their tails in clean gravel sediments.

- Up to 4½ ft (1.4 m)
- Up to 33 lb (15 kg)
- ○ Oviparous
- ♀♂ Male & female
- ♪ Common

Europe, W. Asia, N.W. Africa; introd. worldwide

European smelt Like their close relatives the salmons and trouts, smelts have an adipose fin. This small, fleshy lump on the dorsal side near the tail fin is considered a primitive feature.

- Up to 12 in (30 cm)
- Up to 7 oz (200 g)
- ○ Oviparous
- ♀♂ Male & female
- ♪ Data deficient

N.W. Europe

Atlantic salmon
Salmo salar

Sea trout
Salmo trutta trutta

Cutthroat trout
Oncorhynchus clarki

Red "cutthroat" mark under lower jaw

Brown trout
Salmo trutta fario

Apache trout
Oncorhynchus apache

Large black spots found on head and body; as well as on dorsal, adipose, and caudal fins

European smelt
Osmerus eperlanus

Eulachon
Thaleichthys pacificus

Capelin
Mallotus villosus

Long-based anal fin, strongly arched in males

Inanga
Galaxias maculatus

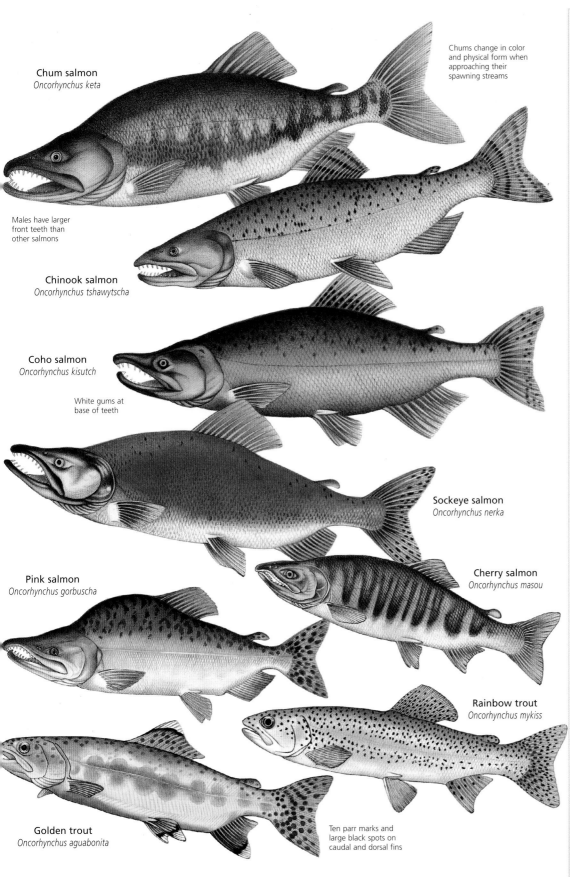

Chum salmon
Oncorhynchus keta

Chums change in color and physical form when approaching their spawning streams

Males have larger front teeth than other salmons

Chinook salmon
Oncorhynchus tshawytscha

Coho salmon
Oncorhynchus kisutch

White gums at base of teeth

Sockeye salmon
Oncorhynchus nerka

Cherry salmon
Oncorhynchus masou

Pink salmon
Oncorhynchus gorbuscha

Rainbow trout
Oncorhynchus mykiss

Golden trout
Oncorhynchus aguabonita

Ten parr marks and large black spots on caudal and dorsal fins

FACT FILE

Chinook salmon This is the largest and the least abundant of the Pacific salmon. An anadromous species, it spends much of its adult life in the ocean and ascends coastal streams and rivers to spawn. The gums at the base of the teeth are black. Around the world the chinook is also known as a quinnat, blackmouth, tyee, king, and tule.

⬱ Up to 58 in (147 cm)
⬛ Up to 126 lb (57 kg)
○ Oviparous, hiders, semelparous
♀♂ Male & female
🗡 Common

Arctic, N. Pacific, N.E. Asia, N.W. North America

Pink salmon Young pink salmon spend very little time in freshwater, migrating to the sea almost immediately after they hatch. They return after 18 months to spawn in the same freshwater in which they were born, after which they die. This species is also known as the "humpback" or "humpy" due to the strongly marked lateral hump on the back of male adults before spawning.

⬱ Up to 30 in (76 cm)
⬛ Up to 15 lb (6.8 kg)
○ Oviparous, hiders, semelparous
♀♂ Male & female
🗡 Common

Arctic, N. Pacific, N.E. Asia, N.W. North America

Rainbow trout This fish has become a freshwater favorite of fly-fishing anglers in the many parts of the world where it has been introduced. Some native North American rainbow trout stocks migrate to the sea as adults and only return to freshwater to spawn. The rainbow trout is known to spawn two or three times in its life. Males spawn when one year old while females are sexually mature at three to four years.

⬱ Up to 4 ft (1.2 m)
⬛ Up to 55 lb (25 kg)
○ Oviparous, hiders
♀♂ Male & female
🗡 Common

N.W. North America; introd. widely

SALMON LIFE-CYCLE

Sockeye salmon make marathon upriver migrations to spawn in freshwater lakes and streams. They return to the same lakes in which they were born, and can travel up to 1,000 miles (1,600 km) on their homeward journey.

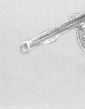

Eggs are laid in gravel nests dug by the females.

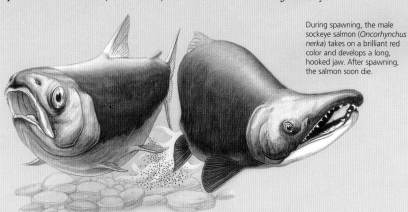

During spawning, the male sockeye salmon (*Oncorhynchus nerka*) takes on a brilliant red color and develops a long, hooked jaw. After spawning, the salmon soon die.

FINDING THEIR WAY HOME

About 80 percent of the millions of sockeye salmon homing to Bristol Bay, Alaska, arrive within a two week period. Just a few months earlier, these fish would have been spread out over a great expanse of ocean. It appears that they can detect changes in day length, which indicates the time of year. This probably tells them when it is time to begin their homeward journey. They may use both Earth's magnetic field and the Sun's position as navigational aids to find their way home, at the same specific time, year after year.

Although early dams were built without provision for migrating salmon, many now have ladders to facilitate their migration.

Brown bears congregate along rivers at known "fishing spots" waiting for the salmon as they head upstream.

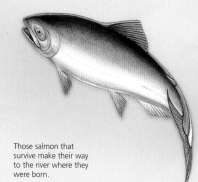

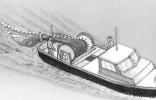

As the salmon return to coastal waters and rivers, fishing boats lie in wait to catch their hauls of fattened, healthy fish.

Those salmon that survive make their way to the river where they were born.

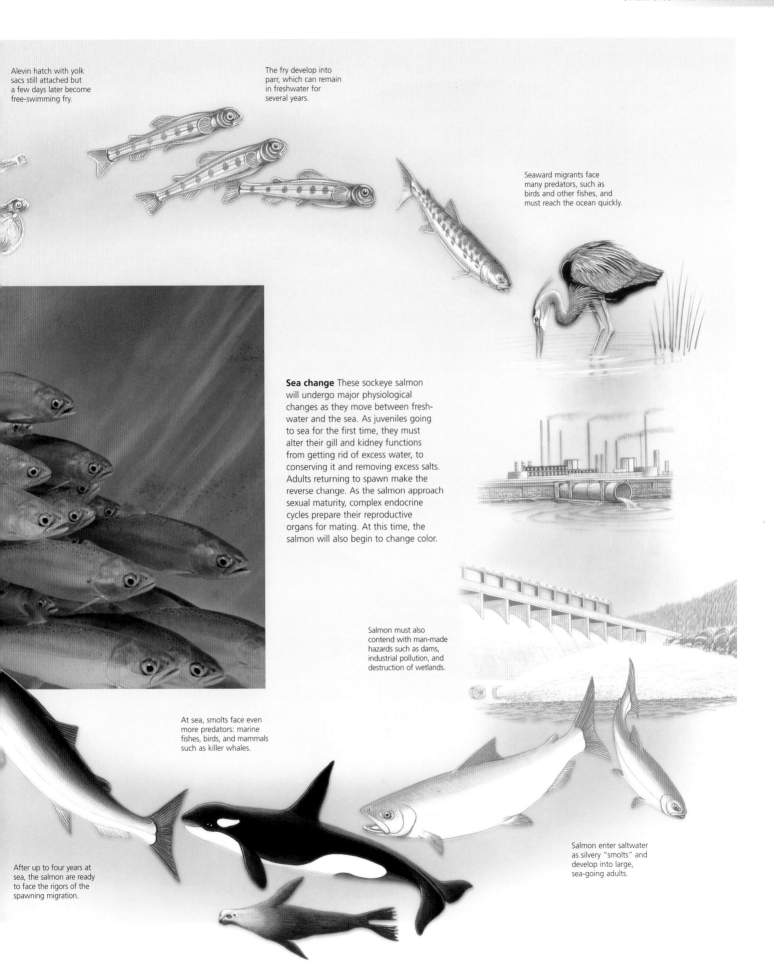

Alevin hatch with yolk sacs still attached but a few days later become free-swimming fry.

The fry develop into parr, which can remain in freshwater for several years.

Seaward migrants face many predators, such as birds and other fishes, and must reach the ocean quickly.

Sea change These sockeye salmon will undergo major physiological changes as they move between fresh-water and the sea. As juveniles going to sea for the first time, they must alter their gill and kidney functions from getting rid of excess water, to conserving it and removing excess salts. Adults returning to spawn make the reverse change. As the salmon approach sexual maturity, complex endocrine cycles prepare their reproductive organs for mating. At this time, the salmon will also begin to change color.

Salmon must also contend with man-made hazards such as dams, industrial pollution, and destruction of wetlands.

At sea, smolts face even more predators: marine fishes, birds, and mammals such as killer whales.

Salmon enter saltwater as silvery "smolts" and develop into large, sea-going adults.

After up to four years at sea, the salmon are ready to face the rigors of the spawning migration.

FACT FILE

Lake trout This deep-dwelling, light-shunning, freshwater species feeds on other fishes, crustaceans, and aquatic insects. Females have been crossed in hatcheries with males of the brook trout (*Salvelinus fontinalis*) to produce fast-growing hybrids known as splakes.

- Up to 4 ft (1.2 m)
- Up to 70 lb (32 kg)
- ○ Oviparous
- ♀♂ Male & female
- Common

N. North America

Grayling Found in unpolluted streams, lakes, and occasionally brackish water throughout northern Europe, graylings spawn en masse during the northern spring when males dig nests into which females bury fertilized eggs. Grayling adults' diets consist mainly of aquatic invertebrates, particularly insects.

- Up to 23½ in (60 cm)
- Up to 6½ lb (3 kg)
- ○ Oviparous, hiders
- ♀♂ Male & female
- Common

N. Europe

Huchen The huchen is one of the world's largest freshwater fishes. Adults are territorial predators that eat other fishes as well as frogs, reptiles, birds, and even small mammals. Its popularity with anglers, pollution, and the damming of the fast-flowing waterways it inhabits, have all contributed to its endangered status.

- Up to 5 ft (1.5 m)
- Up to 46 lb (21 kg)
- ○ Oviparous, hiders
- ♀♂ Male & female
- Endangered

Danube River basin (Europe)

⚡ CONSERVATION WATCH

Disappearing galaxiids The IUCN lists 68 protacanthopterygians, including five that have already gone extinct. Among the eight listed as critically endangered are four galaxiids, each with exceptionally limited freshwater Australian distributions and all threatened by introduced fishes and habitat destruction. Until 1996, one—the Pedder galaxias (*Galaxias pedderensis*)—was considered to be among the world's most endangered fishes. Conservation efforts based on the translocation of individuals to a secure lake, however, appear to have now assured the future of the Pedder galaxias.

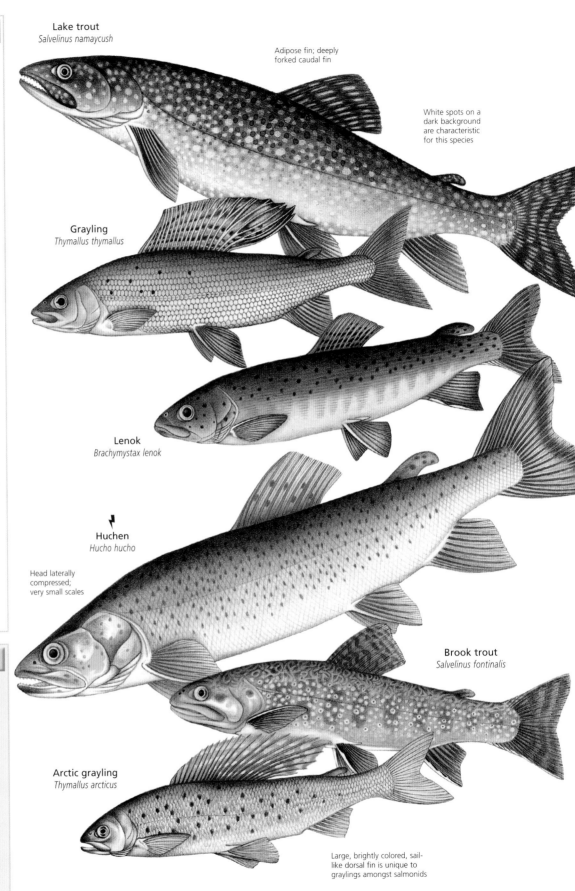

Lake trout
Salvelinus namaycush

Adipose fin; deeply forked caudal fin

White spots on a dark background are characteristic for this species

Grayling
Thymallus thymallus

Lenok
Brachymystax lenok

⚡ Huchen
Hucho hucho

Head laterally compressed; very small scales

Brook trout
Salvelinus fontinalis

Arctic grayling
Thymallus arcticus

Large, brightly colored, sail-like dorsal fin is unique to graylings amongst salmonids

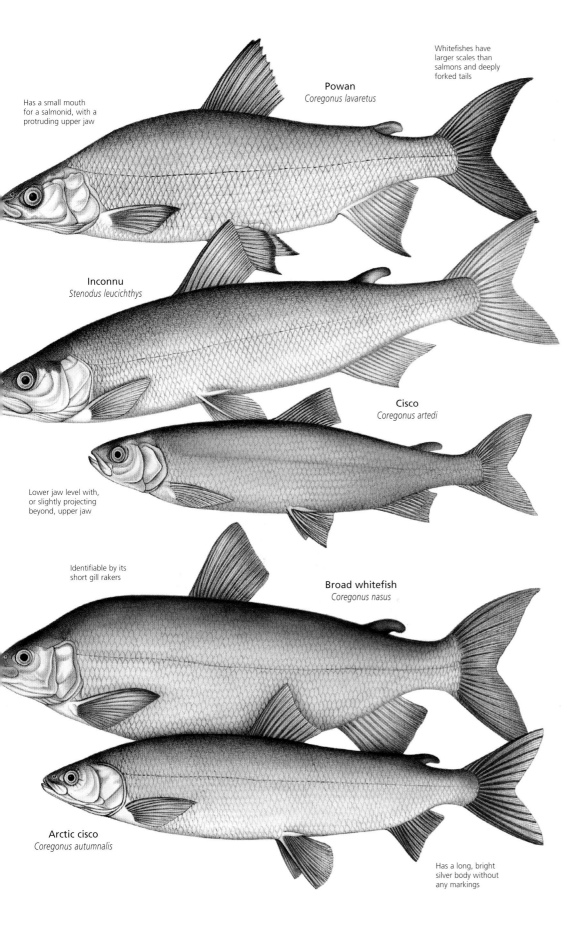

Has a small mouth for a salmonid, with a protruding upper jaw

Powan
Coregonus lavaretus

Whitefishes have larger scales than salmons and deeply forked tails

Inconnu
Stenodus leucichthys

Cisco
Coregonus artedi

Lower jaw level with, or slightly projecting beyond, upper jaw

Identifiable by its short gill rakers

Broad whitefish
Coregonus nasus

Arctic cisco
Coregonus autumnalis

Has a long, bright silver body without any markings

FACT FILE

Powan In the north of its range, this species is only found in brackish water. Populations in the British Isles and the Alps are restricted to mountain lakes where the powan has survived since the end of the last ice age. It feeds on planktonic crustaceans.

- Up to 27½ in (70 cm)
- Up to 22 lb (10 kg)
- ○ Oviparous
- ♀♂ Male & female
- Data deficient

Europe

Inconnu Although it is anadromous near the coasts of North America and also in the northern Caspian Sea, the inconnu is landlocked in inland lakes. It has a large, wide mouth with velvet-like bands of teeth on both jaws. This species feeds on insect larvae and zooplankton when young, but as an adult it feeds exclusively on fishes.

- Up to 49 in (125 cm)
- Up to 88 lb (40 kg)
- ○ Oviparous
- ♀♂ Male & female
- Data deficient

North America & Asia

Cisco Usually found in open waters of lakes and large rivers, this species also occurs in the coastal waters of Hudson Bay. It feeds on invertebrates and small fishes in the water column, as well as benthic invertebrates and fish eggs. It is sometimes known as the "lake herring" and is a much-sought food species.

- Up to 22½ in (57 cm)
- Up to 7¼ lb (3.35 kg)
- ○ Oviparous
- ♀♂ Male & female
- Common

North America

Broad whitefish This species is most frequently found in streams and rivers although lacustrine and brackish water anadromous forms exist. The broad whitefish feeds on crustaceans, insect larvae, and small mollusks.

- Up to 28 in (71 cm)
- Up to 35¼ lb (15.9 kg)
- ○ Oviparous
- ♀♂ Male & female
- Data deficient

North America & Asia

DRAGONFISHES AND ALLIES

Although diverse and widespread, the stomiiforms are rarely encountered by people because of their mid- to deep-water lifestyle. All are predators that are adapted to habitats defined by high pressure, limited light, and low productivity. Most have long teeth and big mouths that can cope with large, infrequently encountered meals. And all but one species are equipped with light organs—photophores. Dotted along their sides and underbellies, these serve as camouflage from predators below by masking their appearance against weak light from above. Most also use them for hunting; suspended from a chin barbel or fin ray they lure prey like moths to a flame.

CLASS	Actinopterygii
SUPERORDER	Stenopterygii
ORDERS	2
FAMILIES	5
SPECIES	415

Deep-sea distribution The stomiiforms are found in the deep, open waters of all major temperate and subtropical oceans. Some extend into polar waters. They are also found over a large depth range, migrating upward at night and returning down during the day.

Fierce predator This deep-sea dragonfish (*Idiacanthus* sp.) has features typical of the family Stomiidae, including photophores along its belly and a long barbel on the lower jaw. These fishes remain in the complete darkness of the ocean's extreme depths by day, but migrate vertically at night to feed at more moderate depths. Males of this genus are much smaller than the females and lack teeth and pelvic fins.

DEEP-SEA LIFE

Stomiiforms typically have big heads, long bodies, and dark coloration, although some are translucent or silvery. Common names such as lightfishes, bristle-mouths, loosejaws, snaggletooths, and viperfishes suggest their often bizarre appearance.

Hermaphroditism is common, an adaptation to a habitat where members of the same species may be infrequently encountered.

Eggs and larvae are buoyant, floating within plankton in surface currents, but young descend as juveniles to pursue deep-sea life. As adults, many stomiiforms rest by day in deep water but migrate at dusk to shallower depths, where food in the form of small fishes and invertebrates is more plentiful.

Hatchetfish
Argyropelecus olfersii

Body deep and extremely compressed; abdominal keel-like structure

Veiled anglemouth
Cyclothone microdon

Dense stellate pigment over head, body, and fins

Scaly dragonfish
Stomias boa

Pacific viperfish
Chauliodus macouni

CONSERVATION WATCH

Deep questions Because deep-sea habitats can be as inaccessible as outer space, very little is known about the population structure, size, or breeding behavior of the stomiiforms. It is possible that one genus, *Cyclothone*, includes more individuals than any other vertebrate genus: billions of these tiny, mesopelagic fishes live in the oceans. It is also possible that some are disappearing as a consequence of oceanic pollution before their existence has even been recorded.

LIZARDFISHES AND ALLIES

ss Actinopterygii

ERORDER
closquamata

ER Aulopiformes

ILIES 13

CIES 229

This marine group, the aulopiforms, is represented in both coastal habitats and great depths. It includes the lizardfishes, Bombay ducks, greeneyes, ipnopids, lancetfishes, daggertooths, and telescopefishes. They exhibit an unusual mix of primitive and advanced features and are of particular interest to scientists for various reasons, including their range of peculiar eye modifications. Many deep-sea species are notable for their mode of reproduction: they are bisexual synchronous hermaphrodites, which means that they function as both sexes at the same time and may even be capable of self-fertilization. The aulopiforms are also known for the often extreme metamorphoses they pass through as they change from larvae into juveniles.

Wide distribution Lizardfishes occur in all warm seas. Greeneyes are found worldwide in tropical to warm-temperate waters. Most Bombay ducks have an Indo-Pacific distribution. The lancetfishes range widely in Atlantic and Pacific mid-waters.

ASSORTED ASSEMBLAGE

Lizardfishes, Bombay ducks, and greeneyes are all inshore bottom-dwelling ambush predators. Typically well-camouflaged, they often sit propped up at the front end by their pelvic fins.

The ipnopids dwell at great depths and usually have flat heads, pencil-like bodies, and poorly developed eyes.

Attaining lengths of nearly 7 feet (2.1 m), lancetfishes are among the largest of all deep-sea predatory fishes. They have huge mouths and large, dagger-like teeth, and have a reputation for destroying undersea cables. They are sometimes seen floundering in the surf.

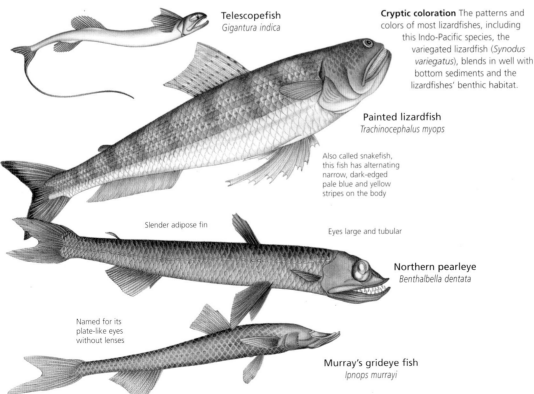

Telescopefish
Gigantura indica

Cryptic coloration The patterns and colors of most lizardfishes, including this Indo-Pacific species, the variegated lizardfish (*Synodus variegatus*), blends in well with bottom sediments and the lizardfishes' benthic habitat.

Painted lizardfish
Trachinocephalus myops

Also called snakefish, this fish has alternating narrow, dark-edged pale blue and yellow stripes on the body

Slender adipose fin

Eyes large and tubular

Northern pearleye
Benthalbella dentata

Named for its plate-like eyes without lenses

Murray's grideye fish
Ipnops murrayi

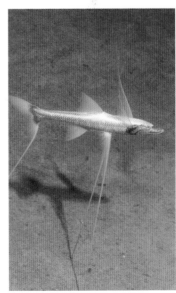

Say cheese Propped up on hugely elongated pelvic and tail fins, tripod fishes hold themselves clear of the substrate at great ocean depths awaiting prey. These ipnopid fishes grow to a maximum length of about 14 inches (36 cm).

LANTERNFISHES

CLASS Actinopterygii
SUPERORDER Scopelomorpha
ORDER Myctophiformes
FAMILIES 2
SPECIES 251

Of all the deep, open-water marine fishes, the lanternfishes are the most widely distributed, diverse, and abundant. Because these small plankton-eaters form large dense schools preyed upon by sea birds (particularly penguins), marine mammals, and a huge range of carnivorous fishes, they play a crucial role in virtually all marine ecosystems. They are fished to a relatively small extent for fish meal and oil but, with a global mass estimated at a staggering 660 million tons (600 million tonnes), they are otherwise regarded as a largely underused commercial resource. Together with their less abundant allies the neoscopelids, lanternfishes make up the group known as the myctophiforms.

Global resource Lanternfishes can be found in all open oceanic waters. Species distributions are related to both ocean currents and the physical and biological characteristics of the water. Many exist at great depths by day but will migrate upward to feed in surface waters by night.

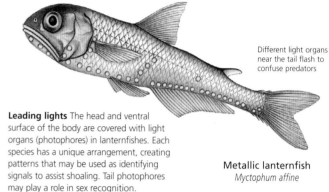

Different light organs near the tail flash to confuse predators

Leading lights The head and ventral surface of the body are covered with light organs (photophores) in lanternfishes. Each species has a unique arrangement, creating patterns that may be used as identifying signals to assist shoaling. Tail photophores may play a role in sex recognition.

Metallic lanternfish
Myctophum affine

BEARDFISHES

CLASS Actinopterygii
SUPERORDER Polymixiomorpha
ORDER Polymixiiformes
FAMILY Polymixiidae
SPECIES 10

Just ten species in one genus make up this small but puzzling group of deep-water marine fishes, which derives its common name from the pair of sensory barbels they all have hanging from the chin. Like the more advanced teleosts (the spiny-rayed fishes), they have true fin spines (as opposed to soft rays): between four and six in the dorsal fin and four in the anal fin. However, along with this modern feature they also exhibit several primitive and unique characteristics, creating a perplexing array of attributes that has fuelled much debate about which other fish groups are their closest relatives.

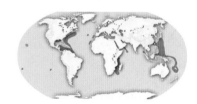

Bottom dwellers Beardfishes are known from tropical and subtropical oceanic waters. They live on the outer continental shelf and upper slope at various depths between 65 and 2,500 feet (20 and 760 m), usually on the bottom.

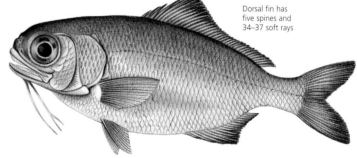

Dorsal fin has five spines and 34–37 soft rays

Rare catch This beardfish (*Polymixia berndti*) is mostly encountered as bycatch taken by commercial trawlers working the deep tropical and subtropical waters of the Indo-Pacific.

Stout beardfish
Polymixia nobilis

OPAHS AND ALLIES

DIVISION Euteleostei
SUPERORDER mpridiomorpha
ORDER Lampridiformes
FAMILIES 7
SPECIES 23

Twenty-three species of deep-sea fishes, known as the lampridiforms, make up this group. Outwardly, their external appearance is extremely variable although most are either large and moon-shaped or elongated and snake-like. They all, however, share four unique and characteristic features, all but one of which relates to an unusual and specialized jaw arrangement that gives them highly protrusible mouths. They usually lack scales, tend to have dorsal fins that run the length of the body, and most have pelvic fins that are well forward on the body. Many have bodies adorned in radiant hues with bright red fins. This group probably arose some 65 million years ago.

Widespread enigmas Lampridiforms are usually found at depths of between 330 and 3,300 feet (100 and 1,000 m). Opahs, ribbonfishes, and tube-eyes have worldwide distributions in warm waters. Velifers are found only in the Indian and Pacific oceans. The open-ocean, deep-water lifestyles of lampridiforms mean that they are rarely encountered by people.

Mythical serpent Accounts of sea monsters probably stem from sightings of the oarfish, the world's longest fish. There has been at least one report of a specimen measuring 56 feet (17 m) long but most probably attain lengths of around 26 feet (8 m). These fish usually inhabit depths up to 660 feet (201 m) but have been seen at the surface and washed up on beaches.

Body oval and compressed; vermilion lips and fins

Opah
Lampris guttatus

Long dorsal fin with high crest on head; unicornfishes are the only fishes with an ink sac

Unicornfish
Lophotus capellei

Ribbon fish
Trachipterus trachypterus

STRANGE LIFESTYLES

The lampridiforms include the crestfish, opahs, ribbonfishes, tube-eyes, and velifers, some of which exhibit unusual feeding behaviors. The tube-eye *Stylephorus chordatus*, for example, rises hundreds of feet (meters) daily from depths of about 2,600 feet (800 m) to feed in a head-up, tail-down position on tiny crustaceans.

The ribbon fish *Trachipterus trachypterus* is thought to adopt a similarly vertical position to feed on other fishes and squid.

All lampridiforms produce large eggs, up to ¼ inch (6 mm) in diameter. Most are bright shades of red, which may protect against ultraviolet rays penetrating the surface waters in which they float for up to a month before hatching. Unlike the eggs of most bony fishes, which produce feeble larvae requiring a rich yolk sac for food, lampridiform embryos develop early and are vigorous swimmers.

CODS, ANGLERFISHES, AND ALLIES

SUBDIVISION	Euteleostei
SUPERORDER	Paracanthopterygii
ORDERS	5
FAMILIES	37
SPECIES	1,382

Several small but significant features of the skeleton indicate relatedness between species in this group. There are also similarities in their habitat preferences. Most, for example, are bottom dwellers although some species (particularly those that are commercially important, such as haddock, hake, and the cods) form large, pelagic schools. All but about 20 species comprising the group are marine. They tend to be active at night or live in dark habitats such as underwater caves or the deep sea. An unusual feature of some is that, by using special muscles located on the swim bladder, they can produce sounds. These may be important in courtship and communicating distress.

Distribution Cods and anglerfishes are found in all oceans. The cods are exclusively marine with the exception of one species—the burbot—which is found in freshwater. Trout perches and allies only live in freshwater and are restricted to North America. Toadfishes live along tropical coastlines.

FACT FILE

Trout perch A native to freshwater streams and lakes in the eastern United States, the trout perch seeks rocky cover by day but ventures out by night to make short feeding migrations to shallower waters. The body is semi-transparent in live specimens.

- ↦ Up to 8 in (20 cm)
- ⚖ Up to 6 oz (170 g)
- ○ Oviparous
- ♀♂ Male & female
- ↯ Locally common

N. North America

Northern cavefish This species of cavefish is found in subterranean water and has no eyes. There are numerous touch-sensitive sensory papillae on the head. It has a low reproductive rate, the eggs are brooded in the gill cavity for up to five months.

- ↦ Up to 4½ in (11.5 cm)
- ⚖ Up to 3 oz (85 g)
- ○ Oviparous
- ♀♂ Male & female
- ↯ Vulnerable

North America

⚠ CONSERVATION WATCH

Threatened futures The critically endangered Alabama cavefish (*Speoplatyrhinus poulsoni*) is entirely white and blind. It is found only in Key Cave, Alabama, in the United States. Interference with bat populations has indirectly affected the cavefish's food chain and the contamination of groundwater is another major threat. An introduced sea star and the increased silt in river sediments due to land clearing have almost certainly contributed to the critically endangered status of the spotted handfish (*Brachionichthys hirsutus*), a marine fish endemic to the Australian island of Tasmania.

CRITICAL FOOD FISHES

Some of the most significant fisheries worldwide exploit species within the family Gadidae, which includes the Alaska pollock and Atlantic cod and annually accounts for well over 10 percent of the world's total fish catch.

These fishes produce enormous numbers of eggs, among the most of any fish. A large Alaskan pollock, for example, may spawn 15 million eggs in a year. Because, however, gadiform fishes are also long-lived and late to mature, they have proved to be highly susceptible to overexploitation and some fisheries are now facing extinction.

Anglerfish Many cod species are strong swimmers that actively search for prey along ocean substrates. Anglerfishes (left), in contrast, are mostly slow-moving and sluggish predators that wait for food to come to them. They can, however, move with lightning speed as they capture unsuspecting prey.

Caught redhanded The red handfish (*Brachionichthys politus*) (right) has a highly restricted distribution and is only found in Tasmania, Australia. It is believed that there are only as few as 1,000 in existence.

Pirate perch
Aphredoderus sayanus

Goatsbeard brotula
Brotula multibarbata

Trout perch
Percopsis omiscomaycus

Pearlfish
Carapus acus

Northern cavefish
Amblyopsis spelaea

FACT FILE

Burbot A freshwater lover of the dark with a circumarctic distribution, the burbot dwells mainly in the depths of lakes and slow-moving rivers. It shelters among vegetation in suitable crevices and down deep holes.

- ⬌ Up to 5 ft (1.5 m)
- ⬖ Up to 75 lb (34 kg)
- ○ Oviparous
- ♀♂ Male & female
- ⚑ Common

N. North America & N. Eurasia

European hake After decades of commercial exploitation, there is wide-spread concern the European hake has been overfished. Although the maximum weight recorded for the species is about 25 pounds (11.5 kg), individuals over 11 pounds (4.9 kg) are now rarely caught.

- ⬌ Up to 4½ ft (1.4 m)
- ⬖ Up to 25 lb (11.5 kg)
- ○ Oviparous
- ♀♂ Male & female
- ⚑ Common

E. North Atlantic, Mediterranean & Black seas

SEXUAL PARASITES

Ceratoid anglerfishes dwell in low-density populations in the high-pressure darkness of oceanic depths. To reduce the hit-or-miss probability of the sexes meeting, males of some species have evolved into little more than parasitic testes. As adults, they live permanently attached to and derive nourishment from their considerably larger female counterparts. In the triplewart seadevil (*Cryptopsaras couesii*) below, females have been found with up to four males attached.

"fishing pole" (illicium) and "lure" (esca)

large median and two small lateral oval caruncles

dwarf parasitic male

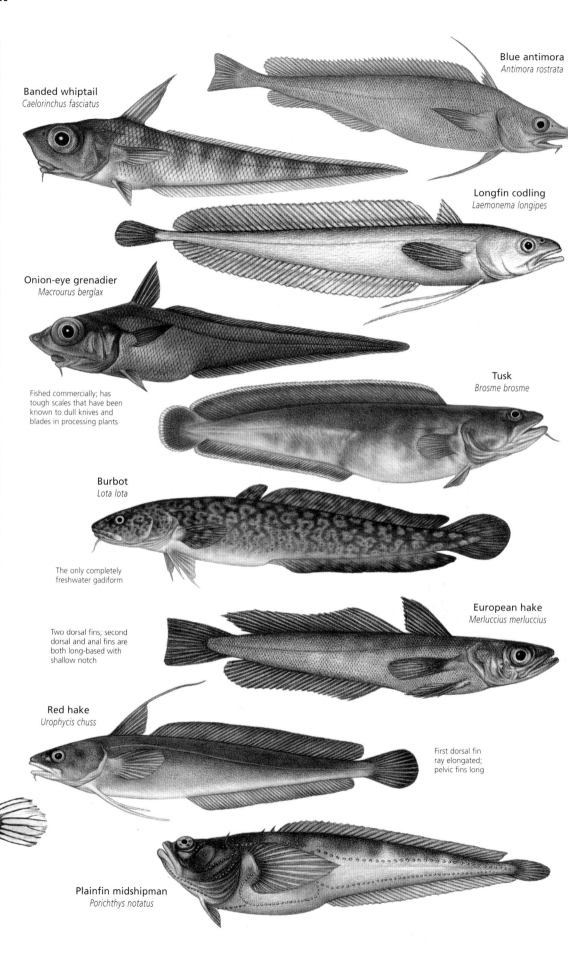

Banded whiptail
Caelorinchus fasciatus

Blue antimora
Antimora rostrata

Longfin codling
Laemonema longipes

Onion-eye grenadier
Macrourus berglax

Fished commercially; has tough scales that have been known to dull knives and blades in processing plants

Tusk
Brosme brosme

Burbot
Lota lota

The only completely freshwater gadiform

Two dorsal fins; second dorsal and anal fins are both long-based with shallow notch

European hake
Merluccius merluccius

Red hake
Urophycis chuss

First dorsal fin ray elongated; pelvic fins long

Plainfin midshipman
Porichthys notatus

Haddock
Melanogrammus aeglefinus

Atlantic cod
Gadus morhua

Two anal fins

Tadpole fish
Raniceps raninus

Stout-bodied with a broad
depressed head; minute first
dorsal fin and small chin barbel

American angler
Lophius americanus

Starry handfish
Halieutaea stellata

Anglerfish
Linophryne arborifera

Bib
Trisopterus luscus

Angler (monkfish)
Lophius piscatorius

Three dorsal fins

FACT FILE

Haddock Both male and female
haddock produce "knocking" sounds
when threatened. Males become
particularly raucous during spawning, so
it is likely that their noises are significant
in the haddock reproductive process.

- Up to 35½ in (90 cm)
- Up to 18 lb (8.2 kg)
- ○ Oviparous
- ♀♂ Male & female
- ↯ Vulnerable

North Atlantic to Spitzbergen

Atlantic cod A cold-water species
exploited in large commercial fisheries
in the North Atlantic, this cod is
usually caught up to weights of
about 25 pounds (11.5 kg) although
it can grow to four times that size.

- Up to 5 ft (1.5 m)
- Up to 100 lb (45 kg)
- ○ Oviparous
- ♀♂ Male & female
- ↯ Vulnerable

North Atlantic to Spitzbergen

Angler One of the anglerfishes,
this eastern Atlantic species has an
enormous mouth and lies in wait for
prey, well-camouflaged among sand
and sediment on the ocean floor. It
usually feeds on other fishes but has
been known to also take seabirds.

- Up to 6½ ft (2 m)
- Up to 127 lb (58 kg)
- ○ Oviparous
- ♀♂ Male & female
- ↯ Common

E. North Atlantic

EXQUISITE CAMOUFLAGE

Anglerfishes have no need for streamlining. Instead, these sit-and-wait
predators are perhaps better served
by being shaped and colored like their
surroundings. The sargassumfish
(*Histrio histrio*), for example, blends
in with sargassum weed, and the
roughbar frogfish (*Antennarius
avalonis*) looks like a rock.

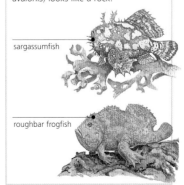

sargassumfish

roughbar frogfish

SPINY—RAYED FISHES

CLASS Actinopterygii	
SUPERORDER Acanthopterygii	
ORDERS 15	
FAMILIES 269	
SPECIES 13,262	

This, the largest single group of fishes, comprises the most advanced and recently evolved teleosts. Known also as acanthopterygians, the spiny-rayed fishes include more than 13,000 species in over 250 families. Common characteristics include a highly mobile and protrusible upper jaw, which has facilitated a wide range of feeding strategies, ctenoid scales that in some cases have become lost or further developed into hardened plates, and hard spines in the fins. As a group, these fishes have a ubiquitous distribution but are particularly abundant in coastal marine waters. They display an enormous breadth of specialized reproductive, behavioral, and anatomical adaptations that has seen them exploit niches not available to other fishes.

Extensive distribution The most widespread of all fish groups, the spiny-rays are found in almost every available aquatic habitat throughout the world from freshwater, through brackish to saltwater, and from coastal shallows to the ocean's depths. Specialized morphological and behavioral adaptations allow them to inhabit a wide range of environments, from frozen seas to ponds that dry up.

Colorful communities With their striking color patterns, wrasses and parrotfishes are among the most conspicuous fishes of coral reefs.

ADVANCED ADAPTATIONS

Almost every variation on the basic fish body plan can be found among the spiny-rayed fishes. The flatfishes, for example, depart dramatically from the normal symmetry seen in most fishes. The wrasses and parrot-fishes have a modified pharyngeal apparatus that acts as a second set of jaws in the throat, facilitating specialized feeding.

The cyprinodontiforms include guppies, swordtails, and other highly resilient freshwater aquarium favorites. Silversides can form large marine schools and many are commercially important baitfish. The flyingfishes are remarkably adapted for above-water gliding.

Gobies are mostly small fishes, such as the amphibious mudskippers, in which the pelvic fins are fused to form a cup-shaped disk.

In many of the triggerfishes and their relatives, scales have developed into protective body armor.

Damselfishes, including the well-known clownfishes, often display highly developed territorial behavior. The cichlids take parental care to its extreme. The groupers are among the most robust of all marine predators, and billfishes such as marlin and sailfish are among the fastest swimming.

The scorpionfishes include some of the deadliest fishes to humans. The drums and croakers make deep, distinctive noises when threatened and the butterflyfishes and angelfishes are among the most exquisitely colored aquatic creatures.

Strong suction Yellowbanded sweetlips (*Plectorhinchus lineatus*) have loose, rubbery lips, well adapted for "vacuuming" the sandy bottom for worms and mollusks.

Goldie River rainbowfish
Melanotaenia goldiei

Forktail rainbowfish
Pseudomugil furcatus

Boeseman's rainbowfish
Melanotaenia boesemani

Macculloch's rainbowfish
Melanotaenia maccullochi

Red-tailed silverside
Bedotia geayi

Brook silverside
Labidesthes sicculus

Threadfin rainbowfish
Iriatherina werneri

Red rainbowfish
Glossolepis incisus

Big-scale sand smelt
Atherina boyeri

Sand smelt
Atherina presbyter

Two dorsal fins, the first with seven or eight slender spines

Males have brighter colors and much longer dorsal and anal fins

Spotted blue-eye
Pseudomugil gertrudae

FLYING TO SAFETY

Flyingfishes inhabit the surface waters of all tropical oceans and are often found in groups around islands. They are well known for their habit of leaping out of water when frightened and gliding above the sea surface. Their ability to glide depends on the size of their pectoral fins. Two-wing flyingfishes (genus *Exocoetus*) build up swimming speed near the surface, set their pectoral fins in position, and launch themselves into the air for distances of 65 to 80 feet (20–25 m). In members of the subfamily Cypselurinae, both pectorals are much larger than the pelvics. They build up speed by taxiing like aircraft and continue to gather speed at the surface by sweeping the tail fin rapidly from side to side, keeping the lower lobe in the water. Toward the end of the taxi, they build up a speed of more than 37 miles per hour (60 km/h); the flight may last as long as 30 seconds and take the fish 650 feet (200 m) or more from the starting point.

Flying high Flyingfishes moving from water to air have to make major adjustments to their body functions. Two important changes are related to respiration and vision. Firstly, they are moving from relatively oxygen-poor water to oxygen-rich air and during gliding they reduce their heart rate, since oxygen uptake from the gills becomes much more efficient. There is also evidence to show that they are able to refocus their eyes to compensate for the drop in the optical density of air compared to water.

Four wings The genus *Cypselurus* has a number of "four-winged" species (right). That is, their pelvic as well as their pectoral fins are modified for gliding. They fly to evade attacks from predators below.

Garfish The garfish has been split into three sub-species. The first is found from the Bay of Biscay northward, the second southward from the Bay of Biscay and the Mediterranean Sea, and the third in the Black Sea. Piscivorous, they live near the surface and are extremely fast and agile swimmers. This species is noted for leaping out of the water when hooked.

⬌ Up to 37 in (95 cm)
⬤ Up to 2¾ lb (1.3 kg)
○ Oviparous
♀♂ Male & female
⚑ Common

N.E. Atlantic, Mediterranean & Black seas

Japanese medaka This medaka prefers slow-moving streams where it feeds on small invertebrates. It is extensively used in research and, along with the zebrafish, has become the equivalent of the laboratory rat. A genetically modified fluorescent variety has been created for the aquarium trade using DNA from jellyfishes.

⬌ Up to 1½ in (4 cm)
⬤ Up to ½ oz (15 g)
○ Oviparous
♀♂ Male & female
⚑ Common

S.E. Asia

Sharpchin flyingfish Members of the genus *Fodiator* are among the weakest "flyers" of the flyingfish. Nevertheless, this species is capable of gliding over water on enlarged, wing-like pectoral fins for 165 feet (50 m) or more. It lives close to the surface of the open ocean, feeds on plankton, and "flies" to evade attacks from predators below.

⬌ Up to 9½ in (24 cm)
⬤ Up to 8 oz (225 g)
○ Oviparous
♀♂ Male & female
⚑ Common

E. Pacific & E. Atlantic

Common halfbeak This species is found in bays and estuaries near the surface in large schools. It is omnivorous and feeds on planktonic invertebrates and phytoplankton. The lower jaw is elongated and blade-like. A food species, in areas such as Venezuela it is caught by attracting schools into shallow water at night with lights, then scooping them out in "mandinga" nets.

⬌ Up to 11 in (28 cm)
⬤ Up to 7 oz (200 g)
○ Oviparous
♀♂ Male & female
⚑ Common

W. Atlantic & E. Pacific

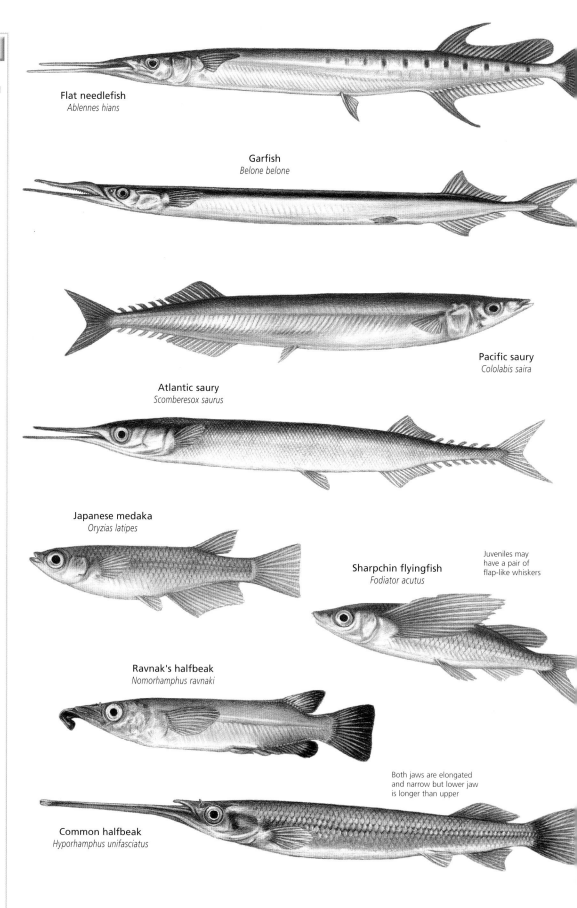

Flat needlefish
Ablennes hians

Garfish
Belone belone

Pacific saury
Cololabis saira

Atlantic saury
Scomberesox saurus

Japanese medaka
Oryzias latipes

Sharpchin flyingfish
Fodiator acutus

Juveniles may have a pair of flap-like whiskers

Ravnak's halfbeak
Nomorhamphus ravnaki

Both jaws are elongated and narrow but lower jaw is longer than upper

Common halfbeak
Hyporhamphus unifasciatus

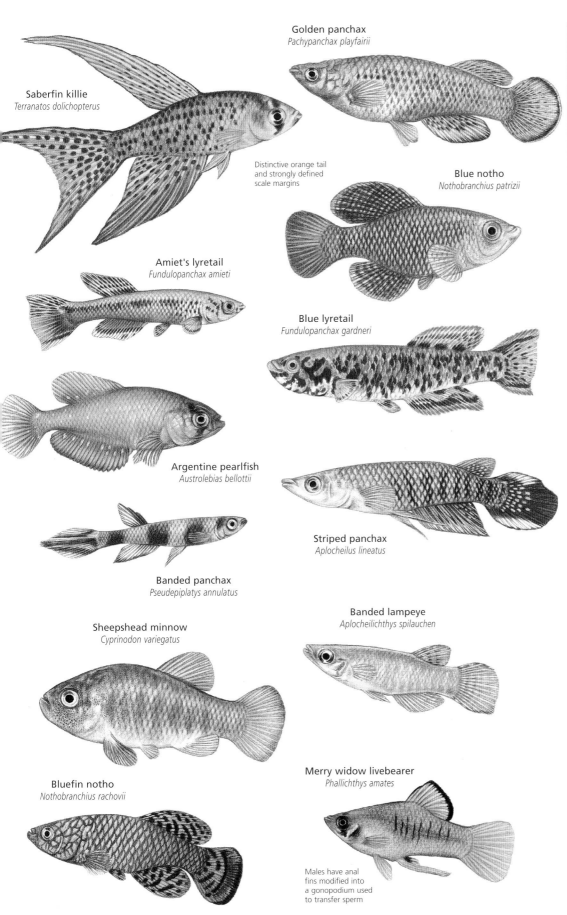

Saberfin killie
Terranatos dolichopterus

Golden panchax
Pachypanchax playfairii

Distinctive orange tail
and strongly defined
scale margins

Blue notho
Nothobranchius patrizii

Amiet's lyretail
Fundulopanchax amieti

Blue lyretail
Fundulopanchax gardneri

Argentine pearlfish
Austrolebias bellottii

Striped panchax
Aplocheilus lineatus

Banded panchax
Pseudepiplatys annulatus

Banded lampeye
Aplocheilichthys spilauchen

Sheepshead minnow
Cyprinodon variegatus

Merry widow livebearer
Phallichthys amates

Bluefin notho
Nothobranchius rachovii

Males have anal
fins modified into
a gonopodium used
to transfer sperm

FACT FILE

Golden panchax This short-lived freshwater species occurs in short-term pools and puddles in West African rain forest. Adults die after spawning, which takes place at the onset of the dry season, leaving fertilized eggs to survive in mud for as long as three months. The eggs hatch with the onset of the rainy season. This species feeds on worms, crustaceans, insects, and small fishes.

⬥ Up to 3 in (7.5 cm)
⬥ Up to 1 oz (30 g)
○ Oviparous, hiders
♀♂ Male & female
↯ Common

W. Africa

Saberfin killie This is another short-lived species in which adults die not long after spawning. Left in drying mud, fertilized eggs enter a resting phase until they are stimulated to hatch by the first raindrops of the rainy season. There is virtually no larval period and the young are sexually mature in just over a month after hatching.

⬥ Up to 1½ in (4 cm)
⬥ Up to ½ oz (15 g)
○ Oviparous, hiders
♀♂ Male & female
↯ Common

Venezuela

Blue notho Temporary pools and swamps on the coastal plains of Kenya and Somalia are the home of the blue notho. It is a seasonal fish. The eggs are laid on the bed and the male pushes them into the mud with a tail flick. When the pools dry up the adults die but the eggs survive in the mud until the next rains. This species cannot yet be bred in captivity.

⬥ Up to 1⅓ in (4.5 cm)
⬥ Up to ¾ oz (20 g)
○ Oviparous
♀♂ Male & female
↯ Locally common

E. Africa

Amiet's lyretail Found in the swampy parts of rain-forest streams of the lower Sanaga system in western Cameroon, this is not a seasonal killifish. Its eggs, which have filaments on the chorion, are laid on the stream-bed and hatch after about a month. It does not survive in aquarium conditions.

⬥ Up to 2¾ in (7 cm)
⬥ Up to 1 oz (30 g)
○ Oviparous
♀♂ Male & female
↯ Locally common

W. Africa

FACT FILE

Striped foureyed fish The striped foureyed fish has eyes divided into aerial and aquatic parts so as to see above and below the water surface. Found in freshwater and sometimes brackish lagoons and mangroves, it has internal fertilization and bears live young. It can remain on the mud bottom exposed to air during low tide.

- Up to 12 in (30 cm)
- Up to 14 oz (400 g)
- Viviparous; live bearers
- Male & female
- Common

South America

Guppy The guppy belongs to one of the few bony fish families (Poeciliidae) with members that give birth to live young. Originally from South America, this popular aquarium fish has been introduced to warm, freshwater lakes throughout the world. It is an adaptable species that tolerates a wide range of habitats and water quality.

- Up to 2 in (5 cm)
- Up to ¾ oz (20 g)
- Viviparous; live bearers
- Male & female
- Common

N.E. South America, Barbados, Trinidad; introd. widely

Valencia toothcarp This species is a non-seasonal killifish found in still waters, rich in vegetation, along the Mediterranean coasts of Spain as well as in Albania and the Island of Corfu. It feeds on invertebrates and can tolerate both brackish and freshwater. The species is considered endangered because of habitat destruction.

- Up to 3 in (7.5 cm)
- Up to 1⅓ oz (40 g)
- Oviparous
- Male & female
- Endangered

S. Europe

Western mosquitofish Native to the fresh and brackish, standing and slow-flowing waters of North America, the western mosquitofish has acquired an almost pan-global distribution. It has been widely introduced for the control of mosquitos, often with detrimental effects on the local fish fauna. It has internal fertilization and bears live young.

- Up to 2½ in (6.6 cm)
- Up to 1¼ oz (35 g)
- Viviparous; live bearers
- Male & female
- Common

North America

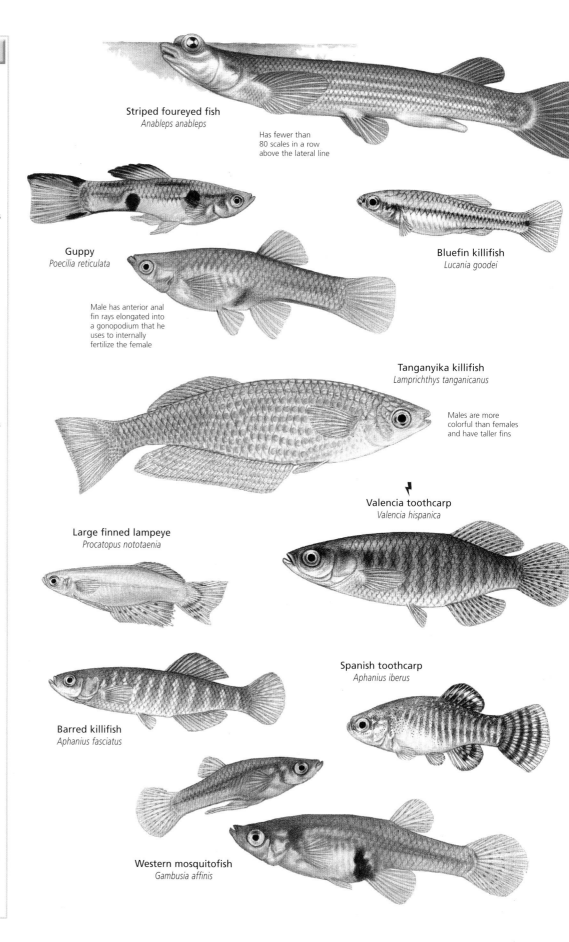

Striped foureyed fish
Anableps anableps

Has fewer than 80 scales in a row above the lateral line

Guppy
Poecilia reticulata

Male has anterior anal fin rays elongated into a gonopodium that he uses to internally fertilize the female

Bluefin killifish
Lucania goodei

Tanganyika killifish
Lamprichthys tanganicanus

Males are more colorful than females and have taller fins

Large finned lampeye
Procatopus nototaenia

Valencia toothcarp
Valencia hispanica

Barred killifish
Aphanius fasciatus

Spanish toothcarp
Aphanius iberus

Western mosquitofish
Gambusia affinis

Velvet whalefish
Barbourisia rufa

Flagfish
Jordanella floridae

Lateral line extends
to deeply forked
caudal fin

Splendid alfonsino
Beryx splendens

Flabby whalefish
Cetomimus craneae

Redmouth whalefish
Rondeletia bicolor

Splitfin flashlightfish
Anomalops katoptron

Alternating broad red
and narrow silvery-white
stripes; anal fin with
four spines

Crown squirrelfish
Sargocentron diadema

Huge, immovable
scales; anal fin
without spines

Pineconefish
Monocentris japonica

Shadowfin soldierfish
Myripristis adusta

FACT FILE

Velvet whalefish Named for its whale-like appearance, not its size, the whalefish is a deep-sea ocean dweller. It has reduced eyes but a highly developed lateral line system to provide information about its environment. It also has a big mouth and highly distensible stomach to cope with the large, infrequently encountered meals typical of life in the deep sea.

- ↔ Up to 14 in (36 cm)
- ▲ Up to 16 oz (455 g)
- ✿ Not known
- ♀♂ Not known
- ⚑ Common

Worldwide in tropical & temperate seas

Crown squirrelfish Most adult squirrelfishes live in shallow water around tropical reefs but their larvae have a long pelagic life and are often found way out to sea. This species has a short, venomous cheek spine. It is active at night, sheltering in caves and under ledges during the day. It feeds on small fishes and invertebrates.

- ↔ Up to 6½ in (16.5 cm)
- ▲ Up to 8 oz (225 g)
- ○ Oviparous
- ♀♂ Male & female
- ⚑ Common

Indo-Pacific, Red Sea, Oceania

Shadowfin soldierfish Inhabiting caves and crevices in coral reefs, either alone or in small groups, this species ventures out at night to feed on plankton.

- ↔ Up to 13⅓ in (35 cm)
- ▲ Up to 18 oz (510 g)
- ○ Oviparous
- ♀♂ Male & female
- ⚑ Common

Indo-Pacific

FACT FILE

John Dory The John Dory is a weak swimmer that leads a mostly solitary life near the ocean floor. A highly compressed body makes its head-on profile extremely narrow, helping it to remain hidden from prey as it stalks from behind. Its highly protrusible jaws are efficient at capturing unsuspecting small fishes and crustaceans.

- Up to 26 in (66 cm)
- Up to 13 lb (6 kg)
- Oviparous
- Male & female
- Common

E. Atlantic, Mediterranean Sea, W. Pacific & W. Indian Ocean

Shrimpfish With a long-snouted, semi-transparent, shrimp-like body, this fish congregates in synchronized schools in a head-down, tail-up vertical position. It lives among sea urchins and staghorn coral branches and feeds on zooplankton. It has been found cast up on Indo-Pacific beaches after storms.

- Up to 6 in (15 cm)
- Up to 4 oz (115 g)
- Oviparous
- Male & female
- Common

Indo-West Pacific

DEVOTED DADS

By cementing plants together with sticky secretions from their kidneys, male sticklebacks build elaborate nests for the females to lay their eggs in. After fertilizing the eggs, the males usually drive the females away but continue to maintain and defend the nests while attending to the eggs, fanning oxygenated water across them with their pectoral fins.

Ninespine stickleback
Pungitius pungitius

7–12 free spines in front of dorsal fin

Three-spined stickleback
Gasterosteus aculeatus

Compressed, scaleless body; mouth at end of long tubular snout

Longspine snipefish
Macrorhamphosus scolopax

Three anal spines with 24–48 soft rays; body highly compressed

Indo-Pacific boarfish
Antigonia rubescens

Long filaments trail from the dorsal spines; large, round, black spot encircled by a yellow ring on each side of the body; minute scales

First dorsal spine long and sharp, located at the extreme end of the body. Soft dorsal and caudal fins displaced ventrally

John Dory
Zeus faber

Massive head with large, highly protrusible jaws

Razor-like body extremely compressed and almost entirely covered by thin bony plates that are expansions of the vertebral column. Lateral line and teeth are absent. Swims in a vertical, head down orientation

Body contained in bony plates; mouth small and toothless; large horizontal pectoral fins

Shrimpfish
Aeoliscus strigatus

Hawaiian sea-moth fish
Eurypegasus papilio

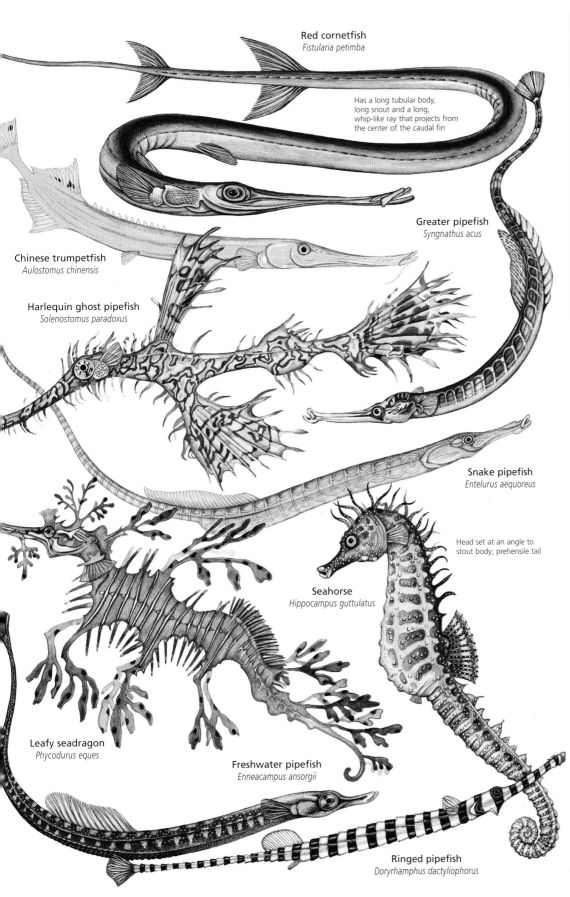

Red cornetfish
Fistularia petimba

Has a long tubular body, long snout and a long, whip-like ray that projects from the center of the caudal fin

Greater pipefish
Syngnathus acus

Chinese trumpetfish
Aulostomus chinensis

Harlequin ghost pipefish
Solenostomus paradoxus

Snake pipefish
Entelurus aequoreus

Head set at an angle to stout body; prehensile tail

Seahorse
Hippocampus guttulatus

Leafy seadragon
Phycodurus eques

Freshwater pipefish
Enneacampus ansorgii

Ringed pipefish
Doryrhamphus dactyliophorus

FACT FILE

Red cornetfish Usually found at depths of more than 33 feet (10 m), this species feeds on shrimps and small fishes.

- Up to 6½ ft (2 m)
- Up to 10¼ lb (4.65 kg)
- ○ Oviparous
- ♀♂ Male & female
- Common

Atlantic & Indo-Pacific

Harlequin ghost pipefish Due to a series of bony plates beneath their skin, pipefishes and seahorses cannot swim by flexing the body like most other fishes, but use rapid fanning movements of the fins instead.

- Up to 4¾ in (12 cm)
- Up to 1 oz (30 g)
- ○ Oviparous, brooder
- ♀♂ Male & female
- Uncommon

Indo-West Pacific

Leafy seadragon Like their relatives the seahorses, male leafy seadragons incubate eggs. Females lay up to 250 onto a patch of spongy tissue on the tail's underside, where they develop for about six weeks before hatching.

- Up to 16 in (40 cm)
- Up to 8 oz (225 g)
- ○ Oviparous, brooder
- ♀♂ Male & female
- Data deficient

S. Australia

SEAHORSE FEEDING

Seahorses are ambush predators that pluck mostly small, planktonic animals from the waters around them. Like their closest relatives, including the seadragons, trumpetfishes, and cornetfishes, they have an elongate, tube-shaped mouth. It functions like a straw, generating a powerful vacuum action to draw in prey.

Toothless predators *Seahorses and their relatives do not have any teeth and so swallow their prey whole.*

MALE PREGNANCY

Seahorse reproduction has a number of interesting features and involves the most extreme form of male parental care known in the animal kingdom—it is the male seahorse that becomes pregnant. Seahorses are sexually dimorphic and the tails and snouts of the males are much longer than those of the females. Mating commences with an elaborate courtship that starts with the male dancing around the female, while he produces clicking sounds. Both sexes change color as the dance progresses. Eventually, the pair will move to a piece of coral or seagrass bed and use their prehensile tails to entwine around an object and each other. In the final stages of courtship they release themselves from the seabed and, still entwined, float in the water column during which time the male pulls his tail back and pumps water in and out of a pouch on his belly. After rinsing out his pouch, the male lengthens his body and pairs up with the female, belly to belly, for egg transfer.

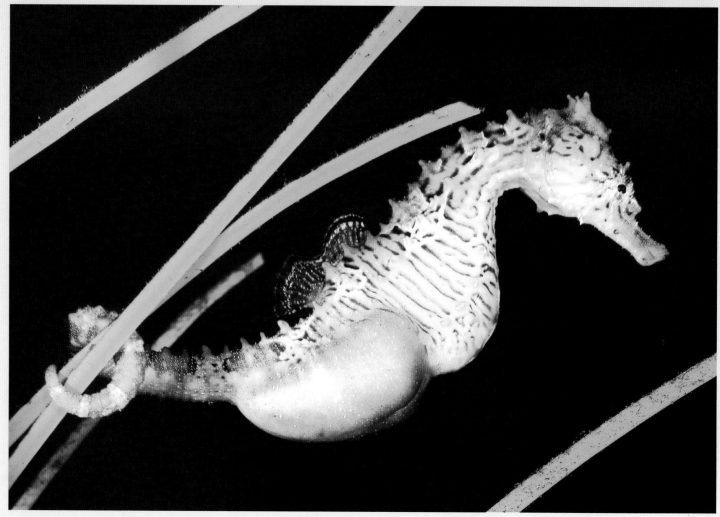

Egg swap After pair bonding displays, the female places her unfertilized eggs into the male's brood pouch (left) using an ovipositor. The presence of the eggs in the brood pouch stimulates the male to produce sperm that fertilizes the eggs. The eggs embed in the pouch wall and become enveloped by the wall lining, which is rich in blood vessels that exchange nutrients, oxygen, and waste products with the pouch fluid. The pouch fluid changes in composition as birth nears, and becomes similar to seawater.

Independent offspring Young (above) are born as miniature adult seahorses that are independent from birth, receiving no further parental care. Although the number of young released averages about 100–200 for most species, it can be as few as 5 for the smaller species, or as many as 1,500.

Ready to mate The presence of a brood pouch (left) is an indicator of sexual maturity in males. Males are able to become pregnant any time during the breeding season, which varies with species and is determined mainly by water temperature. They are pregnant for periods between two and four weeks, the length decreasing with increasing temperature.

Giving birth Males usually go into labor (right) at night and may take several hours, pumping and thrusting, to expel the brood. Throughout pregnancy the female remains close by, regularly "greeting" the male. It has been suggested this ensures that the male and female are ready to re-mate at the same time. Re-mating may take place just a few hours after the end of labor.

East Atlantic red gurnard This species explores the seabed with finger-like pectoral fin rays which are well supplied with sense organs. It feeds on small, buried crustaceans and is often caught in some numbers by trawlers in coastal waters, as well as by anglers—its flesh is very good eating. Gurnards, or sea robins, make audible noises using special muscles attached to the swim bladder.

- Up to 16 in (40 cm)
- Up to 2 lb (900 g)
- Oviparous
- Male & female
- Common

E. Atlantic & Mediterranean Sea

Swamp eel This highly adaptable, air-breathing, freshwater carnivore can survive out of water for long periods. After spending part of its life as a female, some individuals undergo sex reversal, transforming into males. All larger individuals are males. The swamp eel has been labeled a potential "ecological nightmare" in some areas where it has been introduced.

- Up to 18 in (46 cm)
- Up to 24½ oz (700 g)
- Oviparous, guarders
- Hermaphrodite
- Common

S.E. Asia, Australia

Fire eel Although it is often seen in the aquarium trade, the fire eel is becoming rare in the wild where it occurs in slow-flowing rivers and inundated floodplains. It feeds on worms, benthic insect larvae, and some plant material. In aquariums, some appear to recognize their owners and will take food from their hands in an apparently affectionate way.

- Up to 39½ in (1 m)
- Up to 4¼ lb (1.9 kg)
- Oviparous
- Male & female
- Uncommon

S.E Asia

Flying gurnard The flying gurnard has greatly enlarged, wing-like pectoral fins with free, finger-like lower rays. The "wings" are used for underwater gliding and the "fingers" for exploring the seabed. It is able to produce sounds and "walks" on the seafloor by alternate movements of the pelvic fins. It feeds on mollusks, crustaceans, and other fishes.

- Up to 35½ in (90 cm)
- Up to 4 lb (1.8 kg)
- Oviparous
- Male & female
- Common

Atlantic & Mediterranean Sea

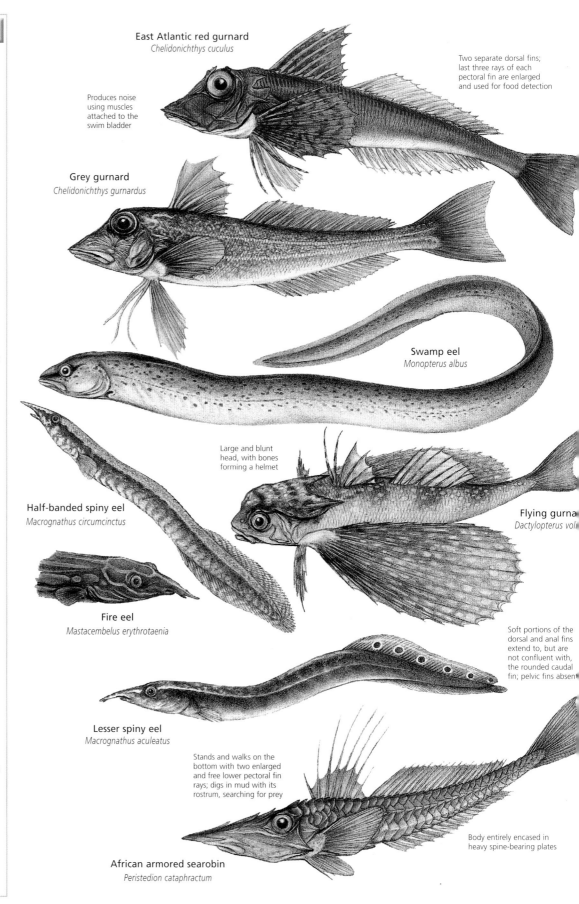

East Atlantic red gurnard
Chelidonichthys cuculus

Two separate dorsal fins; last three rays of each pectoral fin are enlarged and used for food detection

Produces noise using muscles attached to the swim bladder

Grey gurnard
Chelidonichthys gurnardus

Swamp eel
Monopterus albus

Large and blunt head, with bones forming a helmet

Half-banded spiny eel
Macrognathus circumcinctus

Flying gurnard
Dactylopterus volitans

Fire eel
Mastacembelus erythrotaenia

Soft portions of the dorsal and anal fins extend to, but are not confluent with, the rounded caudal fin; pelvic fins absent

Lesser spiny eel
Macrognathus aculeatus

Stands and walks on the bottom with two enlarged and free lower pectoral fin rays; digs in mud with its rostrum, searching for prey

Body entirely encased in heavy spine-bearing plates

African armored searobin
Peristedion cataphractum

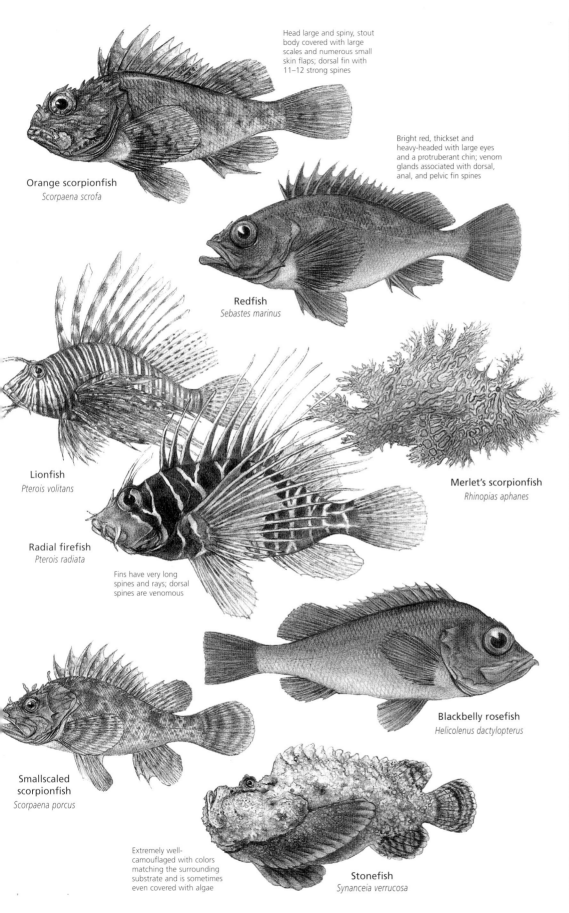

Head large and spiny, stout body covered with large scales and numerous small skin flaps; dorsal fin with 11–12 strong spines

Orange scorpionfish
Scorpaena scrofa

Bright red, thickset and heavy-headed with large eyes and a protruberant chin; venom glands associated with dorsal, anal, and pelvic fin spines

Redfish
Sebastes marinus

Lionfish
Pterois volitans

Radial firefish
Pterois radiata

Fins have very long spines and rays; dorsal spines are venomous

Merlet's scorpionfish
Rhinopias aphanes

Blackbelly rosefish
Helicolenus dactylopterus

Smallscaled scorpionfish
Scorpaena porcus

Extremely well-camouflaged with colors matching the surrounding substrate and is sometimes even covered with algae

Stonefish
Synanceia verrucosa

Flamboyant fish The lionfish (*Pterois volitans*) is the most recognizable and flamboyant member of the scorpion-fishes, Scorpaenidae. The outer half of the pectoral fin rays are free, with relatively broad membranes that give a feather-like appearance.

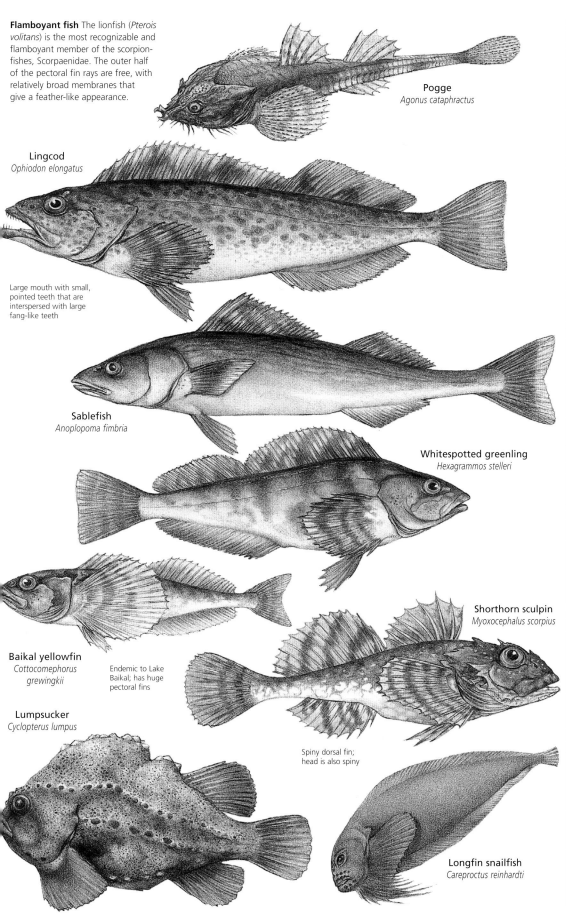

Pogge
Agonus cataphractus

Lingcod
Ophiodon elongatus

Large mouth with small, pointed teeth that are interspersed with large fang-like teeth

Sablefish
Anoplopoma fimbria

Whitespotted greenling
Hexagrammos stelleri

Baikal yellowfin
Cottocomephorus grewingkii

Endemic to Lake Baikal; has huge pectoral fins

Lumpsucker
Cyclopterus lumpus

Shorthorn sculpin
Myoxocephalus scorpius

Spiny dorsal fin; head is also spiny

Longfin snailfish
Careproctus reinhardti

FACT FILE

Sablefish Named because of its sleek black to dark-green skin, the sablefish is an important commercial species in Alaska and to a lesser extent in Canada. It is a deepwater, long-lived fish, with reports of individuals older than 90 years.

- Up to 3¼ ft (1 m)
- Up to 126 lb (57 kg)
- ○ Oviparous
- ♀♂ Male & female
- ⚓ Common

North Pacific

Baikal yellowfin The Baikal yellowfin is endemic to Lake Baikal and its tributaries. It occurs in virtually all regions of the open part of the lake, and can be found down to a depth of 980 feet (300 m). This species feeds on crustaceans and fish larvae.

- Up to 7½ in (19 cm)
- Up to 5 oz (142 g)
- ○ Not known
- ♀♂ Not known
- ⚓ Locally common

Lake Baikal

Shorthorn sculpin Renowned for eating "anything and everything," the shorthorn sculpin has a voracious appetite. Its large mouth can wrap around prey half its size and its stomach readily stretches around any large object it consumes.

- Up to 24 in (61 cm)
- Up to 2 lb (900 g)
- ○ Oviparous
- ♀♂ Male & female
- ⚓ Common

North Atlantic & Arctic oceans

LUMPSUCKER ANATOMY

The female lumpsucker deposits her large egg mass on the shore's edge near the low tide mark. The male guards it aggressively, maintaining his position in the turbulent intertidal zone by attaching to rocks or seaweed with a ventrally located sucking disk formed from modified pelvic fins.

Cheap treat
Lumpsucker eggs are sold commercially as inexpensive caviar.

FACT FILE

Common snook A fish of coastal areas, the common snook is particularly found in mangroves and brackish waters but can also penetrate into freshwaters. The lateral line is prominently outlined in black and it is an active predator of both fishes and crustaceans. It is a prized sport and food species but overfishing in the past has severely reduced its numbers and it is now protected in many places.

- Up to 4 ft (1.2 m)
- Up to 50 lb (23 kg)
- Oviparous
- Hermaphrodite
- Common

W. Atlantic

Striped bass This is a silvery colored fish with seven or eight black stripes on the side. It is found in coastal waters, rarely more than a few miles from the shore. It is able to move into freshwater and some populations are landlocked. The striped bass is a predator of other fishes and crustaceans and is an important sport and food fish, although its numbers have declined in recent years.

- Up to 6 ft (1.8 m)
- Up to 125 lb (56 kg)
- Oviparous
- Male & female
- Common

N.W Atlantic

European bass The European bass is an active schooling fish of inshore waters. Larger fishes frequent reefs with strong currents while smaller fishes are often found in estuaries. Another popular sport fish, it is a predator of fishes, crustaceans, and squid. It is a long-lived species—larger specimens may be more than 20 years old.

- Up to 39½ in (1 m)
- Up to 20 lb (9 kg)
- Oviparous
- Male & female
- Common

N.E Atlantic, Mediterranean & Black seas

Barramundi perch Most barramundi are protandrous hermaphrodites: they begin life as males, reach sexual maturity after about three years, and become females after about five years. As a result, larger individuals are inevitably female, while smaller fishes are mostly males.

- Up to 6 ft (1.8 m)
- Up to 132 lb (60 kg)
- Oviparous
- Hermaphrodite
- Common

Indo-West Pacific

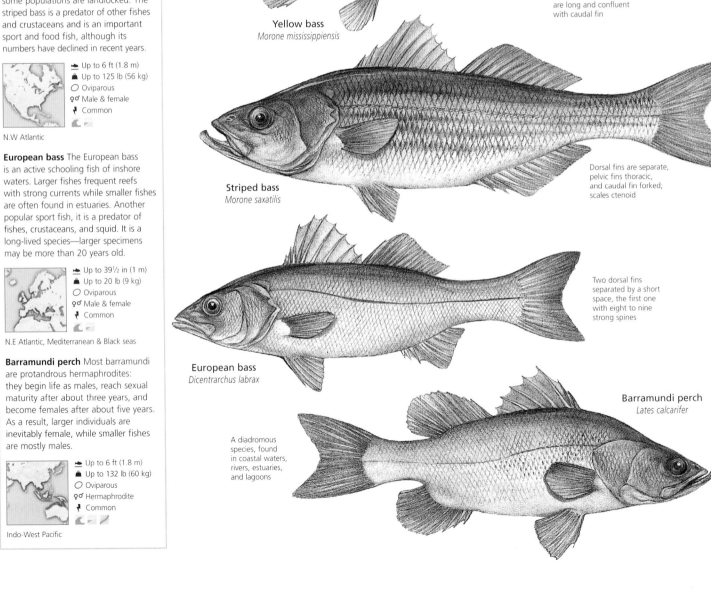

Common snook
Centropomus undecimalis

Sloping forehead, protruding lower jaw, and prominent lateral line that extends to the rear edge of the caudal fin

Striped seasnail
Liparis liparis

Pelvic fins form a suction disc; dorsal and anal fins are long and confluent with caudal fin

Yellow bass
Morone mississippiensis

Striped bass
Morone saxatilis

Dorsal fins are separate, pelvic fins thoracic, and caudal fin forked; scales ctenoid

European bass
Dicentrarchus labrax

Two dorsal fins separated by a short space, the first one with eight to nine strong spines

Barramundi perch
Lates calcarifer

A diadromous species, found in coastal waters, rivers, estuaries, and lagoons

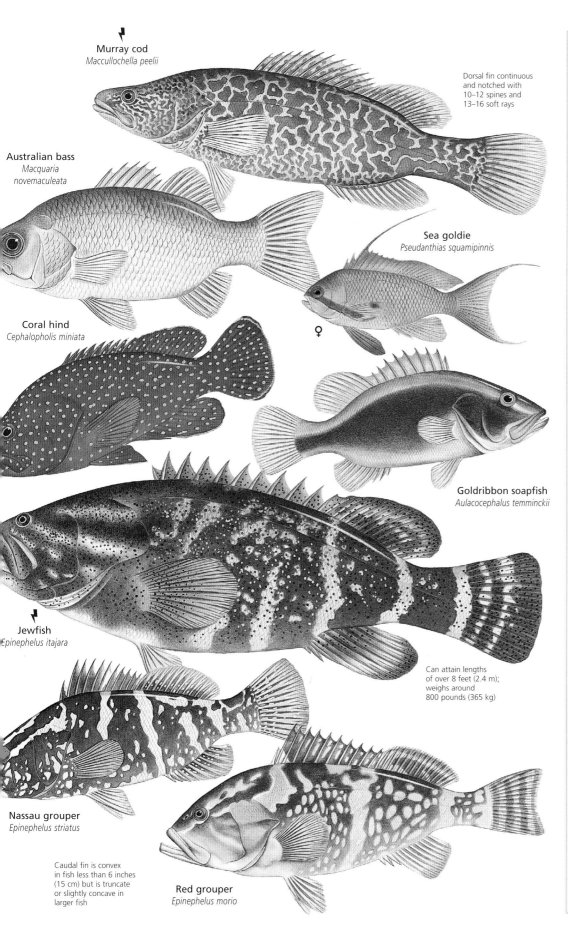

Murray cod
Maccullochella peelii

Dorsal fin continuous and notched with 10–12 spines and 13–16 soft rays

Australian bass
Macquaria novemaculeata

Sea goldie
Pseudanthias squamipinnis

♀

Coral hind
Cephalopholis miniata

Goldribbon soapfish
Aulacocephalus temminckii

Jewfish
Epinephelus itajara

Can attain lengths of over 8 feet (2.4 m); weighs around 800 pounds (365 kg)

Nassau grouper
Epinephelus striatus

Caudal fin is convex in fish less than 6 inches (15 cm) but is truncate or slightly concave in larger fish

Red grouper
Epinephelus morio

FACT FILE

Murray cod One of the world's largest freshwater fish species, the Murray cod mainly inhabits turbid, slow-flowing rivers, especially in deep holes among submerged trees. It may live to an age of 60 years.

- ⟹ Up to 6 ft (1.8 m)
- ⚖ Up to 240 lb (108 kg)
- ○ Oviparous
- ♀♂ Male & female
- ⚡ Critically endangered

E. Australia

Sea goldie The sexes in this fish look like different species. Females are colored orange to yellow while males are mainly purple. Males also have an enormously elongated dorsal fin spine and longer tail-fin lobes.

- ⟹ Up to 6 in (15 cm)
- ⚖ Up to 8 oz (225 g)
- ○ Oviparous
- ♀♂ Sequential hermaphrodite
- ⚡ Common

Indo-West Pacific & Red Sea

Goldribbon soapfish This fish has a deep blue body with a bright yellow band from the snout, through the eye, and along the back to the caudal fin. The skin has a thick mucus coat containing the toxin grammistin, which imparts a bitter taste. When frightened, soapfish produce more toxin.

- ⟹ Up to 16 in (40 cm)
- ⚖ Up to 1¾ lb (800 g)
- ○ Oviparous
- ♀♂ Not known
- ⚡ Uncommon

Indo-Pacific

Jewfish Adults of this solitary species live in shallow inshore areas of reefs and brackish estuaries. Juveniles are common in mangroves. Jewfish are highly territorial and will warn off intruders with a threat display of an open mouth and quivering body. Adults can take large prey items and some large individuals have been known to stalk and attempt to eat divers.

- ⟹ Up to 8¼ ft (2.5 m)
- ⚖ Up to 1,000 lb (455 kg)
- ○ Oviparous
- ♀♂ Hermaphrodite
- ⚡ Critically endangered

Atlantic & E. Pacific

FACT FILE

Yellow-edged lyretail This species prefers offshore reefs rather than continental shores and is usually seen on coral reefs, in clear water, at a depth of more than 50 feet (15 m). Primarily a predator of fishes, it also eats crustaceans such as crabs and shrimps.

- Up to 33 in (85 cm)
- Up to 26½ lb (12 kg)
- ○ Oviparous
- ♀♂ Sequential hermaphrodite
- Common

Indo-Pacific

Cherry bass The cherry bass is found in large schools in rocky areas. The male is scarlet with pearly-white blotches and the female is reddish-orange with a black blotch on the posterior part of the dorsal spines. The third dorsal spine is elongated.

- Up to 5 in (13 cm)
- Up to 6 oz (170 g)
- ○ Oviparous
- ♀♂ Hermaphrodite
- Locally common

N.W. Pacific

INGENIOUS MIMICRY

The comet deters predators by hiding in holes exposing only its tail, which mimics the fierce-looking head of the identically patterned turkey moray eel (*Gymnothorax meleagris*). An ocellus at the base of the dorsal fin looks like an eye. A gap between the anal and tail fins forms a "mouth."

Butterfly effect This type of so-called "Batesian mimicry" is similar to that adopted by many butterflies.

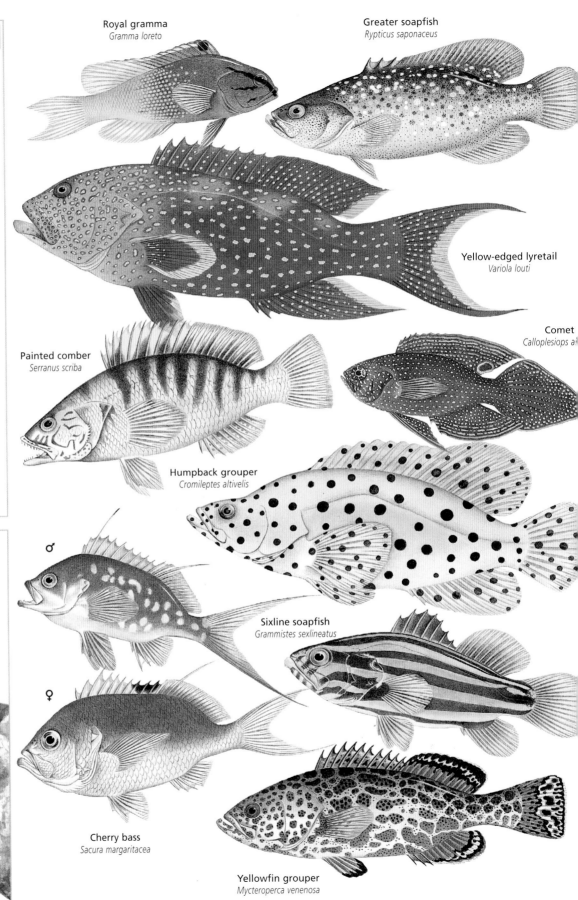

Royal gramma
Gramma loreto

Greater soapfish
Rypticus saponaceus

Yellow-edged lyretail
Variola louti

Comet
Calloplesiops a

Painted comber
Serranus scriba

Humpback grouper
Cromileptes altivelis

♂

♀

Sixline soapfish
Grammistes sexlineatus

Cherry bass
Sacura margaritacea

Yellowfin grouper
Mycteroperca venenosa

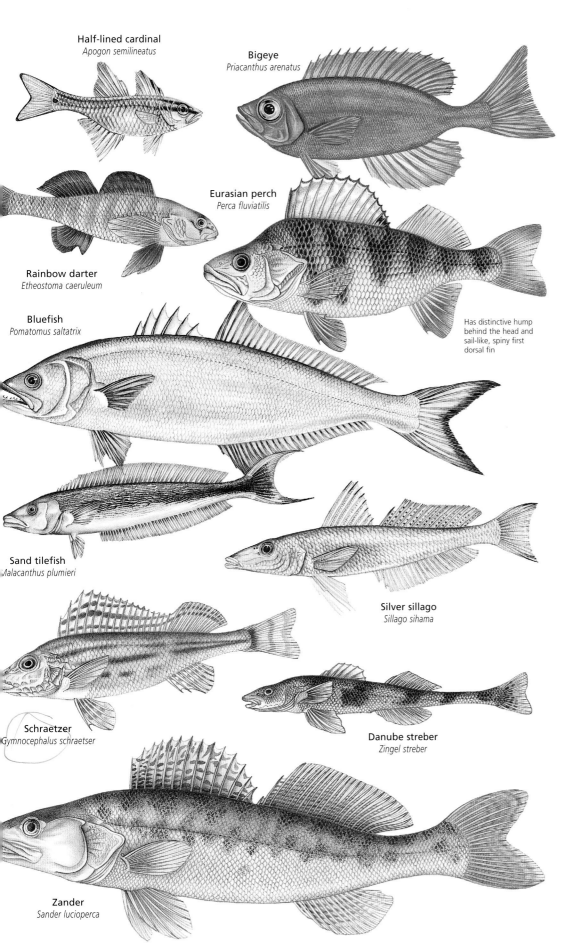

Half-lined cardinal
Apogon semilineatus

Bigeye
Priacanthus arenatus

Eurasian perch
Perca fluviatilis

Rainbow darter
Etheostoma caeruleum

Bluefish
Pomatomus saltatrix

Has distinctive hump behind the head and sail-like, spiny first dorsal fin

Sand tilefish
Malacanthus plumieri

Silver sillago
Sillago sihama

Schraetzer
Gymnocephalus schraetser

Danube streber
Zingel streber

Zander
Sander lucioperca

FACT FILE

Bigeye A nocturnal predator of small fishes, crustaceans, and polychaetes, the bigeye is usually found in small aggregations near the bottom of coral reefs and rocky areas at depths of 50 to 250 feet (15–75 m).

Up to 19½ in (50 cm)
Up to 6¼ lb (2.8 kg)
Oviparous
Not known
Common

Atlantic

Eurasian perch The females of this species lay their eggs, several tens of thousands at a time, connected in long, white, sticky mucus ribbons. These can be up to 40 inches (1 m) in length and are left draped over submerged rocks and vegetation.

Up to 20 in (51 cm)
Up to 10½ lb (4.7 kg)
Oviparous
Male & female
Common

N. Eurasia

Bluefish The bluefish is found in large schools in oceanic and coastal waters; juveniles enter estuaries. The female produces between 400,000 and 2,000,000 eggs.

Up to 51 in (1.3 m)
Up to 29¾ lb (14 kg)
Oviparous
Male & female
Common

Widespread in subtropical seas

BURROW AND BROOD

Jawfishes use their capacious mouths to excavate large burrows in sand that are lined with pebbles and shell fragments. They sit just inside the burrow but on seeing food they float out of their hole to grab the food and then rush back in. The burrow entrance can be closed with a large piece of shell.

Brooding male
After fertilization, the male scoops up the eggs left by the female and broods them in his mouth for about seven days.

FACT FILE

Cobia The cobia is the sole member of the family Rachycentridae and is related to the remoras and jacks. Found in coastal and open waters, it often congregates around buoys and other floating objects. This species is generally encountered singularly or in small groups but it has been occasionally known to school.

- Up to 6½ ft (2 m)
- Up to 150 lb (68 kg)
- Oviparous
- ♀♂ Male & female
- Common

Tropical & subtropical seas worldwide

Common dolphinfish This species has a rapid growth rate and a short lifespan, few live longer than four years. It is a schooling species, but often hunts in pairs or small groups. It feeds on fishes and squid near the surface of oceans, frequently near drift lines and flotsam.

- Up to 6¾ ft (2.1 m)
- Up to 88 lb (40 kg)
- Oviparous
- ♀♂ Male & female
- Common

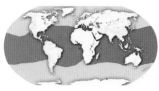

Tropical & subtropical seas worldwide

Pilotfish The common name of this species stems from its habit of swimming with sharks and other large marine creatures, feeding on food scraps and parasites. Sailors once thought they guided their "hosts" to food.

- Up to 27½ in (70 cm)
- Up to 15 lb (6.8 kg)
- Oviparous
- ♀♂ Male & female
- Common

Tropical seas worldwide

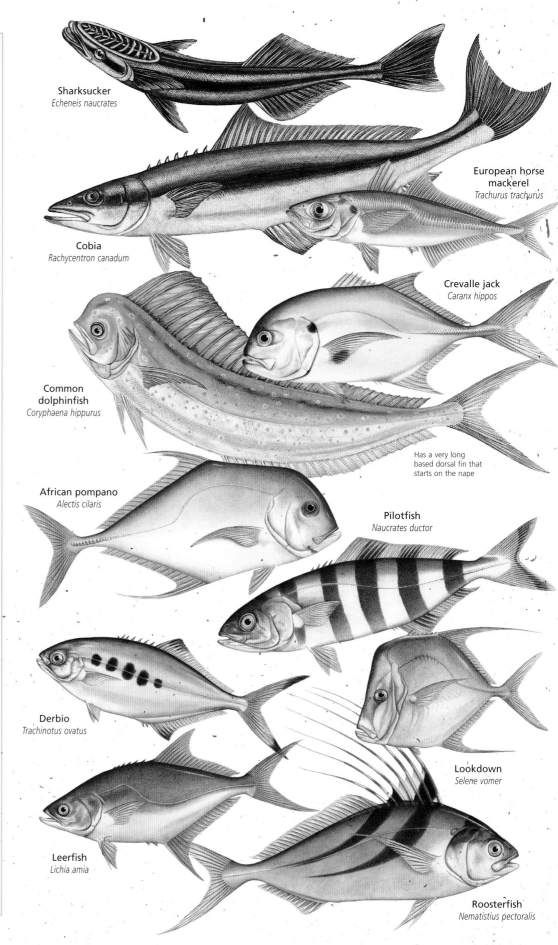

Sharksucker
Echeneis naucrates

European horse mackerel
Trachurus trachurus

Cobia
Rachycentron canadum

Crevalle jack
Caranx hippos

Common dolphinfish
Coryphaena hippurus

Has a very long based dorsal fin that starts on the nape

African pompano
Alectis ciliaris

Pilotfish
Naucrates ductor

Derbio
Trachinotus ovatus

Lookdown
Selene vomer

Leerfish
Lichia amia

Roosterfish
Nematistius pectoralis

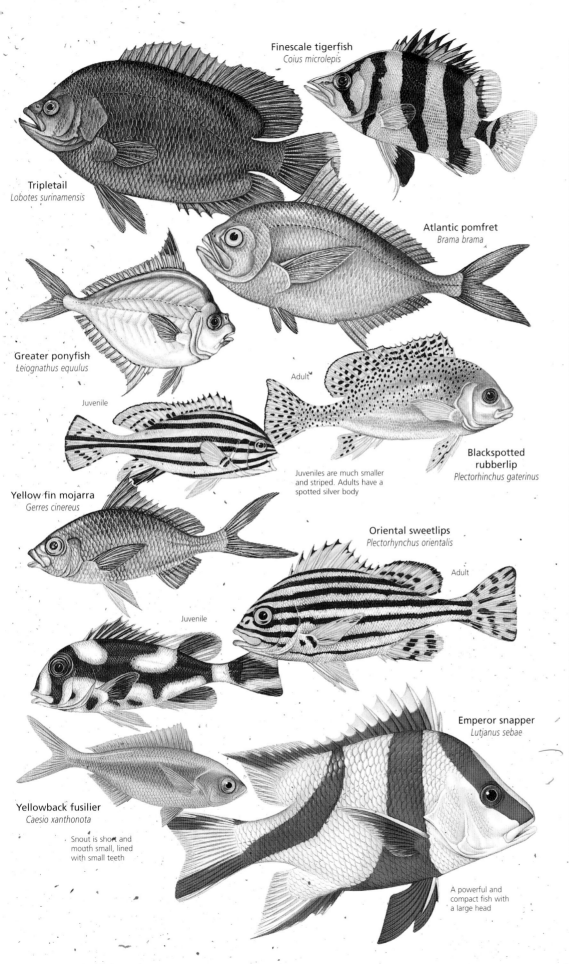

Finescale tigerfish
Coius microlepis

Tripletail
Lobotes surinamensis

Atlantic pomfret
Brama brama

Greater ponyfish
Leiognathus equulus

Juvenile

Adult

Blackspotted
rubberlip
Plectorhinchus gaterinus

Juveniles are much smaller
and striped. Adults have a
spotted silver body

Yellow fin mojarra
Gerres cinereus

Oriental sweetlips
Plectorhynchus orientalis

Adult

Juvenile

Emperor snapper
Lutjanus sebae

Yellowback fusilier
Caesio xanthonota

Snout is short and
mouth small, lined
with small teeth

A powerful and
compact fish with
a large head

FACT FILE

Tripletail Found from the lower reaches of large rivers, estuaries and bays to open water offshore, the tripletail often floats on its side near floating objects, mimicking a drifting leaf. Its common name is derived from the rounded lobes of the caudal, dorsal, and anal fins.

- Up to 43½ in (1.1 m)
- Up to 42½ lb (19.2 kg)
- ○ Oviparous
- ♀♂ Male & female
- Common

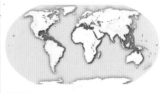

Tropical & subtropical seas worldwide

Oriental sweetlips The loose rubbery lips of sweetlips are adapted for "vacuuming" invertebrates from sandy bottoms. They feed so vigorously that silt sweeps back through their gill arches to emerge as a cloud in the water behind. As part of the grunt family (Haemulidae), this species is also able to produce sounds by grinding its pharyngeal teeth.

- Up to 20 in (51 cm)
- Up to 4 lb (1.8 kg)
- ○ Oviparous
- ♀♂ Male & female
- Common

Indo-West Pacific

Yellowback fusilier A bright yellow stripe runs across the upper third of the body in this species. Found in coastal areas, primarily around coral reefs but also in deep lagoons, it feeds on zooplankton in large, midwater groups.

- Up to 16 in (40 cm)
- Up to 1½ lb (680 g)
- ○ Oviparous
- ♀♂ Male & female
- Common

Indian Ocean

Emperor snapper Juveniles live in shallow tropical waters, often in close association with sea urchins. Large adults, which dwell at greater depths, are sometimes implicated in cases of ciguatera poisoning. The vivid red stripes that characterize young fish of this species fade with age.

- Up to 3¼ ft (1 m)
- Up to 35½ lb (16 kg)
- ○ Oviparous
- ♀♂ Male & female
- Common

Indo-West Pacific, Red Sea

Twoband bream The twoband bream has two distinctive black bands, one behind the head and the other across the caudal peduncle and the rear bases of the dorsal and anal fins. It is usually found in water less than 165 feet (50 m) deep, with a rocky seabed or sometimes sand. This species feeds on mollusks, crustaceans, and worms.

- Up to 17½ in (45 cm)
- Up to 2¾ lb (1.3 kg)
- Oviparous
- Not known
- Common

E. Atlantic & Mediterranean Sea

Dentex The sexes in this porgy (seabream) are usually separate, but some specimens are hermaphroditic. It is found over hard bottoms and is a predator of fishes, cephalopods, and other mollusks. The adults are solitary but the juveniles are gregarious.

- Up to 47 in (1.2 m)
- Up to 26½ lb (12 kg)
- Oviparous
- Male & female
- Common

E. Atlantic, Mediterranean & Black seas

Bogue The bogue is a slender bodied porgy (seabream) with moderately large eyes and a small mouth. It lives in schools of often 100 or more fishes, found near the shore to depths of 500 feet (150 m) on sandy bottoms, seagrass beds, and near rocks. It ascends toward the surface at night. A commercially exploited species, the bogue is often used for fishmeal and oil, as well as bait in tuna fisheries.

- Up to 15 in (38 cm)
- Up to 1½ lb (680 g)
- Oviparous
- Hermaphrodite
- Common

E. Atlantic, Mediterranean & Black seas

Sheepshead This striped fish is common in bays and estuaries and is often found around pilings. It feeds mainly on mollusks and crustaceans. Adults migrate to offshore waters to spawn, later returning to nearshore waters and estuaries. Spawning frequency ranges from once a day to once every 20 days. It is a member of the Sparidae family, many of which have been found to be hermaphroditic.

- Up to 36 in (92 cm)
- Up to 20 lb (9 kg)
- Oviparous
- Not known
- Common

W. Atlantic

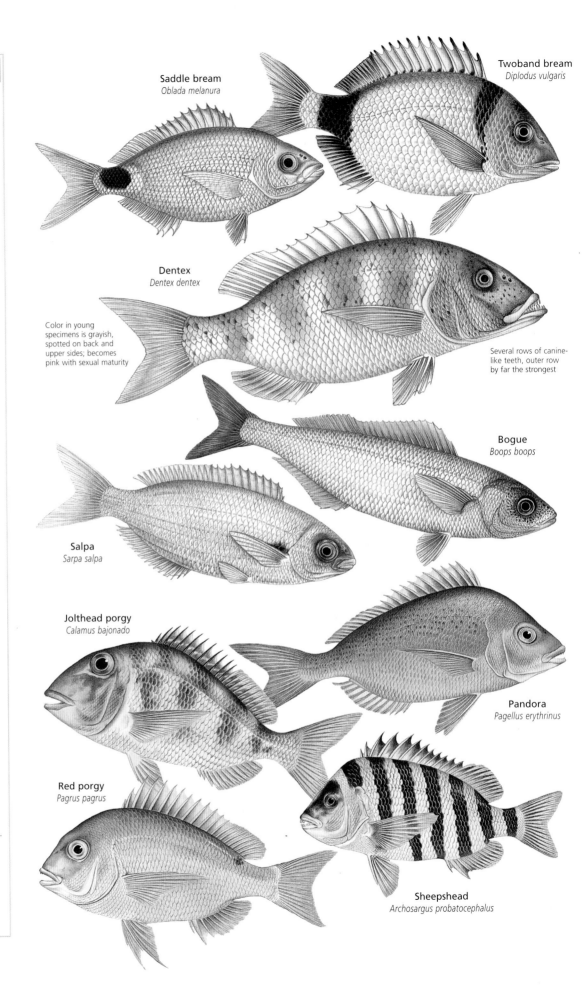

Saddle bream
Oblada melanura

Twoband bream
Diplodus vulgaris

Dentex
Dentex dentex

Color in young specimens is grayish, spotted on back and upper sides; becomes pink with sexual maturity

Several rows of canine-like teeth, outer row by far the strongest

Bogue
Boops boops

Salpa
Sarpa salpa

Jolthead porgy
Calamus bajonado

Pandora
Pagellus erythrinus

Red porgy
Pagrus pagrus

Sheepshead
Archosargus probatocephalus

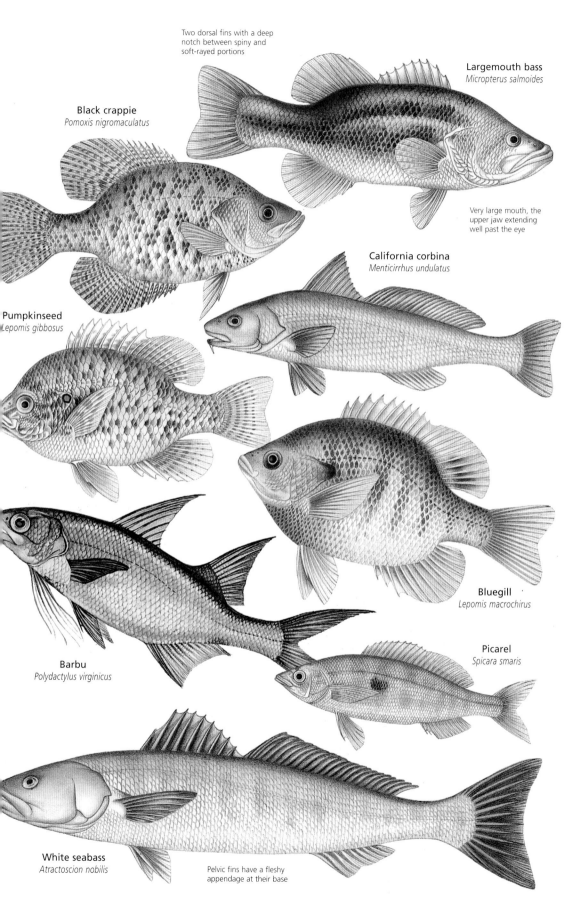

Black crappie
Pomoxis nigromaculatus

Largemouth bass
Micropterus salmoides

Two dorsal fins with a deep notch between spiny and soft-rayed portions

Very large mouth, the upper jaw extending well past the eye

Pumpkinseed
Lepomis gibbosus

California corbina
Menticirrhus undulatus

Bluegill
Lepomis macrochirus

Barbu
Polydactylus virginicus

Picarel
Spicara smaris

White seabass
Atractoscion nobilis

Pelvic fins have a fleshy appendage at their base

FACT FILE

California corbina Unlike other members of the drum family, the California corbina cannot produce croaking sounds because it does not have a swim bladder. It is found along sandy shores and in bays, usually in the surf on exposed beaches. It usually occurs in small groups, but larger fishes tend to be solitary. The adults eat crustaceans and worms.

- Up to 28 in (71 cm)
- Up to 8½ lb (3.9 kg)
- ○ Oviparous
- ♀♂ Male & female
- ♚ Common

E. Pacific

Pumpkinseed This species occurs in vegetated ponds, lakes, and slow-flowing areas of creeks and small rivers. The males build nests in shallow water near the shore and swim in a circular path with a female, over the nest, releasing sperm and eggs—up to 1,000—at intervals. The male then guards the eggs and larvae for about 11 days after they hatch.

- Up to 16 in (40 cm)
- Up to 1⅓ lb (630 g)
- ○ Oviparous
- ♀♂ Male & female
- ♚ Common

North America

Bluegill The bluegill is found in vegetated ponds, lakes, and rivers. There is a black or dark blue "ear" which is an extension of the gill cover called the opercular flap. As nest builders, small males sometimes fertilize eggs in a larger male's nest by darting in while the large male's attention is concentrated on the female, or by mimicking a female and joining a pair over the nest.

- Up to 16 in (40 cm)
- Up to 4¾ lb (2.2 kg)
- ○ Oviparous
- ♀♂ Male & female
- ♚ Common

North America

Barbu A member of the threadfins (*Polynemidae*), the barbu is distinguished by its pectoral fins that are divided into two parts. The lower part consists of elongate free rays. This fish is common in shallow water along beaches, around islands, and in estuaries.

- Up to 12½ in (32 cm)
- Up to 12 oz (340 g)
- ○ Oviparous
- ♀♂ Not known
- ♚ Common

W. Atlantic

FACT FILE

Red mullet This species is not a true mullet but a goatfish (family Mullidae). It has the long sensory chin barbels, characteristic of its family, and uses these to probe bottom sediments for small invertebrates. Goatfishes, like their mammalian namesakes, have a reputation for an omnivorous diet. The red mullet spawns from May to July, eggs and larvae are pelagic.

- ↔ Up to 16 in (40 cm)
- ⬤ Up to 35 oz (1 kg)
- ○ Oviparous
- ♀♂ Male & female
- ↟ Common

E. North Atlantic & Mediterranean Sea

Red drum Found over sand and sandy mud bottoms in coastal waters and estuaries, the red drum is also abundant in the surf zone. It feeds mainly on other fishes, crustaceans, and mollusks. There is a conspicuous black spot or spots on the caudal peduncle of this important game fish. Recent stock enhancement has halted a decline in numbers.

- ↔ Up to 60 in (1.5 m)
- ⬤ Up to 100 lb (45 kg)
- ○ Oviparous
- ♀♂ Male & female
- ↟ Common

N.W. Atlantic & Gulf of Mexico

Spotted seatrout Feeding mainly on crustaceans and fishes, this sea-trout is found in estuaries and shallow coastal waters, over sandy bottoms and seagrass beds. It is a member of the drums or croakers (Sciaenidae), which get their common name from drumming sounds produced by special muscles on the wall of the swim bladder. Females in this species are generally larger than males.

- ↔ Up to 39½ in (1 m)
- ⬤ Up to 17½ lb (7.9 kg)
- ○ Oviparous
- ♀♂ Male & female
- ↟ Common

N.W. Atlantic & Gulf of Mexico

Jack-knifefish A greatly elongated dorsal fin gives this species, which is endemic to the western Atlantic and Caribbean, the most recognizable appearance of all the drums and croakers (Sciaenidae). It is a nocturnal fish and hides in coral caves by day.

- ↔ Up to 10 in (25 cm)
- ⬤ Up to 10 oz (285 g)
- ○ Oviparous
- ♀♂ Male & female
- ↟ Common

W. Atlantic

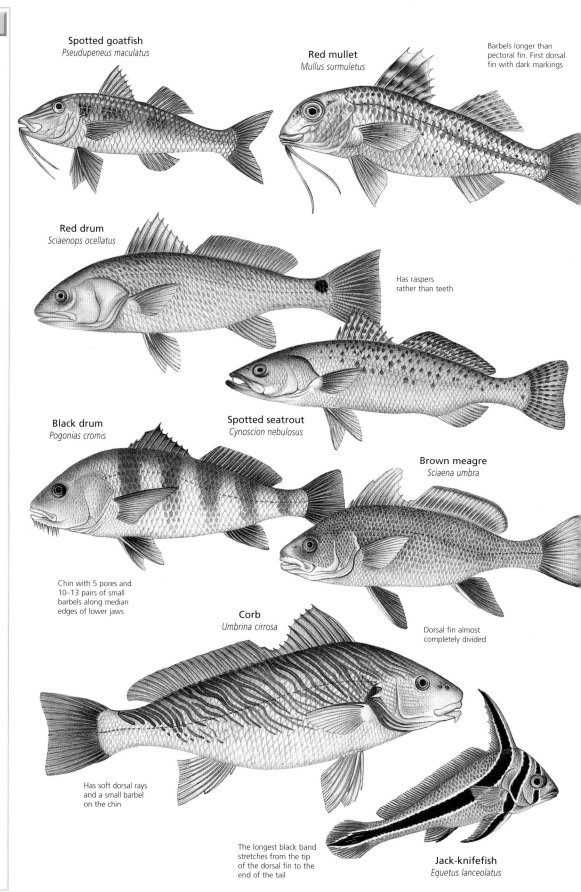

Spotted goatfish
Pseudupeneus maculatus

Red mullet
Mullus surmuletus

Barbels longer than pectoral fin. First dorsal fin with dark markings

Red drum
Sciaenops ocellatus

Has raspers rather than teeth

Black drum
Pogonias cromis

Spotted seatrout
Cynoscion nebulosus

Brown meagre
Sciaena umbra

Chin with 5 pores and 10–13 pairs of small barbels along median edges of lower jaws

Corb
Umbrina cirrosa

Dorsal fin almost completely divided

Has soft dorsal rays and a small barbel on the chin

The longest black band stretches from the tip of the dorsal fin to the end of the tail

Jack-knifefish
Equetus lanceolatus

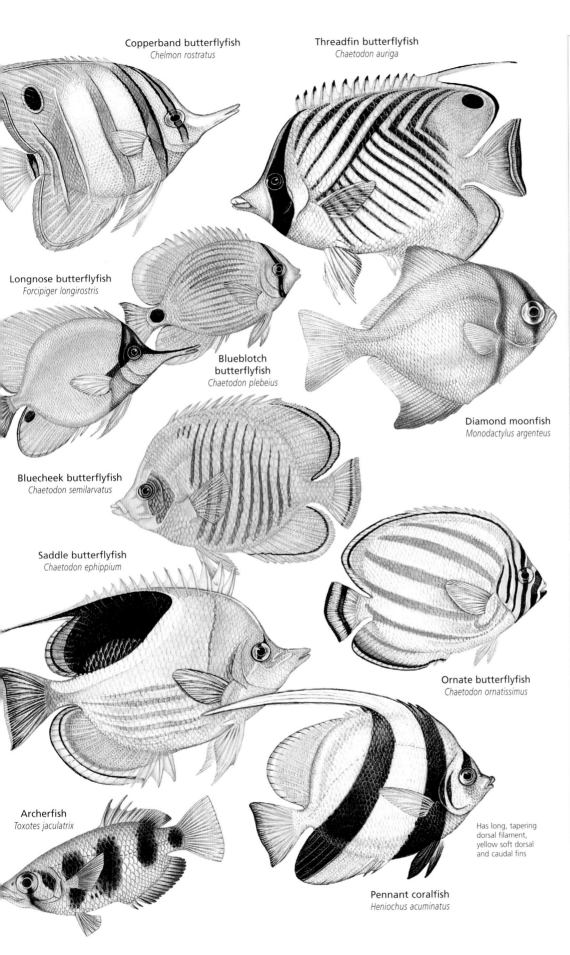

Copperband butterflyfish
Chelmon rostratus

Threadfin butterflyfish
Chaetodon auriga

Longnose butterflyfish
Forcipiger longirostris

Blueblotch
butterflyfish
Chaetodon plebeius

Diamond moonfish
Monodactylus argenteus

Bluecheek butterflyfish
Chaetodon semilarvatus

Saddle butterflyfish
Chaetodon ephippium

Ornate butterflyfish
Chaetodon ornatissimus

Archerfish
Toxotes jaculatrix

Has long, tapering
dorsal filament,
yellow soft dorsal
and caudal fins

Pennant coralfish
Heniochus acuminatus

FACT FILE

Longnose butterflyfish This butterflyfish is usually seen in pairs on seaward reefs to depths greater than 200 feet (60 m), where it feeds on small invertebrates such as crustaceans. It is very similar in appearance to the much wider ranging *Forcipiger flavissimus* but its snout is one-half to one-third longer.

- Up to 8¾ in (22 cm)
- Up to 7 oz (200 g)
- ○ Oviparous
- ♀♂ Male & female
- Uncommon

Indo-Pacific

Diamond moonfish A deep, compressed body is characteristic of the diamond moonfish. This species is able to tolerate freshwater and is found in estuaries and mangroves, and sometimes on silty coastal reefs. It feeds on detritus and plankton.

- Up to 10 in (25 cm)
- Up to 14 oz (400 g)
- ○ Oviparous
- ♀♂ Not known
- Common

Indo-Pacific

TAKING AIM

Archerfishes fire water jets from the mouth to knock insects and other prey from overhanging branches. Rapid oral cavity compressions force water through a tube formed by the tongue pressing against the specially grooved palate. The archerfish *Toxotes jaculatrix* has a shooting range of about 5 feet (1.5 m). They will also shoot at swarms of flying insects hovering above the surface.

CLOSE ASSOCIATIONS

Close interactions between unrelated organisms are known as mutualisms. In fishes these range from loose associations, such as multispecies shoaling as a defense against predators, to intimate associations that last a lifetime. The most well known fish-to-fish interactions are cleaner associations found in both freshwater and marine species. In these associations, one species allows another to pick off parasites, damaged scales, and skin—in some cases even their mouths and delicate, highly vulnerable gills are cleaned. Some cleaner species, such as the bluehead wrasse *Thalassoma bifasciatum,* are cleaners only as juveniles. Others are cleaners throughout their lives and have highly modified mouths and teeth. Not all mutualisms are between fishes. For example, some species benefit from regular grooming by shrimps or use anemones for protection. In other cases, fishes actually live with an invertebrate host—pearlfishes live in the lower intestines of sea cucumbers, as well as inside large sea squirts.

Free ride This manta ray (far right) is carrying two remoras or sucker-fish. Remoras have a powerful sucker disk on their heads that allows them to attach very tightly to a larger host. The sucker's grip can be released almost instantaneously, allowing the remora to dart forward and pick up scraps as the larger host feeds.

Dainty dentist A juvenile cleaner wrasse (below) touches the coral hind so that it will allow it to enter its mouth and clean between its teeth in safety. Studies have shown that cleaner fishes are vital to the health of coral reef communities.

Gill inspection This mappa pufferfish (top right) is allowing a cleaner wrasse to clean its gills. Some species have exploited cleaning behavior and mimic cleaners so that they can get close enough to tear off flesh from unsuspecting client fishes.

House mates This goby and shrimp (right) share a burrow excavated by the shrimp. The goby sits at the entrance and alerts the shrimp to danger and the shrimp, followed by the goby, retreats down the burrow. The goby usually reappears before the shrimp.

Varied clientele Not all cleaner fish clients are other fishes. Other species can recognize "cleaning stations" and benefit from them. For example, this turtle (bottom right) is being cleaned by a group of goldring surgeonfish.

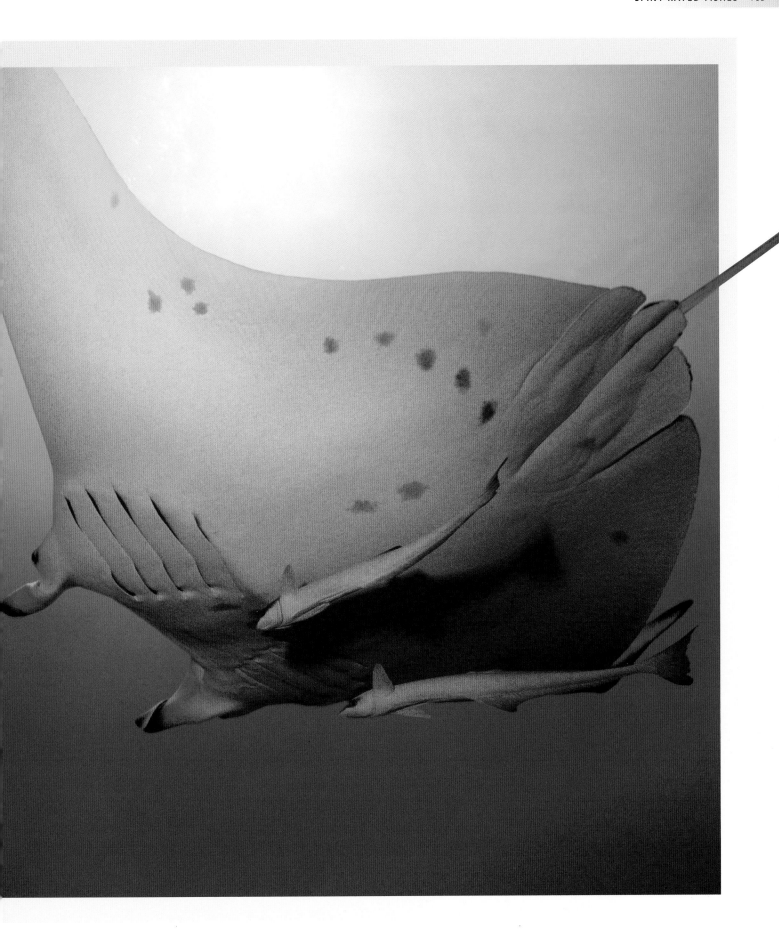

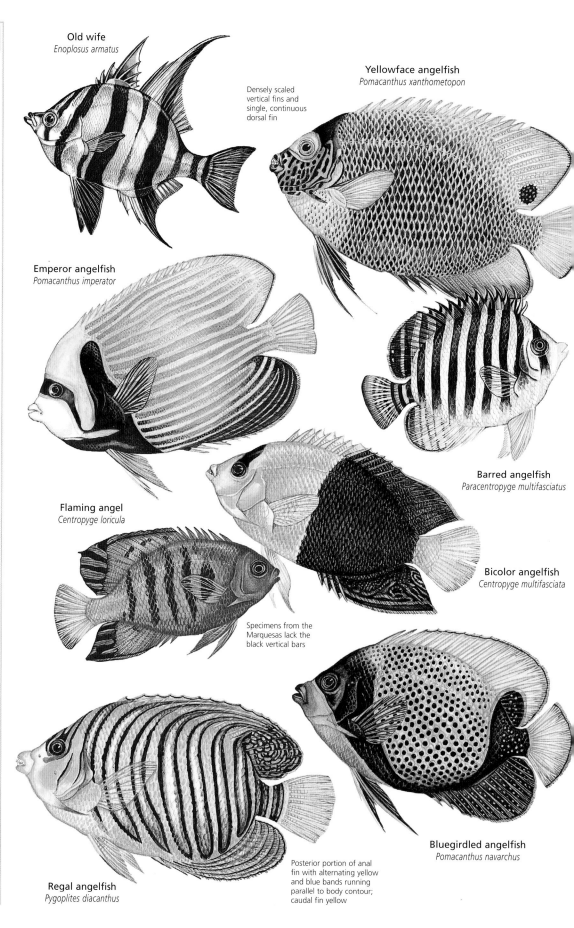

Old wife
Enoplosus armatus

Yellowface angelfish
Pomacanthus xanthometopon

Densely scaled vertical fins and single, continuous dorsal fin

Emperor angelfish
Pomacanthus imperator

Barred angelfish
Paracentropyge multifasciatus

Flaming angel
Centropyge loricula

Bicolor angelfish
Centropyge multifasciata

Specimens from the Marquesas lack the black vertical bars

Bluegirdled angelfish
Pomacanthus navarchus

Regal angelfish
Pygoplites diacanthus

Posterior portion of anal fin with alternating yellow and blue bands running parallel to body contour; caudal fin yellow

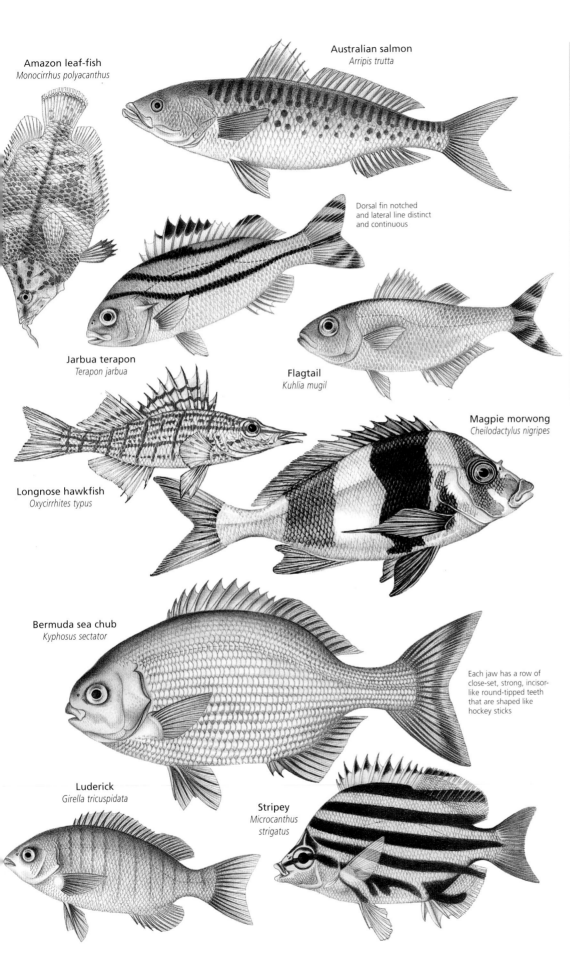

Amazon leaf-fish
Monocirrhus polyacanthus

Australian salmon
Arripis trutta

Dorsal fin notched
and lateral line distinct
and continuous

Jarbua terapon
Terapon jarbua

Flagtail
Kuhlia mugil

Longnose hawkfish
Oxycirrhites typus

Magpie morwong
Cheilodactylus nigripes

Bermuda sea chub
Kyphosus sectator

Each jaw has a row of
close-set, strong, incisor-
like round-tipped teeth
that are shaped like
hockey sticks

Luderick
Girella tricuspidata

Stripey
*Microcanthus
strigatus*

PATTERNS AND COLORS

Angelfishes are associated with coral and rock reefs in many tropical ecosystems, especially those in the Indo-Pacific and western Atlantic oceans. They are active during the day but seek shelter in holes and crevices at night. These fish generally have disk shaped bodies, small mouths, comb-like teeth, and vibrant colors. Once believed to be related to butterflyfish and classified as part of the family Chaetodontidae, they are now placed in the family Pomacanthidae—distinguished from butterflyfishes by a sharp spine on each cheek. Many characteristics, such as coloration, change during the transition from juvenile to adult life stages. When the dominant male in the habitat leaves, a female often undergoes a sex change and takes over the role of dominant male. Some species, however, are known to mate for life. Their bright colors, long life, and resistance to diseases have made the angelfishes popular aquarium species.

Body shape Angelfishes have tall, narrow bodies. Because they are so thin, they can maneuver down into narrow cracks between corals to hunt prey. They swim by rowing with their pectoral fins. Long dorsal, anal, and caudal fins allow them to turn quickly.

Growing up There are striking differences in coloration and pattern between adult and juveniles of the same species. To the right is the adult French angelfish (*Pomacanthus paru*). Juveniles in this species are black with five bold, vertical bands of golden yellow.

FACT FILE

Oscar This cichlid feeds on small fishes, crayfishes, worms, and insect larvae. Both males and females clean a suitable spawning site on branches or in a circular nest excavated in shallow water.

⟹ Up to 18 in (46 cm)
⛰ Up to 3½ lb (1.6 kg)
○ Oviparous, guarder
♀♂ Male & female
⚑ Common

South America

Freshwater angelfish Eggs laid onto a submerged leaf are guarded and fanned constantly by parents for three days until hatching. Fry are gathered into a dense pack for ease of protection.

⟹ Up to 3 in (7.5 cm)
⛰ Up to 8 oz (225 g)
○ Oviparous, guarder
♀♂ Male & female
⚑ Common

N.E. South America

Blue discus Territorial during breeding, pairs clean chosen breeding spots. Both parents care for eggs and larvae. They secrete white mucus from their skin that the post-larvae eat for the first few days.

⟹ Up to 5½ in (14 cm)
⛰ Up to 8 oz (225 g)
○ Oviparous, guarder
♀♂ Male & female
⚑ Common

South America

ORAL NURSERIES

All of the cichlids show some form of parental care, the most advanced being continuous mouth-brooding. Usually the female scoops her eggs up into her mouth quickly after laying them, nuzzles the male near his genital opening, and then draws his ejaculated sperm into her mouth where she may brood embryos and young for more than three weeks. Toward the end of that period, the young are released at intervals to forage.

Redhead cichlid
Vieja synspila

Rio Grande cichlid
Herichthys cyanoguttatus

Breeding males have bright purple coloration over front third of head and body

Oscar
Astronotus ocellatus

Freshwater angelfish
Pterophyllum scalare

Pearl eartheat⟨er⟩
Geophagus brasilier

Peacock cichlid
Cichla ocellaris

Has large, upward facing mouth and prominent eyespot on tail

Blue discus
Symphysodon aequifasciatus

Red devil
Amphilophus labiatus

Agassiz's dwarf cichlid
Apistogramma agassizii

Lionhead cichlid
Steatocranus casuarius

Burton's haplo
Haplochromis burtoni

Zebra cichlid
Haplochromis obliquidens

Marlier's julie
Julidochromis marlieri

Small cichlid that
spawns in caves
and guards its eggs

Blunthead cichlid
Tropheus moorii

Bluegray mbuna
Melanochromis johannii

♀

♂

Rainbow krib
Pelvicachromis pulcher

Blood-red jewel cichlid
Hemichromis lifalili

Orange chromide
Etroplus maculatus

Colors brighten during
breeding periods and
red margin on the tail
becomes prominent

FACT FILE

Lionhead cichlid The lionhead
cichlid has a distinctive large bump
on the forehead. It is found in Malebo
(Stanley) Pool and the lower Congo
River, sitting on the bottom in fast-
flowing water. Its swim bladder is
poorly developed, so it cannot swim
for any length of time off the bottom.
Both parents are brood guarders and
eggs are large and pear-shaped.

⬅ Up to 4 in (10 cm)
⬛ Up to 4¼ oz (120 g)
○ Oviparous, guarder
♀♂ Male & female
🗡 Locally common

W. Africa

Rainbow krib This species occurs
in the mouth of the Niger River in
southern Nigeria and the coastal
zone of Cameroon—in both fresh
and brackish water. It feeds on insects,
worms, and crustaceans and is known
to spawn in caves. The female stays
close to the eggs while the male
guards both the female and the eggs.

⬅ Up to 4 in (10 cm)
⬛ Up to 3¼ oz (90 g)
○ Oviparous, guarder
♀♂ Male & female
🗡 Locally common

W. Africa

Orange chromide An inhabitant of
lagoons and small streams, the orange
chromide is found among marginal
roots and weeds but has also been
known to enter estuaries. It spawns
in shallow water on a soft depression
excavated by both parents. The parents
guard and fan the eggs, one parent
always present while the other forages.
The fry are guarded until they almost
reach sexual maturity.

⬅ Up to 3¹⁄₁₀ in (8 cm)
⬛ Up to 3½ oz (100 g)
○ Oviparous, guarder
♀♂ Male & female
🗡 Common

S. Asia

Blood-red jewel cichlid Found only in
pools in the Congo basin, the blood-red
jewel cichlid does not inhabit swampy
areas or rapids. The male is a much
brighter red than the female. During
breeding, the pair clean a surface on
which to spawn and the male then
guards the eggs and larvae. It produces
about 300 larvae in each brood.

⬅ Up to 3¹⁄₁₀ in (8 cm)
⬛ Up to 3½ oz (100 g)
○ Oviparous, guarder
♀♂ Male & female
🗡 Common

W. Africa

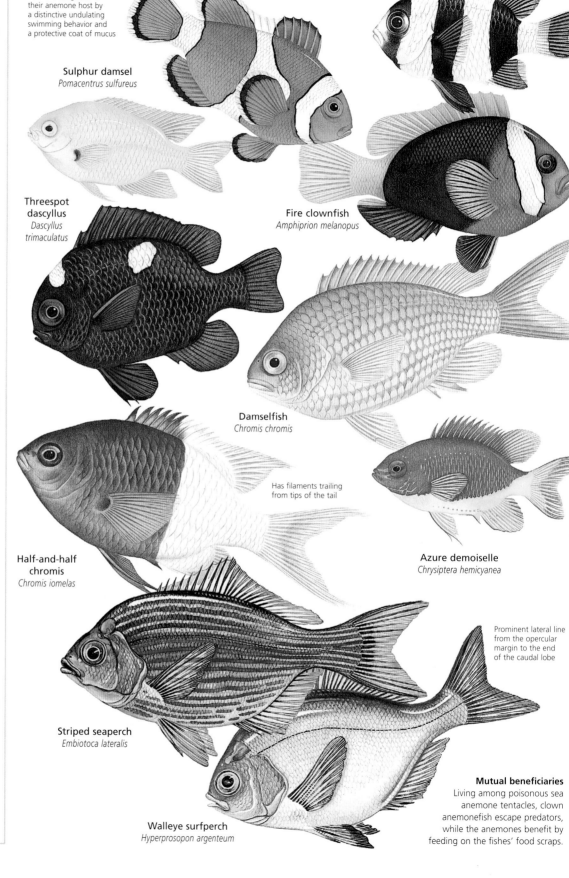

Clown anemonefish A popular fish, this species is found in calm, shallow lagoons and the male is an egg guarder. It is well known for its commensal associations with the anemones and probably has a factor in the skin that inhibits nematocyst discharge. A nearly identical species, *A. percula*, occurs at New Guinea and Queensland, Australia.

➣ Up to 4⅓ in (11 cm)
🏋 Up to 4¼ oz (120 g)
○ Oviparous, guarder
♀♂ Hermaphrodite
🍴 Common

Indo–W. Pacific

Threespot dascyllus Found on coral and rocky reefs, the juveniles are often commensal with sea urchins, large sea anemones, or small coral heads. Courtship is characterized by the male "signal-jumping," and spawning may occur two or three times a month, the male guarding the eggs.

➣ Up to 4⅓ in (11 cm)
🏋 Up to 4¼ oz (120 g)
○ Oviparous
♀♂ Male & female
🍴 Common

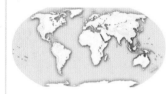

Indo-Pacific

Damselfish This species is found in small shoals in mid-water, near or above reefs and seagrass beds. Courtship and nesting occurs on rocky and occasionally sandy bottoms. The breeding male is vivid mauve and takes care of the eggs which have a tuft of adhesive filaments.

➣ Up to 10 in (25 cm)
🏋 Up to 12 oz (340 g)
○ Oviparous
♀♂ Not known
🍴 Common

E. Atlantic & Mediterranean Sea

Striped seaperch Fertilization in this species is internal, aided by the thickened forward end of the male's anal fin. The female gives birth to few but relatively large young. They feed on mollusks, worms, and small crustaceans.

➣ Up to 15 in (38 cm)
🏋 Up to 35 oz (1 kg)
🐟 Viviparous
♀♂ Male & female
🍴 Common

N.E. Pacific

Clown anemonefish are protected from harm from the sting cells of their anemone host by a distinctive undulating swimming behavior and a protective coat of mucus

Clown anemonefish
Amphiprion ocellaris

Blacktail humbug
Dascyllus melanurus

Sulphur damsel
Pomacentrus sulfureus

Threespot dascyllus
Dascyllus trimaculatus

Fire clownfish
Amphiprion melanopus

Damselfish
Chromis chromis

Has filaments trailing from tips of the tail

Half-and-half chromis
Chromis iomelas

Azure demoiselle
Chrysiptera hemicyanea

Prominent lateral line from the opercular margin to the end of the caudal lobe

Striped seaperch
Embiotoca lateralis

Walleye surfperch
Hyperprosopon argenteum

Mutual beneficiaries
Living among poisonous sea anemone tentacles, clown anemonefish escape predators, while the anemones benefit by feeding on the fishes' food scraps.

FACT FILE

California sheepshead Found near rocky areas of seabed, particularly where there is kelp, the California sheepshead can live for more than 50 years. Populations have declined and large males are now increasingly rare because of fishing pressure and habitat destruction. The females change into males at about 12 inches (30 cm). Stout canine teeth give this wrasse a bucktooth appearance.

- Up to 35¾ in (91 cm)
- Up to 35½ lb (16 kg)
- ○ Oviparous
- ♀♂ Hermaphrodite
- Uncommon

E. Pacific

Bluestreak cleaner wrasse Pairs or small groups of bluestreak cleaner wrasses set up permanent "cleaning stations," near cave entrances and beneath rocky overhangs, in tropical reefs throughout the Indo-Pacific. Here they service "clients"—larger fishes looking to be picked free of parasites.

- Up to 4½ in (11.5 cm)
- Up to 3 oz (85 g)
- ○ Oviparous
- ♀♂ Hermaphrodite
- Common

Indo-Pacific & Red Sea

Harlequin tuskfish This is a solitary and territorial species that inhabits seaward sides of reefs. It feeds on crustaceans, mollusks, echinoderms, and worms. It has prominent and distinctive blue canine teeth.

- Up to 12 in (30 cm)
- Up to 1½ lb (680 g)
- ○ Oviparous
- ♀♂ Not known
- Common

W. Pacific

Bird wrasse Found in lagoons and coral-rich reef areas, its snout is used to probe crevices for crustaceans, brittle stars, mollusks, and small fishes. Small juveniles lack the elongate snout.

- Up to 15 in (38 cm)
- Up to 13 oz (370 g)
- ○ Oviparous
- ♀♂ Not known
- Common

Indo-Central Pacific

California sheepshead
Semicossyphus pulcher

Only breeding males have the dark coloration over the front and rear thirds of the body

Bluestreak cleaner wrasse
Labroides dimidiatus

Bird wrasse
Gomphosus varius

Harlequin tuskfish
Choerodon fasciatus

Spotted wrasse
Anampses meleagrides

♂

♀

Juvenile

Clown wrasse
Coris aygula

Juvenile

Adult females have a bright yellow caudal fin

Yellowtail coris
Coris gaimard

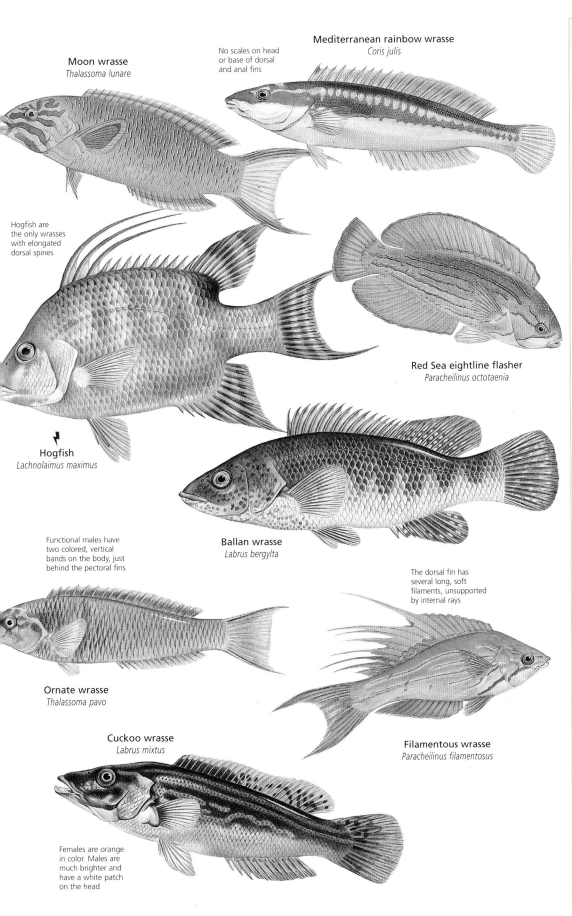

Moon wrasse
Thalassoma lunare

Mediterranean rainbow wrasse
Coris julis

No scales on head
or base of dorsal
and anal fins

Hogfish are
the only wrasses
with elongated
dorsal spines

Red Sea eightline flasher
Paracheilinus octotaenia

Hogfish
Lachnolaimus maximus

Ballan wrasse
Labrus bergylta

Functional males have
two colored, vertical
bands on the body, just
behind the pectoral fins

The dorsal fin has
several long, soft
filaments, unsupported
by internal rays

Ornate wrasse
Thalassoma pavo

Cuckoo wrasse
Labrus mixtus

Filamentous wrasse
Paracheilinus filamentosus

Females are orange
in color. Males are
much brighter and
have a white patch
on the head

FACT FILE

Green humphead parrotfish This is the largest and wariest of the parrot-fishes. It sleeps in caves at night and feeds on benthic algae and live coral during the day. The adults have a very large hump dorso-anteriorly to the eye. They are colored dull green to blue-green, apart from the anterior of the head which is often pink.

- Up to 4⅓ ft (1.3 m)
- Up to 101 lb (46 kg)
- ○ Oviparous
- ♀♂ Not known
- Common

Indo-Pacific

Stoplight parrotfish An abundant and colorful species, this parrotfish produces a significant amount of sediment through bioerosion, using its strong jaws and constantly regrowing teeth. Adults are found on coral reefs while young frequent sea grass and other heavily vegetated seabeds.

- Up to 25 in (64 cm)
- Up to 3½ lb (1.6 kg)
- ○ Oviparous
- ♀♂ Hermaphrodite
- Common

W. Atlantic

Blue parrotfish Large adults develop a prominent blunt snout and extended upper and lower lobes on the caudal fin. Colored sky to royal blue overall, with a duller colored head, it feeds on benthic plants and small invertebrates and forms large groups for spawning.

- Up to 4 ft (1.2 m)
- Up to 77 lb (35 g)
- ○ Oviparous
- ♀♂ Hermaphrodite
- Common

W. Atlantic

Queen parrotfish At night, the queen parrotfish sleeps in a veil-like mass of mucus that it secretes around itself. It is often seen in groups with one larger "super male" accompanied by several smaller adults that are probably female.

- Up to 24 in (61 cm)
- Up to 3¼ lb (1.5 kg)
- ○ Oviparous
- ♀♂ Hermaphrodite
- Common

W. Atlantic

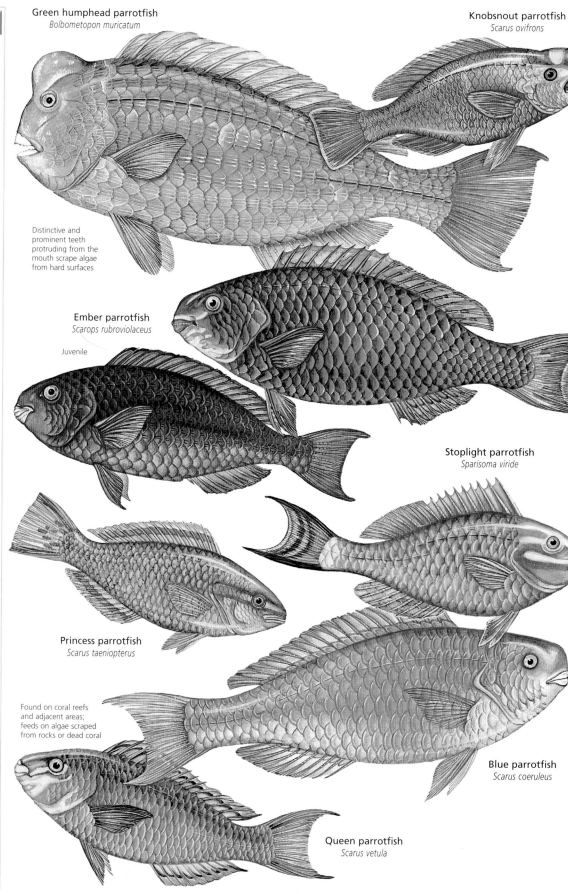

Green humphead parrotfish
Bolbometopon muricatum

Knobsnout parrotfish
Scarus ovifrons

Distinctive and prominent teeth protruding from the mouth scrape algae from hard surfaces

Ember parrotfish
Scarops rubroviolaceus

Juvenile

Stoplight parrotfish
Sparisoma viride

Princess parrotfish
Scarus taeniopterus

Found on coral reefs and adjacent areas; feeds on algae scraped from rocks or dead coral

Blue parrotfish
Scarus coeruleus

Queen parrotfish
Scarus vetula

Greater weaver
Trachinus draco

Lies buried in sand; spines
of the first dorsal fin and
gill cover have venom

Sailfin sandfish
Arctoscopus japonicus

Atlantic wolffish
Anarhichas lupus

Hairy blenny
Labrisomus nuchipinnis

Sand stargazer
Dactyloscopus tridigitatus

Rock gunnel
Pholis gunnellus

Thick, fleshy lips and
small, conical teeth

Viviparous blenny
Zoarces viviparus

Atlantic stargazer
Uranoscopus scaber

Lesser sandeel
Ammodytes tobianus

Hibernates in the winter,
buried at 8 to 19½ inches
(20–50 cm) in the sand

FACT FILE

Atlantic wolffish A solitary species
found on rocky seabeds and sometimes
over sand or mud, the Atlantic wolffish
feeds on sea urchins, crustaceans, and
hard-shelled mollusks. Fertilization of
eggs is internal in the oviduct of the
female but they are then deposited as
a spherical mass on the seabed, where
the male guards them until they hatch.

🐟 Up to 5 ft (1.5 m)
⚖ Up to 52 lb (24 kg)
○ Oviparous
♀♂ Male & female
🗡 Common

N. Atlantic

Viviparous blenny This is the most
common member of the eelpout family
(Zoarcidae). It is found among algae, in
tide pools, and under stones on rocky
shores where it can breathe air out of
water. Ovoviviparous, eggs develop
within the female before hatching after
three to four weeks. Between 30 and
400 young then continue to develop,
nourished by specialized ovary tissues,
before being released.

🐟 Up to 20½ in (52 cm)
⚖ Up to 18 oz (510 g)
⊘ Ovoviviparous
♀♂ Male & female
🗡 Common

N.E. Atlantic

Atlantic stargazer A camouflaged
bottom dweller, the Atlantic stargazer
has a small, worm-like appendage on
its bottom lip that it wriggles to attract
prey. Adaptations to a life spent almost
completely buried in sandy sediments
include a high-set mouth, nostrils, and
eyes. A venomous spine behind the
operculum and electric organs behind
the eyes make good defense weapons.

🐟 Up to 16 in (40 cm)
⚖ Up to 33 oz (940 g)
○ Oviparous
♀♂ Male & female
🗡 Locally common

E. Atlantic; Mediterranean & Black seas

Lesser sandeel Preyed upon by a
wide variety of fishes and seabirds, the
lesser sandeel alternates between lying
buried in clean, fine sand—into which
it can burrow with great rapidity—or
swimming in schools. It is found in
inshore waters including the intertidal
zone and estuaries.

🐟 Up to 8 in (20 cm)
⚖ Up to 1⅓ oz (40 g)
○ Oviparous
♀♂ Male & female
🗡 Common

N.E. Atlantic

Rippled rockskipper Common along rocky shores and shallow reefs, adults can jump out of the water from one tidepool to another in energetic skippings if pursued. This species can breathe air when hiding under rocks and seaweeds, sheltering in cracks and holes, or grazing on rock surfaces.

⚓ Up to 6¼ in (16 cm)
⚖ Up to 3⅓ oz (95 g)
○ Oviparous
♀♂ Male & female
🏴 Common

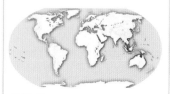

Indo-Pacific

Shore clingfish A powerful, ventral, sucking disk, formed partly from the pelvic fins, gives this species its name. The disk is used to cling to the underside of rocks and kelp on the lower shore. The clingfish has a flattened, scaleless body with a long snout that gives it a "duck-billed" appearance. Eggs are laid in clusters on the underside of boulders and guarded by one of the parents.

⚓ Up to 2½ in (6.5 cm)
⚖ Up to 1 oz (30 g)
○ Oviparous
♀♂ Male & female
🏴 Common

E. Atlantic & Mediterranean Sea

Bluestriped fangblenny This blenny mimics the bluestreak cleaner wrasse *Labroides dimidiatus*, which large fishes seek out for the removal of parasites. It attacks fishes at cleaning stations, removing mucus, skin, and sometimes scales. It can also mimic and conceal itself among other shoaling fishes by changing color and striping pattern. It then nips at passing fishes. Found in coral-rich areas of lagoons and reefs, it hides in holes and deserted worm tubes when alarmed.

⚓ Up to 4¾ in (12 cm)
⚖ Up to 2½ oz (70 g)
○ Oviparous
♀♂ Male & female
🏴 Common

Indo-Pacific

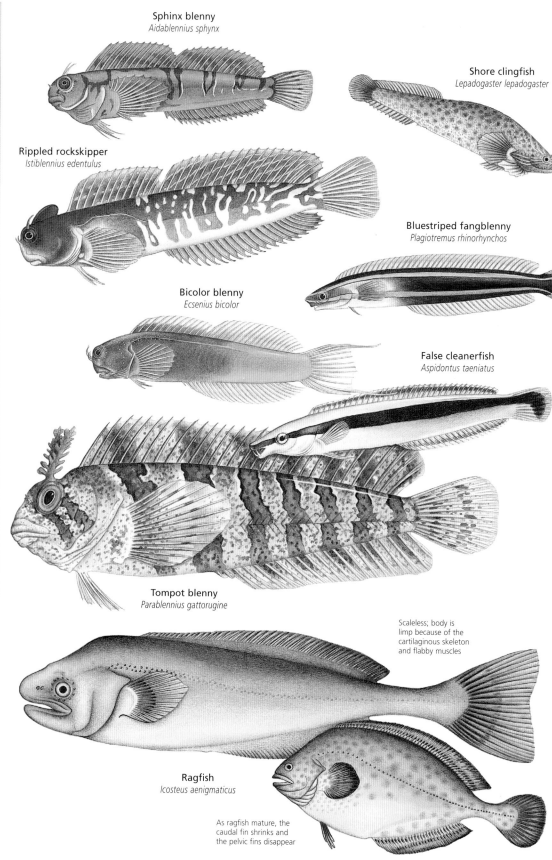

Sphinx blenny
Aidablennius sphynx

Shore clingfish
Lepadogaster lepadogaster

Rippled rockskipper
Istiblennius edentulus

Bluestriped fangblenny
Plagiotremus rhinorhynchos

Bicolor blenny
Ecsenius bicolor

False cleanerfish
Aspidontus taeniatus

Tompot blenny
Parablennius gattorugine

Scaleless; body is limp because of the cartilaginous skeleton and flabby muscles

Ragfish
Icosteus aenigmaticus

As ragfish mature, the caudal fin shrinks and the pelvic fins disappear

Juvenile

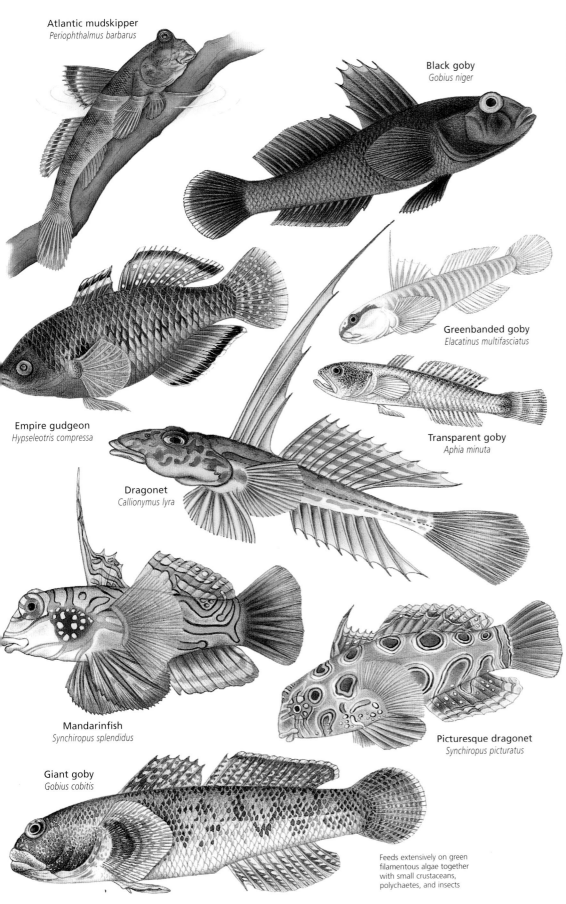

Atlantic mudskipper
Periophthalmus barbarus

Black goby
Gobius niger

Greenbanded goby
Elacatinus multifasciatus

Transparent goby
Aphia minuta

Empire gudgeon
Hypseleotris compressa

Dragonet
Callionymus lyra

Mandarinfish
Synchiropus splendidus

Picturesque dragonet
Synchiropus picturatus

Giant goby
Gobius cobitis

Feeds extensively on green
filamentous algae together
with small crustaceans,
polychaetes, and insects

FACT FILE

Dragonet The male dragonet has a tall first dorsal fin and is spectacularly colored, especially during spawning when it performs an elaborate courtship display. The males are territorial and aggressive to each other.

- Up to 12 in (30 cm)
- Up to 6⅓ oz (180 g)
- Oviparous
- Male & female
- Common

E. Atlantic & Mediterranean Sea

Mandarinfish A brilliantly colored little dragonet, this species is found in protected shallow lagoons and inshore reefs, to a depth of about 59 feet (18 m). Dragonet species are scaleless and have a strongly protrusible upper jaw. The mandarinfish is popular in the aquarium trade.

- Up to 2⅓ in (6 cm)
- Up to 1¼ oz (35 g)
- Oviparous
- Male & female
- Common

W. Pacific

Giant goby A fish of the intertidal zone, the giant goby is found among weeds, rocks, and in pools—often where the water is brackish because of freshwater run-off. It is the largest goby in European seas.

- Up to 10½ in (27 cm)
- Up to 9¼ oz (262 g)
- Oviparous
- Male & female
- Common

E. Atlantic & Mediterranean Sea

AMPHIBIOUS FISHES

Mudskippers use their muscular tail and pectoral fins to "skip" over mud at low tide and even climb trees with the aid of a pelvic fin "suction cup." There are more than 30 species of mudskipper, found mainly in the muddy, intertidal mangrove forests of Southeast Asia and Africa. They take in oxygen through their moist skin, which is richly endowed with blood vessels.

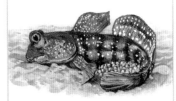

Land lovers *The males of some mudskipper species display their masculine prowess and define territories by leaping about in the mud.*

FACT FILE

Narrowbanded batfish Omnivorous, the narrowbanded batfish feeds on algae, invertebrates, and small fishes. Adults are found in open water over sandy areas of deep lagoons, channels, and seaward facing reefs. Juveniles occur in mangroves and sheltered lagoons.

- Up to 19½ in (50 cm)
- Up to 7¼ lb (3.3 kg)
- ○ Oviparous
- ♀♂ Male & female
- ⚑ Common

Indo-Pacific

Moorish idol Using its tubular snout and small mouth containing many long, bristle-like teeth, the moorish idol feeds on small encrusting animals. It is found in inner reef lagoons, reef flats, and the seaward faces of rock and coral reefs.

- Up to 9 in (23 cm)
- Up to 14 oz (400 g)
- ○ Oviparous
- ♀♂ Male & female
- ⚑ Common

Indo-Pacific

Foxface Juveniles and subadults are sometimes found in large schools but adults are only seen singly or in pairs. It is thought that this species pairs for life and patrols territories together.

- Up to 9½ in (24 cm)
- Up to 7¾ oz (220 g)
- ○ Oviparous
- ♀♂ Male & female
- ⚑ Common

W. Pacific

Spotted scat Although the spotted scat also feeds on worms, crustaceans, insects, and plant material, it gets its name, *Scatophagus*, from eating feces. The spines are believed to be venomous.

- Up to 15 in (38 cm)
- Up to 2.6 lb (1.2 kg)
- ○ Oviparous
- ♀♂ Male & female
- ⚑ Common

Indo-Pacific

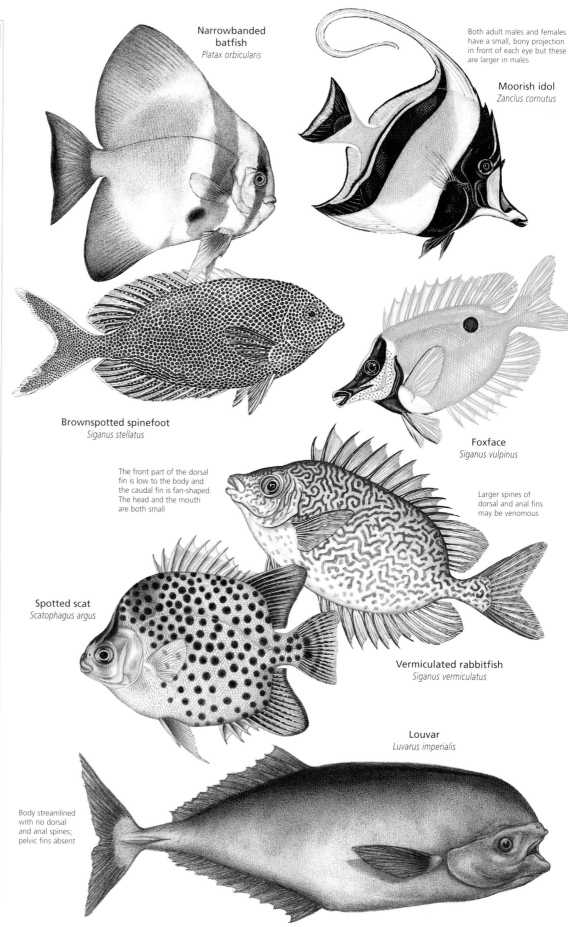

Narrowbanded batfish
Platax orbicularis

Both adult males and females have a small, bony projection in front of each eye but these are larger in males

Moorish idol
Zanclus cornutus

Brownspotted spinefoot
Siganus stellatus

Foxface
Siganus vulpinus

Larger spines of dorsal and anal fins may be venomous

The front part of the dorsal fin is low to the body and the caudal fin is fan-shaped. The head and the mouth are both small

Spotted scat
Scatophagus argus

Vermiculated rabbitfish
Siganus vermiculatus

Louvar
Luvarus imperialis

Body streamlined with no dorsal and anal spines; pelvic fins absent

Clown surgeonfish
Acanthurus lineatus

Caudal spines are venomous and can cause painful wounds to the unwary

Yellow tang
Zebrasoma flavescens

Convict tang
Acanthurus triostegus

Palani
Acanthurus dussumieri

Redtail surgeonfish
Acanthurus achilles

Easily recognized by its blue body with black markings and yellow tail

Palette surgeonfish
Paracanthurus hepatus

Red Sea surgeonfish
Acanthurus sohal

May occur singly or in large groups. Feeds on the film of algae on the seabed, on larger clumps of algae, and small growths in crevices

This delicately colored surgeonfish has long been a favorite of the aquarium trade. In nature, it is usually found on reef flats and along upper seaward slopes of Indian Ocean coral reefs

Powderblue surgeonfish
Acanthurus leucosternon

FACT FILE

Clown surgeonfish A territorial and aggressive species, large males guard feeding areas and control a harem of females. This surgeonfish is often encountered in the turbulent, but well-aerated, water of the surge zone on the seaward face of exposed reefs—usually in less than 10 feet (3 m) of water.

- Up to 15 in (38 cm)
- Up to 1¾ lb (800 g)
- ○ Oviparous
- ♀♂ Male & female
- Common

Indo-Pacific

Yellow tang Found singly or in loose groups around food sources, the yellow tang uses its markedly tubular snout to pick filamentous algae from hard surfaces. Spawning behavior is variable—both group and pair-spawning has been observed—with territorial males courting passing females.

- Up to 8 in (20 cm)
- Up to 9 oz (255 g)
- ○ Oviparous
- ♀♂ Male & female
- Common

West-Central Pacific

Redtail surgeonfish A striking species, this territorial fish grazes on filamentous and small, fleshy algae. Its retractile, scalpel-like blades at the base of the tail are modified peduncular spines that may be venomous. Juveniles lack the large, orange spot seen on the flanks of adults.

- Up to 9½ in (24 cm)
- Up to 12 oz (340 g)
- ○ Oviparous
- ♀♂ Male & female
- Common

West-Central Pacific

FACT FILE

Snake mackerel Larvae and juveniles in this species live close to the surface. Adults migrate up from the depths at night to feed as solitary hunters, preying on smaller fishes, squid, and crustaceans.

- Up to 3¼ ft (1 m)
- Up to 10 lb (4.5 kg)
- Oviparous
- Male & female
- Common

Tropical & temperate seas worldwide

Atlantic cutlassfish Fished commercially, this species is favored for sashimi. During the day, juveniles can be found schooling at about 330 feet (100 m). At night, they migrate toward the surface to feed on zooplankton and small fishes. Mature adults migrate in reverse, moving to the surface during the day to pursue larger prey.

- Up to 8¼ ft (2.5 m)
- Up to 11⅓ lb (5 kg)
- Oviparous
- Male & female
- Common

Tropical & temperate seas worldwide

Great barracuda Though it is responsible for attacks on humans, ironically, most fatalities are caused by ciguatera poisoning—when the fish is eaten. Adults are solitary hunters in a wide range of habitats, from harbors to the open sea, while juveniles live in groups in mangroves and in shallow, sheltered inner reef areas.

- Up to 6½ ft (2 m)
- Up to 110¼ lb (50 kg)
- Oviparous
- Male & female
- Common

Tropical & temperate seas worldwide

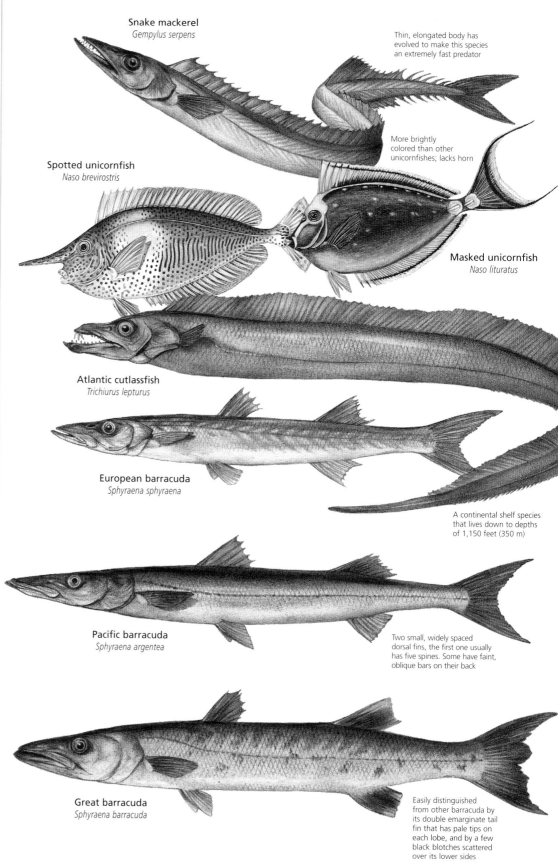

Snake mackerel
Gempylus serpens

Thin, elongated body has evolved to make this species an extremely fast predator

Spotted unicornfish
Naso brevirostris

More brightly colored than other unicornfishes; lacks horn

Masked unicornfish
Naso lituratus

Atlantic cutlassfish
Trichiurus lepturus

European barracuda
Sphyraena sphyraena

A continental shelf species that lives down to depths of 1,150 feet (350 m)

Pacific barracuda
Sphyraena argentea

Two small, widely spaced dorsal fins, the first one usually has five spines. Some have faint, oblique bars on their back

Great barracuda
Sphyraena barracuda

Easily distinguished from other barracuda by its double emarginate tail fin that has pale tips on each lobe, and by a few black blotches scattered over its lower sides

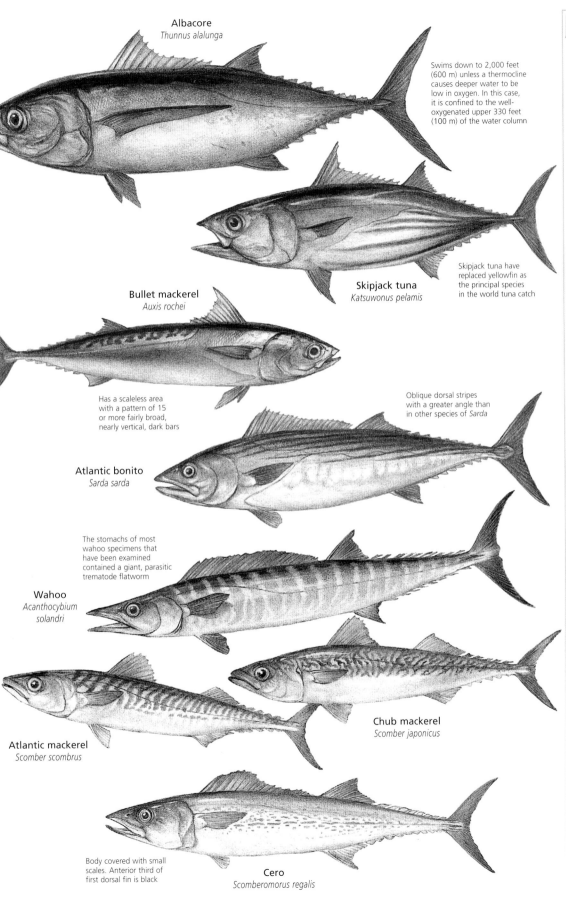

Albacore
Thunnus alalunga

Swims down to 2,000 feet (600 m) unless a thermocline causes deeper water to be low in oxygen. In this case, it is confined to the well-oxygenated upper 330 feet (100 m) of the water column

Skipjack tuna have replaced yellowfin as the principal species in the world tuna catch

Skipjack tuna
Katsuwonus pelamis

Bullet mackerel
Auxis rochei

Has a scaleless area with a pattern of 15 or more fairly broad, nearly vertical, dark bars

Oblique dorsal stripes with a greater angle than in other species of *Sarda*

Atlantic bonito
Sarda sarda

The stomachs of most wahoo specimens that have been examined contained a giant, parasitic trematode flatworm

Wahoo
Acanthocybium solandri

Chub mackerel
Scomber japonicus

Atlantic mackerel
Scomber scombrus

Body covered with small scales. Anterior third of first dorsal fin is black

Cero
Scomberomorus regalis

FACT FILE

Albacore One of the fastest swimmers in the sea; the high rates of metabolism and consequent oxygen demand created by such an active lifestyle may account for the vertical distribution of this species. It is an important game fish and commercial species but many stocks are threatened by overfishing.

- Up to 4½ ft (1.4 m)
- Up to 132 lb (60 kg)
- ○ Oviparous
- ♀♂ Male & female
- ⚑ Data deficient

Tropical & temperate seas worldwide

Skipjack tuna This tuna spawns several times a year in equatorial waters. The spawning period shortens with increasing distance from the equator. There is also a temperature-related difference in adult and larval distributions, adults prefer waters with an average temperature of 60°F (15°C) and larvae are restricted to those with a temperature of at least 80°F (25°C).

- Up to 3½ ft (1.1 m)
- Up to 76 lb (34.5 kg)
- ○ Oviparous
- ♀♂ Male & female
- ⚑ Common

Tropical & temperate seas worldwide except Black Sea

Atlantic mackerel This fast-swimming mackerel is a predator of pelagic crustaceans and small schooling fishes, especially sprats, herrings, and sand eels. It winters in deep water offshore and moves inshore in spring, once the water temperature is above 52°F (11°C). The Atlantic mackerel is an important commercial fish species but the increasing efficiency of fishing equipment and fishing activity has caused a serious decline in its numbers.

- Up to 23½ in (60 cm)
- Up to 7½ lb (3.4 kg)
- ○ Oviparous
- ♀♂ Male & female
- ⚑ Common

North Atlantic

FACT FILE

Swordfish Adult swordfish lack scales, teeth, and a lateral line. They mostly feed on pelagic fishes—taken anywhere from surface waters to depths of about 2,100 feet (650 m)—using their sword to slash prey. This species is the only member of the family Xiphiidae.

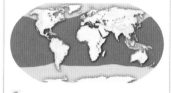

- Up to 16 ft (4.9 m)
- Up to 1,435 lb (650 kg)
- ○ Oviparous
- ♀♂ Male & female
- ↯ Data deficient

Tropical & temperate seas worldwide

Indo-Pacific sailfish No other fish is known to swim faster than the sailfish, which has been clocked in excess of 68 miles per hour (110 km/h). It uses its rapier-like beak to stun and maim prey, which it then scoops up with toothless jaws.

- Up to 11½ ft (3.5 m)
- Up to 220 lb (100 kg)
- ○ Oviparous
- ♀♂ Male & female
- ↯ Common

Tropical & temperate Indian & Pacific oceans

↯ CONSERVATION WATCH

Big decline The blue marlin is one of the most sought-after gamefishes, but sportfishing is not its biggest threat. Huge numbers are caught and killed accidentally on long-lines set for tuna and swordfish by commercial fishing operations. Being predators at the top of the food chain, they occur at naturally low levels of abundance, making their populations vulnerable to overexploitation of any sort.

The results of a 10-year study by German and Canadian scientists, published in 2003 in the international science journal *Nature*, indicate that blue marlin numbers, along with those of other large fishes in the world's oceans, declined dramatically during the last half of the 20th century.

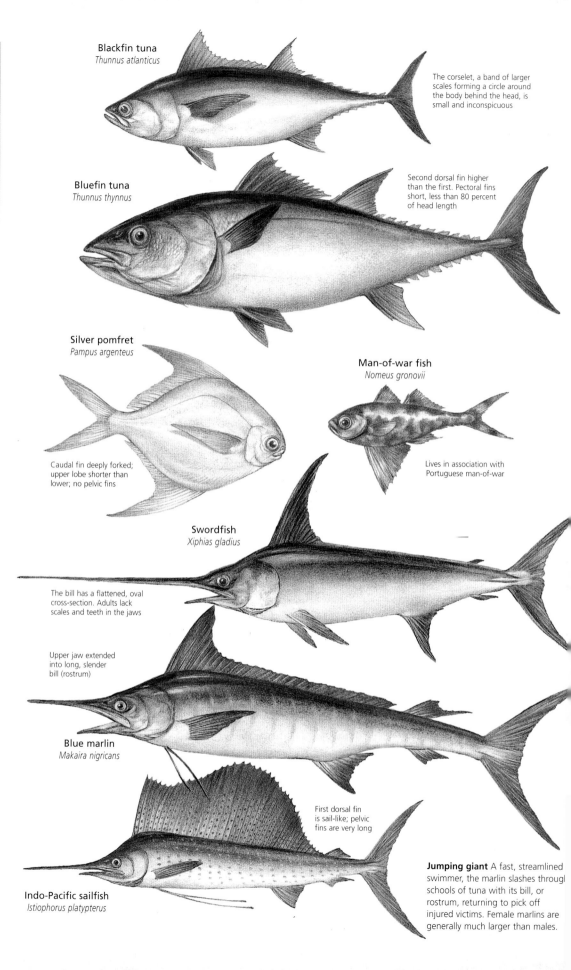

Blackfin tuna
Thunnus atlanticus

The corselet, a band of larger scales forming a circle around the body behind the head, is small and inconspicuous

Bluefin tuna
Thunnus thynnus

Second dorsal fin higher than the first. Pectoral fins short, less than 80 percent of head length

Silver pomfret
Pampus argenteus

Man-of-war fish
Nomeus gronovii

Caudal fin deeply forked; upper lobe shorter than lower; no pelvic fins

Lives in association with Portuguese man-of-war

Swordfish
Xiphias gladius

The bill has a flattened, oval cross-section. Adults lack scales and teeth in the jaws

Upper jaw extended into long, slender bill (rostrum)

Blue marlin
Makaira nigricans

First dorsal fin is sail-like; pelvic fins are very long

Indo-Pacific sailfish
Istiophorus platypterus

Jumping giant A fast, streamlined swimmer, the marlin slashes through schools of tuna with its bill, or rostrum, returning to pick off injured victims. Female marlins are generally much larger than males.

FACT FILE

Siamese fighting fish The males of this freshwater species create egg nests by blowing bubbles around leaves, which they then guard aggressively. The male-male fighting for which the species is famous involves threat displays and fin-nipping.

➤ Up to 2½ in (6.6 cm)
⬛ Up to 1 oz (30 g)
○ Oviparous, guarder
♀♂ Male & female
🗡 Common

Mekong basin (Asia)

Paradise fish The natural habitat of the paradise fish is shallow, standing, or slow-flowing freshwater over dark soil. Its tolerance of a range of water conditions and its bubble-nest building has made the paradise fish a popular aquarium species, but the need to keep it in pairs and in a separate tank, because of its aggressive nature, has caused it to be overtaken by more colorful and sociable species.

➤ Up to 2¾ in (7 cm)
⬛ Up to 3¾ oz (110 g)
○ Oviparous
♀♂ Male & female
🗡 Common

S.E. Asia

Kissing gourami This species has become a partial air-breather in order to cope with low oxygen conditions. It absorbs oxygen from air trapped in its gill chamber with a leaf-like outgrowth on the first gill arch. This supplements oxygen absorbed from the water by the rest of its gills. It is named for its thick, protuberant lips that are seemingly used to "kiss" other individuals. Ironically, it actually uses "kissing" as a threat display, not as an act of affection.

➤ Up to 12 in (30 cm)
⬛ Up to 15 oz (425 g)
○ Oviparous
♀♂ Male & female
🗡 Common

S.E. Asia

Climbing perch With an accessory air-breathing organ associated with the gills, this fish is well adapted to life in oxygen-depleted environments. When ponds dry up it will "walk," using its fins, in search of water and reportedly it will even climb low trees.

➤ Up to 10 in (25 cm)
⬛ Up to 16 oz (455 g)
○ Oviparous, guarder
♀♂ Male & female
🗡 Common

S.E. Asia

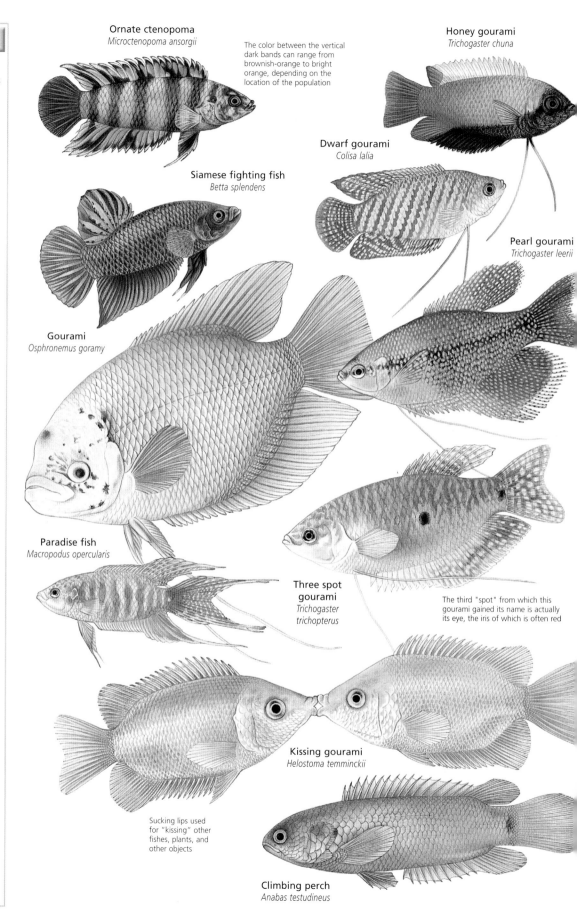

Ornate ctenopoma
Microctenopoma ansorgii

The color between the vertical dark bands can range from brownish-orange to bright orange, depending on the location of the population

Honey gourami
Trichogaster chuna

Dwarf gourami
Colisa lalia

Siamese fighting fish
Betta splendens

Pearl gourami
Trichogaster leerii

Gourami
Osphronemus goramy

Paradise fish
Macropodus opercularis

Three spot gourami
Trichogaster trichopterus

The third "spot" from which this gourami gained its name is actually its eye, the iris of which is often red

Kissing gourami
Helostoma temminckii

Sucking lips used for "kissing" other fishes, plants, and other objects

Climbing perch
Anabas testudineus

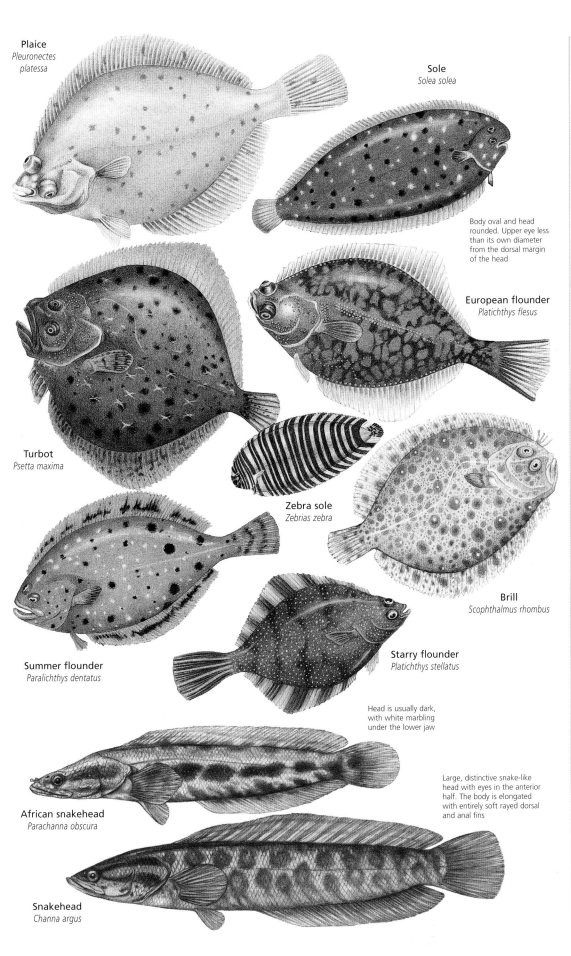

Plaice
*Pleuronectes
platessa*

Sole
Solea solea

Body oval and head
rounded. Upper eye less
than its own diameter
from the dorsal margin
of the head

European flounder
Platichthys flesus

Turbot
Psetta maxima

Zebra sole
Zebrias zebra

Brill
Scophthalmus rhombus

Summer flounder
Paralichthys dentatus

Starry flounder
Platichthys stellatus

Head is usually dark,
with white marbling
under the lower jaw

Large, distinctive snake-like
head with eyes in the anterior
half. The body is elongated
with entirely soft rayed dorsal
and anal fins

African snakehead
Parachanna obscura

Snakehead
Channa argus

FACT FILE

European flounder Although it
spawns in seawater between February
and June, juveniles in this species use
estuaries as nursery grounds. Both
juveniles and adults can tolerate
reduced salinities down to freshwater,
and can penetrate far inland.

⬆ Up to 20 in (51 cm)
🏋 Up to 6½ lb (3 kg)
○ Oviparous
♀♂ Male & female
🍴 Common

N.E Atlantic, Mediterranean & Black seas

Brill Like all other flatfishes, this
marine species relies extensively on
camouflage to hide it from both
predators and prey, and can change its
body color to match the surrounding
seabed environment.

⬆ Up to 29½ in (75 cm)
🏋 Up to 16 lb (7.3 kg)
○ Oviparous
♀♂ Male & female
🍴 Common

E. North Atlantic; Mediterranean & Black seas

Starry flounder Adults are found in
coastal waters all around the North
Pacific, moving inshore in summer and
into deeper water in winter. The young
have safe nursery grounds in estuaries—
fluctuating salinity conditions exclude
many potential predators. This species
lives on sand or mud sediments and
feeds on buried invertebrates.

⬆ Up to 35¾ in (91 cm)
🏋 Up to 20 lb (9 kg)
○ Oviparous
♀♂ Male & female
🍴 Common

North Pacific

Snakehead The snakehead's body
shape is adapted to moving through
thick, aquatic vegetation. It can survive
for long periods out of water because
it is a partial air-breather, able to absorb
oxygen from air in its gill chamber that
has an elaborately folded lining to
increase its surface area.

⬆ Up to 33 in (85 cm)
🏋 Up to 13 lb (6 kg)
○ Oviparous
♀♂ Male & female
🍴 Common

S.E Asia

MIGRATING BODY PARTS

One of the most radical departures from the "normal" fish body is seen in flatfishes, which have deep bodies—flattened sideways—and eyes that have migrated to the same side of the body. This remarkable rearrangement of body parts occurs during larval development. Flatfish larvae look similar to most other larval fishes when they first emerge from eggs but after periods between one to three months, they undergo metamorphosis into the adult form. During this process, one side of the body becomes the upper side, carrying both eyes, and pigmented to blend with surrounding sea or riverbed. The blind, lower side is pale or unpigmented. Most can be classified according to their preferred upper side; the right-eyed groups are from the family Pleuronectidae and the left-eyed groups are from the family Bothidae. In the primitive spiny flatfishes (family Psettodidae), however, there are equal numbers of left and right-eyed forms.

Chameleons of the sea Using information from their eyes, that can resolve the fine detail of hues and textures of the seabed, flatfishes such as the peacock flounder (*Bothus lunatus*) (top left), are able to control the size and shape of pigmented cells in their skin to match exactly surrounding sediments in which they bury themselves.

Tracking migration Scientists can identify which side the eye of a flatfish started on by tracing the path of optic nerves between eye and brain in adult species. In left-eyed forms, including the peacock flounder (bottom left), the optic nerves have an unusual twist. In right-eyed forms, such as the starry flounder, the optic nerve of the migrating left eye always crosses behind that of the right eye.

Twisted jaws Once the eyes have migrated, they become hooded, raised structures that protrude above the surface while the fish lies immobile and camouflaged. Eye migration is accompanied by twisting of the jaws (below), so they open on the upper side.

EYE MIGRATION

At metamorphosis, one of the eyes begins a slow journey to the other side of the body, finishing near the other eye. The distance of this migration varies among flatfishes. It can be as little as one-fifth of an inch (5 mm) in some American soles or as much as five inches (120 mm) in *Chasconopsetta*—a genus of left-eyed flounders. The path taken by the eye also varies; in some it follows a groove that forms between the eyes, just ahead of the developing dorsal fin. Once the eye is close to its final position, the dorsal fin will extend forward and take up the position it will occupy in the adult form. In other flatfishes, the dorsal fin base is established in its final position and the eye has to pass through a slit between the fin base and the skull.

Larva with normal eye position

Left eye migrates to top of head

Adult eyes both on the right side

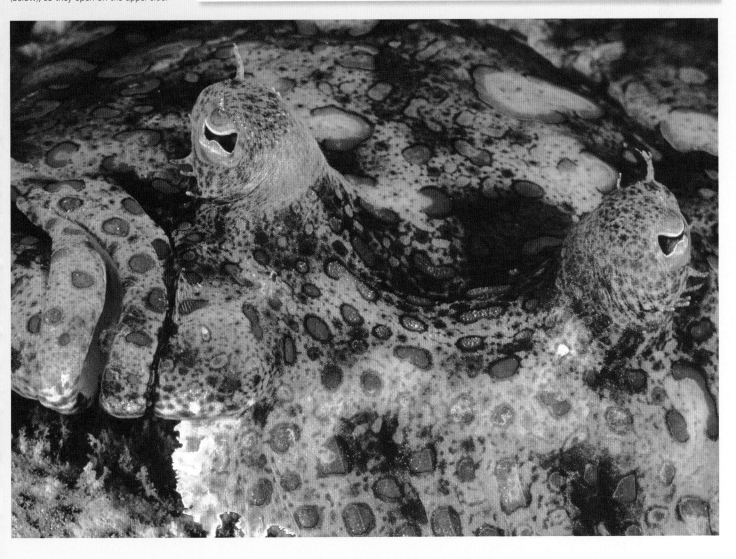

FACT FILE

Whitespotted filefish Although it is not common, this is a conspicuous filefish. It usually swims in pairs, well off the bottom, and often in an unusual, tilted posture. Males are distinguished from females by longer and deeper-orange peduncular spines, tail, and eyes. Juveniles and immature adults have small, white spots on the head and body.

- Up to 15 in (38 cm)
- Up to 2 lb (900 g)
- Oviparous
- Male & female
- Uncommon

Indo-Pacific

Harlequin filefish The presence of this tropical coral reef specialist is a sign of environmental health. It lives almost exclusively on coral polyps and is one of the first species to disappear from reefs affected by pollution or global warming.

- Up to 4¾ in (12 cm)
- Up to 3 oz (85 g)
- Oviparous
- Male & female
- Common

Indo-West Pacific

Clown triggerfish In the wild, the clown triggerfish is found over coral, rubble, and sand on the seaward side of coral reefs. It feeds on crabs, mollusks, and sea urchins. Females defend egg masses and are armed with strong jaws and sharp teeth that can inflict serious bites on divers who venture too close.

- Up to 19½ in (50 cm)
- Up to 5½ lb (2.5 kg)
- Oviparous
- Male & female
- Uncommon

Indo-Pacific

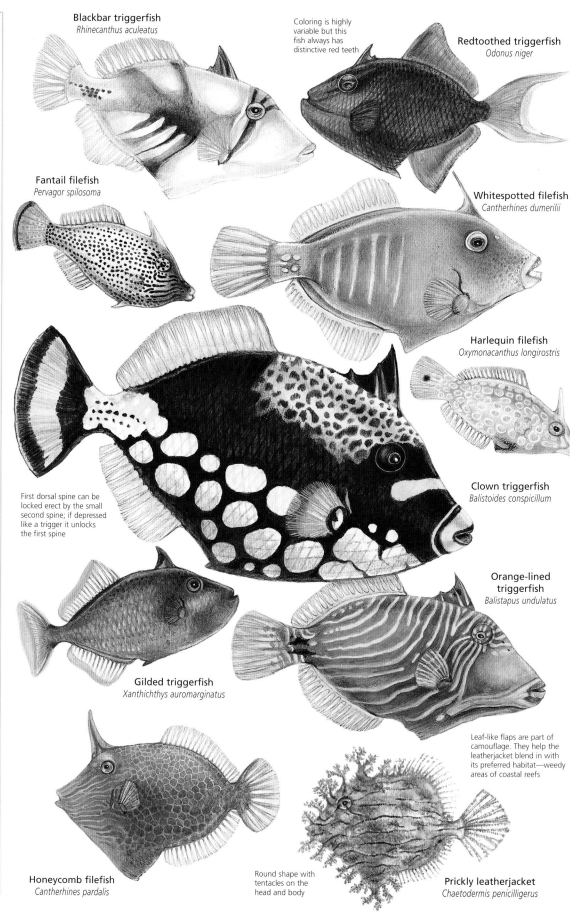

Blackbar triggerfish
Rhinecanthus aculeatus

Coloring is highly variable but this fish always has distinctive red teeth

Redtoothed triggerfish
Odonus niger

Fantail filefish
Pervagor spilosoma

Whitespotted filefish
Cantherhines dumerilii

Harlequin filefish
Oxymonacanthus longirostris

First dorsal spine can be locked erect by the small second spine; if depressed like a trigger it unlocks the first spine

Clown triggerfish
Balistoides conspicillum

Orange-lined triggerfish
Balistapus undulatus

Gilded triggerfish
Xanthichthys auromarginatus

Leaf-like flaps are part of camouflage. They help the leatherjacket blend in with its preferred habitat—weedy areas of coastal reefs

Honeycomb filefish
Cantherhines pardalis

Round shape with tentacles on the head and body

Prickly leatherjacket
Chaetodermis penicilligerus

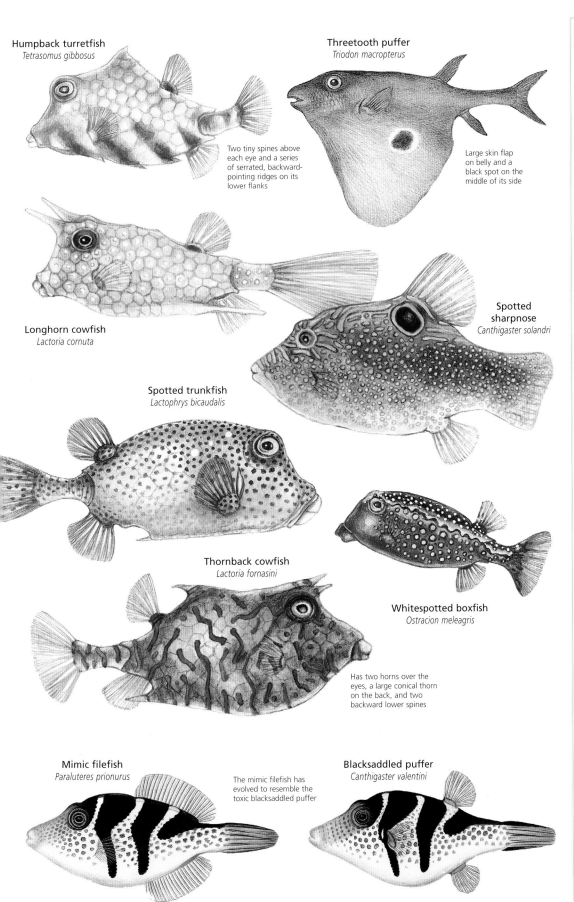

Humpback turretfish
Tetrasomus gibbosus

Threetooth puffer
Triodon macropterus

Two tiny spines above each eye and a series of serrated, backward-pointing ridges on its lower flanks

Large skin flap on belly and a black spot on the middle of its side

Longhorn cowfish
Lactoria cornuta

**Spotted
sharpnose**
Canthigaster solandri

Spotted trunkfish
Lactophrys bicaudalis

Thornback cowfish
Lactoria fornasini

Whitespotted boxfish
Ostracion meleagris

Has two horns over the eyes, a large conical thorn on the back, and two backward lower spines

Mimic filefish
Paraluteres prionurus

The mimic filefish has evolved to resemble the toxic blacksaddled puffer

Blacksaddled puffer
Canthigaster valentini

PROTECTIVE ARMOR

Also known as trunk or boxfishes, cowfishes have evolved a covering of enlarged, thickened, and sutured scale plates. These plates are partially or completely fused together to form an extremely strong, rigid structure—as complete as any of the now extinct armored fishes of the Paleozoic era (more than 245 million years ago). The hard covering, or shell, that encloses most of their bodies makes adult cowfishes relatively immune to predation from all but the largest of fishes. Some may be adorned with horn-like projections to further deter predators. When threatened, captured, or handled, they exude a toxic substance called ostracitoxin into the surrounding water. This toxin is poisonous enough to kill other fishes kept with them in aquariums, and in some cases, the actual cowfish as well.

Extreme specialist The honeycomb cowfish (*Acanthostracion polygonius*) (right) belongs to an advanced group that has lost the typical torpedo-shaped streamlining. The plate-like armor prevents body movement but the fins are able to facilitate finely controlled "hovering."

Fine movements Cowfishes and their relatives have a unique form of swimming, known as ostraciform swimming, that is a result of the rigidity of their bodies. They are propelled by rapid undulations or complex scullings of the soft dorsal and anal fins. Short bursts of high speed are produced by the powerful caudal fin. The paired pectoral fins are in an almost constant state of rapid vibration that gives the cowfish exquisite control to its movements—unusual even among fishes.

FACT FILE

Shosaifugu The shosaifugu (fugu) is found close to shore in areas of semi-enclosed shallow sea and in the lower reaches of estuaries. Its dried flesh has been used for centuries in traditional Chinese medicine and its freshly prepared flesh is one of the most-prized of Japanese delicacies. Its liver, ovaries, and gut contain large amounts of tetrodotoxin that is one of the most potent toxins found in nature. Despite this, some predatory fishes are able to eat puffers without apparent harm.

↠ Up to 12 in (30 cm)
⚖ Up to 24 oz (680 g)
○ Oviparous
♀♂ Not known
⚑ Common

N.W Pacific

Blackspotted pufferfish This species feeds on live coral, biting off the tips of branching corals, particularly staghorn corals. It also noses through sand to find crustaceans, mollusks, sponges, and tunicates, and grazes on the algal turf of reefs. Like all puffers, it contains the poison tetrodotoxin.

↠ Up to 13 in (33 cm)
⚖ Up to 25 oz (710 g)
○ Oviparous
♀♂ Not known
⚑ Common

Indo-Pacific

Stellate puffer Considered to be a giant among puffers, the stellate puffer can grow to more than 3 feet (1 m) long. Its skin is flexible and scaleless but covered with hard, dermal prickles. When threatened, it inflates itself with seawater by filling a special sac near the stomach, and becomes a nearly spherical ball of spines.

↠ Up to 4 ft (1.2 m)
⚖ Up to 22 lb (10 kg)
○ Oviparous
♀♂ Not known
⚑ Common

Indo-C. Pacific & S.E Atlantic

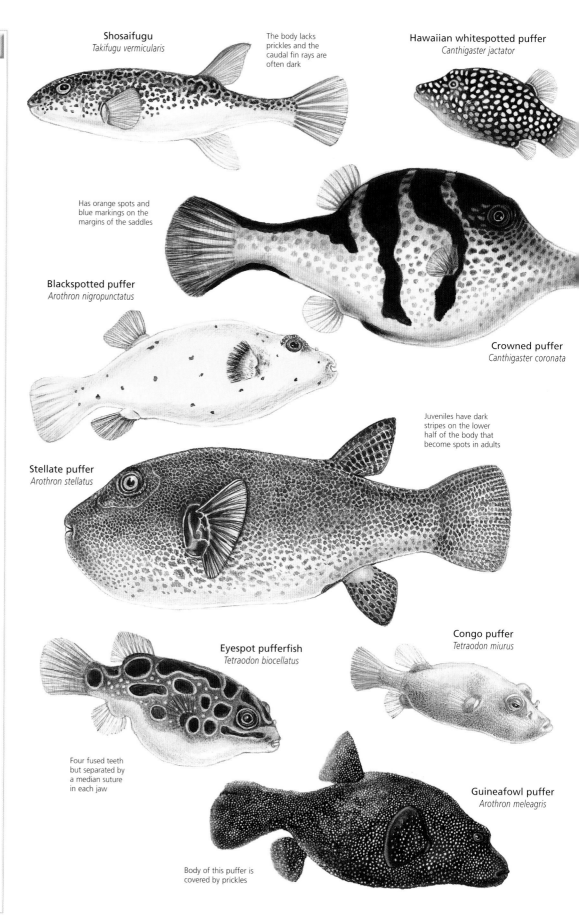

Shosaifugu
Takifugu vermicularis

The body lacks prickles and the caudal fin rays are often dark

Hawaiian whitespotted puffer
Canthigaster jactator

Has orange spots and blue markings on the margins of the saddles

Blackspotted puffer
Arothron nigropunctatus

Crowned puffer
Canthigaster coronata

Stellate puffer
Arothron stellatus

Juveniles have dark stripes on the lower half of the body that become spots in adults

Eyespot pufferfish
Tetraodon biocellatus

Congo puffer
Tetraodon miurus

Four fused teeth but separated by a median suture in each jaw

Guineafowl puffer
Arothron meleagris

Body of this puffer is covered by prickles

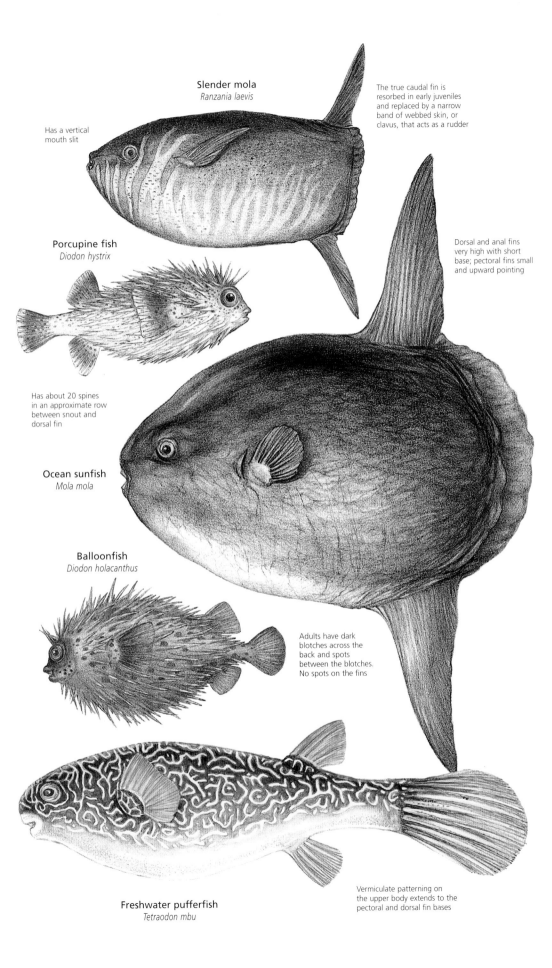

Slender mola
Ranzania laevis

Has a vertical mouth slit

The true caudal fin is resorbed in early juveniles and replaced by a narrow band of webbed skin, or clavus, that acts as a rudder

Porcupine fish
Diodon hystrix

Has about 20 spines in an approximate row between snout and dorsal fin

Dorsal and anal fins very high with short base; pectoral fins small and upward pointing

Ocean sunfish
Mola mola

Balloonfish
Diodon holacanthus

Adults have dark blotches across the back and spots between the blotches. No spots on the fins

Freshwater pufferfish
Tetraodon mbu

Vermiculate patterning on the upper body extends to the pectoral and dorsal fin bases

FACT FILE

Ocean sunfish The disk-shaped body of the sunfishes has an abbreviated appearance at the back end because there is no tail fin. Forward motion is provided instead, by sculling with the dorsal and anal fins, which have shifted toward the rear.

- Up to 11 ft (3.3 m)
- Up to 3,300 lb (1,500 kg)
- ○ Oviparous
- ♀♂ Male & female
- Common

Widespread in warm & temperate oceans

Freshwater pufferfish When they are threatened, pufferfishes pump air or water into a distensible stomach sac to greatly increase the size of their bodies and appear more formidable. This also forces spines and scales to protrude, making them harder to swallow.

- Up to 26½ in (67 cm)
- Up to 15 lb (6.8 kg)
- ○ Oviparous
- ♀♂ Male & female
- Common

Central Africa

PUFFERFISH POISON

Some pufferfishes are highly poisonous, particularly those of the Indo-Pacific. Tetrodotoxin, which is found throughout the body but concentrated in the liver, ovaries, and gut, is a powerful nerve poison considerably stronger than cyanide. These fishes also release this toxin into the surrounding water when frightened by a potential predator.

Dicey dining *The specially prepared poison-free flesh of certain pufferfish species is highly prized, particularly in Japan and Korea, even though their organs are imbued with deadly tetrodotoxin.*

GLOSSARY

adaptation A change in a fish's behavior or body that allows it to survive and breed in new conditions.

adipose eyelid An immovable, transparent outer covering or partial covering of the eye of some groups of bony fishes, such as mullets and jacks, which performs protective and streamlining functions.

adipose fin A small, fleshy fin without rays found on the back behind the dorsal fin of some primitive teleost fishes such as the lizardfishes, salmons, and characids.

alevin Larval salmon that have hatched but have not completely absorbed their yolk sacs.

algae The simplest forms of plant life.

allopatric Existing in different areas; populations or species occupying mutually exclusive geographic areas, opposite of sympatric.

ampullae of Lorenzini Jelly-filled canals found on the head of sharks that can detect weak electric fields.

anadromous Living in the ocean but returning to freshwater to spawn, as in salmon.

anal fin An unpaired fin on the lower surface of a fish's abdomen. It plays an important role in swimming.

annulus (pl. annuli) A marking resembling a growth ring, as on a scale of a fish, that is used in estimating age.

aquaculture Cultivation of the resources of the sea or inland waters, as opposed to their exploitation.

axil The acute, angular region between a fin and the body; usually used in reference to the underside of the pectoral fin toward the base.

band An oblique or irregular marking.

bar An elongate vertical color marking, with straight sides.

barbel A slender, fleshy outgrowth on a fish's lips or near its mouth. It is equipped with sensory and chemical receptors and is used by bottom-dwelling fishes to find food.

bathymetry Measurement of the ocean depths and the contours of the seabed.

batoid A member of the group of fishes that includes all rays and skates.

benthic Relating to or occurring at the bottom of a body of water or the depths of the ocean; bottom-dwelling (as in fishes).

biodiversity The total number of species of plants and animals in a particular location.

bioluminescence The generation of light by living organisms using the enzyme luciferase.

bony fish A fish with a bony skeleton. Other characteristics are a covering over the gills, and a swim bladder. Most bony fishes also have scales on their skin.

canine A prominent, slender, sharp-pointed tooth.

cartilaginous fish A fish with a skeleton made of cartilage, such as a shark, ray, or chimaera.

catadromous Living in freshwater but returning to the sea to spawn, as in freshwater eels.

caudal Relating to an animal's tail. In fishes, the caudal fin is the tail fin.

caudal peduncle The part of the body between the posterior basal parts of the dorsal and anal fins and the base of the caudal fin.

cavity A chamber within a fish that can contain some of the fish's organs.

cephalic Of, relating to, or situated on or near the head.

cephalic flaps The forward-pointing projections on either side of the mouth of manta and devil rays.

cephalopod An advanced group of mollusks that includes the squids, octopuses, and cuttlefishes.

ciguatera An illness caused by eating fresh fish that have ciguatoxin in their flesh. The organism that initially produces the toxin is a dinoflagellate.

claspers The modified inner edges of the pelvic fins of male sharks, rays, and chimaeras, used for the transferring of sperm to the female.

cloaca An internal chamber in fishes into which the contents of the reproductive ducts and the waste ducts empty before being passed from the body.

compressed Laterally flattened, deep and thin.

conspecific Of the same species.

convergent evolution The situation in which totally unrelated groups develop similar structures to cope with similar evolutionary pressures.

coral reef A structure made from the skeletons of coral animals, or polyps, found in warm water.

crustaceans Invertebrates with jointed limbs and hard, chalky shells, such as lobsters, crabs, shrimps, and copepods.

ctenoid scales Bony fish scales which have tiny tooth-like projections (ctenii) along the posterior margin and part of the exposed portion.

cycloid scales Bony fish scales that lack tiny tooth-like projections and are therefore smooth.

demersal Living on or near the bottom.

denticles Tooth-like projections such as the scales of cartilaginous fishes.

depressed Dorso-ventrally flattened, shallow and wide.

dimorphic Having two distinct forms within a species. Sexual dimorphism is the situation in which the male and female of a species differ in size and/or appearance.

dioecious Born either male or female and remaining that way through life.

display Behavior used by a fish to communicate with its own species, or with other animals. Displays can include postures, actions, or showing brightly colored parts of the body, and may signal threat, defense, or readiness to mate.

divergent evolution The situation in which two or more similar species become more and more dissimilar due to environmental adaptations.

dorsal fin The large fin on the back of some fishes and aquatic mammals, which helps the animal keep its balance as it moves through the water. Some fishes have two or three dorsal fins.

echinoderms Exclusively marine invertebrates with five-way symmetry and a water vascular system, including starfishes, sea cucumbers, and brittlestars.

ecosystem A community of plants, animals, and the environment to which they are adapted.

elasmobranch A subclass of cartilaginous fishes including sharks and rays.

electroreceptors Specialized organs found in some fishes (such as sharks) that detect electrical activity from the bodies of other animals. They also help the fish to navigate by detecting distortions in the electrical field of its surroundings—for example, those caused by a reef.

emarginate Concave, used to describe the posterior edge of a caudal fin that is inwardly curved.

embryo An unborn animal in the earliest stages of development. An embryo may grow inside its mother's body, or in an egg outside her body.

epipelagic Pertaining to the surface layer of the open sea.

esca The lure or bait of lophiiform fishes (see illicium).

evolution Gradual change in plants and animals, over many generations, in response to their environment.

falcate Sickle-shaped, used to describe the shape of fins.

fins Folds of skin supported by cartilaginous tissue in elasmobranchs and by bony rays in bony fishes. Used for locomotion, display, and sometimes specialized functions such as fertilization.

forked Inwardly angular; used to describe the shape of a caudal fin that is divided into two equal lobes which have relatively straight posterior borders.

fry Young or small fishes.

gas bladder Gas-filled buoyancy organ in most bony fishes.

gestation period The period of time during which a female fish is pregnant with her young.

gill arch Bony or cartilaginous arches in the throat of fish to which the filaments and rakers of the gills are attached. Bony fishes usually have four gill arches.

gills Organs that collect oxygen from water and are used for respiration.

gonad The reproductive organs.

gravid Full of eggs; pregnant.

habitat The area in which an animal naturally lives. Many different kinds of animals live in the same environment, but each kind lives in a different habitat within that environment. For example, some animals live in the deep sea, while others live in coral reefs.

hermaphrodite A fish possessing both male and female sex organs at the same time, and thus able to fertilize itself (known as simultaneous hermaphroditism), or one that starts life as one sex and later changes to the other (sequential hermaphroditism).

hybrid The offspring of parents of two different species.

illicium An elongate dorsal spine of lophiiform fishes, tipped by an expanded structure called the esca, which is used to attract prey close to the mouth.

invertebrate An animal that has no backbone. Sea urchins, sea stars, shellfishes, and worms are all kinds of invertebrates.

keel A lateral strengthening ridge on the caudal peduncle on some swift-swimming fishes.

krill Small, shrimp-like crustaceans that live in huge numbers in Arctic and Antarctic waters.

lateral line A sensory canal system along the sides of a fish from behind the eye to the tip of the tail, and also extends in various directions around the head. It detects moving objects by registering disturbances (or pressure changes) in the water.

live-bearing Giving birth to young that are fully formed.

luminous Reflecting or radiating light. Some deep-sea fishes can produce their own light source by using luminous bacteria.

lunate Sickle-shaped, used to describe a caudal fin that is deeply emarginate with narrow lobes.

median fins The fins in the median plane, hence the dorsal, anal, and caudal fins.

mesopelagic Of or associated with the deep sea, from about 650 to 3,280 feet (200 to 1,000 m).

migration A usually seasonal journey from one habitat to another. Fishes may migrate vast distances to another location to find food, or to mate and lay eggs or give birth. Some deep-sea fishes migrate vertically at night to feed.

morph A color or other physical variation within, or a local population of, a species.

nape The part of the back that extends from the margin of the skull to the dorsal fin origin; also, the region of the head above and behind the eyes.

nictitating eyelid A transparent, moveable membrane or inner eyelid that protects and helps keep the eye clean. Found particularly in sharks.

nocturnal Active at night. Nocturnal fishes have special adaptations, such as large, sensitive eyes to help them find their way in the dark. Many nocturnal fishes rest during the day.

ocellus An eye-like marking with a ring of one color surrounding a spot of another.

omnivore An animal that eats both plant and animal food. Omnivores have teeth and a digestive system designed to process almost any kind of food.

opercle The large bone that forms the upper posterior part of the operculum.

operculum Bony gill cover; comprised of four bones: opercle, preopercle, interopercle, and subopercle.

osmoregulation The regulation of the concentration of body fluids by aquatic animals.

oviparous Reproducing by laying eggs. Little or no development occurs within the mother's body; instead, the embryos develop inside the egg.

ovoviviparous Reproducing by giving birth to live young that have developed from eggs within the mother's body. The eggs may hatch as they are laid or soon after.

paired fins Collective term for the pectoral and pelvic fins.

papilla (pl. papillae) A small fleshy protuberance.

parallel evolution The situation in which related groups living in isolation develop similar structures to cope with similar evolutionary pressures.

parasitism The situation in which an animal or plant lives and/or feeds on another living animal or plant, sometimes with harmful effects.

pectoral fins Paired fins attached to each side of the fish and used for lift and control of movement. They are usually located just behind the gills.

pelagic Swimming freely in the open ocean; not associated with the bottom.

pelvic fins Paired fins, located on the lower part of a fish's body.

pharyngeal teeth Opposing patches of teeth which occur on the upper and lower elements of the gill arches.

pheromone A chemical released by a fish that sends a signal and affects the behavior of others of the same species. Many fishes use pheromones to attract mates, or to signal danger.

photophores Luminous organs on some deep-sea fishes.

phytoplankton Tiny, single-celled algae that float on or near the surface of the sea.

placoid scale A type of scale, typically thorn-shaped, found on the skin of Elasmobranchii and claspers of Holocephali. Also called denticle, dermal denticle, or odontoid.

plankton The plant (phytoplankton) or animal (zooplankton) organisms that float or drift in the open sea. Plankton forms an important link in the food chain.

polyp The sedentary body form of coelenterates, notably corals.

predator A fish that lives mainly by killing and eating other animals.

protandrous Of sequential hermaphrodites (as in some fishes), starting life as a male and later becoming female.

protogynous Of sequential hermaphrodites (as in some fishes), starting life as a female and later becoming male.

ray The supporting bony elements of fins, including spines and soft rays.

rounded A caudal fin shape where the terminal border is smoothly convex.

rudimentary Describes a simple, undeveloped, or underdeveloped part of a fish, such as an organ or fin. The rudimentary parts of some modern-day fishes are the traces of the functional parts of an early ancestor, but now serve no purpose.

scales Small plates that form part of the external body covering.

scavenger A fish that eats carrion—often the remains of animals killed by predators.

scute An external bony plate or enlarged scale.

sediment Fine organic or mineral particles found in the seafloor.

social Living in groups. Social fishes can live in breeding pairs, sometimes together with their young, or in a school of up to thousands of fishes.

soft ray A segmented fin ray which is composed of two closely joined lateral elements. It is nearly always flexible and often branched.

spawn To release eggs and sperm together directly into the water.

species A group of fishes with very similar features that are able to breed together and produce fertile young.

spermatophore A container or package of sperm that is passed from male to female during mating.

spine An unsegmented bony process consisting of a single element, usually rigid and sharply pointed. Spines that support fins are never branched.

spiracle In cartilaginous fishes, spiracles are located behind the eyes. They take in water for respiration when the fish is at rest, or when the mouth is used for feeding.

squalene A substance found in the liver oil of sharks. It is refined and used as a high-grade machine oil in high-technology industries, as a human health and dietary supplement, and in cosmetics.

stereoscopic vision Vision in which both eyes face forward, giving an animal two overlapping fields of view and thus allowing it to judge depth.

streamlined Having a smooth body shape to reduce drag.

stripe Horizontal color marking with straight sides.

swim bladder A gas-filled, bag-like organ in the abdomen of bony fishes. It enables the fishes to remain at a particular depth in the water.

symbiosis An alliance between two species that is usually (but not always) beneficial to both. Fishes form symbiotic relationships with microorganisms and other animals.

sympatric Of two or more species, occurring in the same area.

taxonomy The system of classifying living things into various groups and subgroups according to similarities in features and adaptations.

teleost Refers to the Teleostei, the highest superorder of the ray-finned bony fishes.

territory An area inhabited by a fish and defended against intruders. The area often contains all the living resources required by the fish, such as food and a nesting site.

torpid In a sleep-like state in which bodily processes are greatly slowed. Torpor helps fishes to survive difficult conditions such as lack of food or water. Estivation and hibernation are types of torpor.

truncate With square ends; used to describe a caudal fin with a vertically straight terminal border and angular or slightly rounded corners.

vertebral column The series of vertebrae running from head to tail along the back of vertebrates, and which encloses the spinal cord.

vertebrate An animal with a backbone. All vertebrates have an internal skeleton of cartilage or bone. Fishes, reptiles, birds, amphibians, and mammals are vertebrates.

vestigial Relating to an organ that is non-functional or atrophied.

viviparous Reproducing by means of young that develop inside the mother's body and are born live; sometimes called placental viviparity. Some fishes (such as sharks) are viviparous.

vomer A median unpaired bone on the roof of the mouth, its anterior end often bears teeth.

zooplankton The tiny animals that, together with phytoplankton, form the plankton that drifts on or near the sea's surface. Zooplankton are eaten by whales, fishes, and seabirds.

INDEX

Page numbers in italics refer to illustrations, photographs, and to information in captions. Species are listed by both their common name/s and scientific name, although page references to scientific names often relate only to mentions in the text of common names.

shosaifugu 198, *198*
shrimpfish 150, *150*
shrimps *103*, 168, *168*
Siganidae 184, *184*
Siganus
    S. stellatus 184
    S. vermiculatus 184
    S. vulpinus 184, *184*
sight 22, 69, 70, 72
silky shark 77, *77*
sillago, silver 161
Silurus glanis 123, *123*
silver pomfret 188
silver sillago 161
silversides 142
    brook 143, *143*
Simenchelys parasitica 102
sixgill shark 79
skates 22, 68, 84, *86*
    blue 86, *86*
    rays *see* rays
skipjack tuna 187, *187*
skunk botia 116
slickhead, California 127
small-eyed ray 86
smell 22, 70, 72, 73
smelts 128, *128*, 143, *143*
snailfish, longhorn 157
snake mackerel 186, *186*
snake pipefish 151
snakeheads 191, *191*
    African 191
snapper, Emperor 163, *163*
snipefish, longspine 150
snook, common 158, *158*
soapfishes 159, *159*, 160
sockeye salmon 130-1, *130-1*
soldierfish, shadowfin 149, *149*
sole 191
    zebra 191
Solea solea 191
Solenostomus paradoxus 151, *151*
Somniosus microcephalus 79
sorubim, barred 125
soupfin shark 74
South American pilchard 106, *106*
spangled perch 32, *32*
Spanish toothcarp 148
Sparisoma viride, 180, *180*
spawning 26, 66, 91
Speoplatyrhinus poulsoni 138
sphinx blenny 182
Sphyraena
    S. argentea 186
    S. barracuda 25, *25*, 186, *186*
    S. sphyraena 186
Sphyrna zygaena 74, *74*
Spicara smaris 165
spinefoot, brownspotted 184
spiny eel 100, *154*
spiny-rayed fish 20, 142-85
spiracles 69
splash tetra 118, *118*
spookfishes 68
spotbreast angelfish 107, *107*
spotted eagle ray 69, *69*, 88
spotted hoplo 125
spotted pike characin 118
spotted unicornfish 186
spotted wrasse 178
sprats 106

Squalus acanthias 79
Squatina squatina 79
squeaker, angel 124
squid 50, *51*
    deep-sea 50, *51*
squirrelfish, crown 149, *149*
stargazers 57
    Atlantic 181, *181*
    sand 181
starry, flounder 191, *191*
Steatocranus casuarius 175, *175*
Stegostoma fasciatum 71
stellate pufferfish 198, *198*
stellate sturgeon 95, *95*
Stenodus leucichthys 133, *133*
Stenopterygii 20, 134
sterlet 95, *95*
sticklebacks 28, *150*
stinging catfish 124, *124*
stingrays 55, *55*, 57, 84, *84*, 86, *86*, 87
    Atlantic 86, *86*
    Ocellate river 87, *87*
    rays *see* rays
Stomias boa 134
Stomiidae 134
Stomiiformes 134
stonefishes 56, *56*, 155, *155*
stoplight parrotfish 180, *180*
streams and rivers 31, *31*
streber, Danube 161
striped bass 158, *158*
striped eel-catfish 124, *124*
striped seaperch 176, *176*
stripey 171
sturgeons 58, 62, 94
    Atlantic 95
    Beluga 95, *95*
    European 95
    stellate 95, *95*
    white 95, *95*
Stylephorus chordatus 137
suckerfishes 113, *113*, 168, *169*
summer flounder 191
surfperch, walleye 176
surgeonfishes 168, 185
    clown 185, *185*
    palette 185
    powderblue 185
    Red Sea 14, *14-15*, 185
    redtail 185, *185*
swai 123
swallower 102
swallowtail seaperch 39, *39*
swamp eel 154, *154*
sweetlips 21, *21*, 142, 163, *163*
swordfishes 46, 94, *94*, 188, *188*
swordtail characin 120, *120*
swordtails 142
Symphysodon aequifasciatus 174, *174*
Synanceia 56, *56*
    S. verrucosa 155, *155*
Synchiropus
    S. picturatus 183
    S. splendidus 26, *26*, 183, *183*
Syngnathus acus 151
Synodontis
    S. angelicus 124
    S. nigriventris 124
Synodus variegatus 135, *135*

T

tadpole fish *141*
Taeniura lymma 69, *69*, 87, *87*
tagging 75, *75*
Takifugu vermicularis 198, *198*
Tandanus tandanus 124, *124*
tangs
    convict 185
    yellow 185, *185*
Tanichthys albonubes 111, *111*
tarpons 100, *100*
tasseled wobbegong 24, *24*, 76, *76*
taste 73
teeth 68, 83, *83*, 108, *108*, 127, *127*
Teleostei 20, 105-6
teleosts 136, 142
telescopefishes 135, *135*
temperate regions 39
tench 110
Tenualosa thibaudeaui 106
terapon, Jarbua 171
Terranatos dolichopterus 147, *147*
Tetraodon
    T. biocellatus 198
    T. mbu 199, *199*
    T. miurus 198
tetrapods 90
tetras 31, 108, *108*
    bleeding-heart 120
    cardinal 120
    Congo 119
    emperor 119
    firehead 120
    garnet 120
    longfin 120
    neon 120, *120*
    splash 118, *118*
Thalassoma
    T. bifasciatum 168
    T. lunare 179, *179*
    T. pavo 179
Thaleichthys pacificus 128
Thayeria boehkei 119
thornback ray 86
threadfin butterflyfish 167
threadfin rainbowfish 143, *143*
three spot gourami 190
threetooth pufferfish 195
thresher shark 71, 72, *72*, 77, *77*, 78
Thunnus
    T. alalunga 187, *187*
    T. atlanticus 188
    T. thynnus 91, *91*, 188
Thymallus
    T. arcticus 132
    T. thymallus 132, *132*
tides 37
tiger shark 71, 73, 74, 83, *83*
tigerfishes 119, *119*, 163
tilefish, sand 161
Tinca tinca 110
toadfishes 57
tompot blenny 182
toothcarp, Spanish 148, *148*
toothcarp, Valencia 148, *148*
Tor putitora 110, *110*
torpedo, ocellated 85
Totoaba macdonaldi 60
touch 73
toxins 196, 199 *see also* venom
Toxotes jaculatrix, 167, *167*

Trachinocephalus myops 135
Trachinotus ovatus 162
Trachinus draco 181
trachipterids 137
Trachipterus trachypterus 137, *137*
Trachurus trachurus 162
trade 62
trahira 117, *117*
transparency 55, *55*
transparent goby 183
trevallies 46
Trichiurus lepturus 186, *186*
Trichogaster
    T. chuna 190
    T. leerii 190
    T. trichopterus 190
triggerfishes 142, 194, *194*
    black 46, *46*
    blackbar 194
    gilded 194
    orange-lined 194
    redtooth 194
Triodon macropterus 195
tripletail 163, *163*
tripodfishes 50, *51*, 135, *135*
Trisopterus luscus 141
Tropheus moorii 175
tropical regions 38, *38*, 42
trout 31, *129*
    brook 132
    brown 128, *128*
    farming 126, *126*
    lake 132, *132*
    rainbow 126, 129, *129*
    reproduction 26
    sea 128, *128*
trout perch 138
trout perches 138, *138*
trumpetfish, chinese 151
trunkfishes 195, 196
tube-eyes 137
tunas 46
    blackfin 188
    bluefin 91, *91*, 188
    commercial fishing 62
    skipjack 187, *187*
turbots 191
tusk 140
tuskfish, harlequin 178, *178*
Twee redfin 109
twoband bream 164, *164*

U

Ubangi shovelnose catfish 121, *121*
Umbra krameri 127, *127*
Umbrina cirrosa 166
unicornfishes 186
    masked 186
    spotted 186
Uranoscopidae 181
Uranoscopus scaber 181, *181*
Urobatis halleri 87
Urophycis chuss 140

V

Valencia hispanica 148, *148*
Valenciennea puellaris 47, *47*
Variola louti 160, *160*
venom 57 *see also* toxins

spines 57
vermiculated rabbitfish 184
Vieja synspila 174
viperfishes 50, *51*
    Pacific 134
viviparous blenny 181, *181*

W

wahoo 187
walking catfish 30, *123*
weatherfishes 116, *116*
weaver, greater 181
Weberian apparatus 108
weeverfishes 57
wels catfish 123, *123*
whale shark 68, *68*, 71, *71*, 76-7, 77
whalefish 149, *149*
    flabby 149
    redmouth 149
    velvet 149, *149*
whales
    sperm 50, *51*
whiptail 125
    banded 139
white cloud mountain fish 111, *111*
white shark 76, *76*, 78, 82-3, *82*
white sturgeon 95, *95*
whitefishes 126, 133, *133*
whitespotted filefish 194, *194*
wimple piranha 120, *120*
wobbegong, tasseled 24, *24*, 76, *76*
wolffish 181, *181*
wrasses 45, *103*, 142, *142*, 168
    bird 178, *178*
    bluestreak cleaner 178, *178*, 182
    clown 178
    cuckoo 179, *179*
    filamentous 179
    Mediterranean rainbow 179
    moon 179, *179*
    spotted 178

X

Xanthichthys auromarginatus 194
Xenomystus nigri 98, *98*
Xiphias gladius 188, *188*

Y

yellow bass 158
yellow tang 185, *185*
yellow-edged lyretail 160, *160*
yellowfin, Baikal 157, *157*
yellowfin grouper 160
yellowtail coris 178

Z

Zanclus cornutus 184, *184*
zander 161
zebra cichlid 175
zebra shark 52, *52*, 71
zebra sole 191
Zebrasoma flavescens 185, *185*
Zebrias zebra 191
Zeus faber 150, *150*
ziege 110
Zoarces vivparus 181, *181*
zooplankton 23, *23*, 46, 50, 90

ACKNOWLEDGMENTS

t=top; l=left; r=right; tl=top left; tcl=top center left; tr=top right; cl=center left; c=center; cr=center right; b=bottom; bl=bottom left; bcl=bottom center left; bc=bottom center; bcr=bottom center right; br=bottom right

AFP = Agence France-Presse; APL = Australian Picture Library; APL/CBT = Australian Picture Library/Corbis; APL/MP = Australian Picture Library/Minden Pictures; AUS = Auscape International; GI = Getty Images; IFR = Ifremer; IQ3D = imagequestmarine.com; N_EO = NASA/Earth Observatory; N_ES = NASA/Earth from Space; N_V = NASA/Visible Earth; NHPA = Natural History Photographic Agency; NPL=Nature Picture Library; PL = photolibrary.com; SP=Seapics.com; TSA = Tom Stack & Associates.

PHOTOGRAPHS

Front cover tl, tc, c GI; tr Corel Corp.

1c GI; 2c GI; 4c GI; 6cl GI; 8cl APL/CBT; 12c GI; 14bcl GI; cr PL; 16b TSA; 18bl APL/CBT; br PL; 19b PL; 21b, tr GI; 22br PL; tr GI; 23tl GI; tr NHPA; 24b GI; 25b GI; tr AUS; 26cl APL/MP; tl AUS/Clive Bromhall; 27c GI; 28b, tr APL/MP; 29br NHPA; tr APL/CBT; 30b PL; tr GI; 31r NHPA; 32bl PL; br AUS; tl GI; 33b APL/MP; tr APL/CBT; 34c N_EO/Goddard Space Flight Center; 35br GI; 36cl N_V; cr N_EO; 37tr NHPA; 38br APL/CBT; 39b PL; tc APL/CBT; 40b APL/MP; tl PL; 41br N_ES; tr APL/CBT; 42br APL/CBT; t GI; 43c APL/CBT; 44c PL; 45b PL; 46b PL; tc NHPA; 47br APL/CBT; t PL; 48b PL; 49b, tr APL/CBT; 52b APL/MP; 53c GI; 54c PL; 55b PL; c Digital Stock; t Corel Corp.; 56bl, tl GI; 57b APL/MP; 58b PL; 59bl, br APL/MP; tr PL; 60t GI; 61b PL; tr APL/CBT; 62br AFP; tr APL/CBT; 63b APL/CBT; tr PL; 64c GI; 66b NPL/Reijo Juurinen/Naturbild; c AUS 68cl PL; tr APL/CBT; 69br SP/Doug Perrine; c SP/Phillip Colla; 70c AFP; cl PL; 72tc APL; 73bc GI; cr APL/CBT; tr PL; 75c APL/MP; tl PL; tr APL/CBT; 81cr GI; 82br APL/CBT; l, tr PL; 83bc SP/Ben Cropp Productions; 84bc APL/CBT; br PL; cl GI; 87br PL; 88c APL/CBT; 90bc NHPA; cl AUS; 91cr SP; tl AUS; tr APL/CBT; 92cr PL; 93br GI; 94c AUS; cl PL; 96cl APL/CBT; cr SP; 97c Norbert Wu Productions; 98c PL; cl naturalvisions.co.uk; 100c PL; 103c APL; 104tl PL; tr NPL; 105br APL/MP; c IQ3D/Masa Ushioda; 107tl PL; 108bc, br PL; cl APL/MP; 114cr PL; l NHPA; 122c PL; 126bl APL/CBT; c SP/Mark Conlin; cl APL; 130c GI; 134cl AUS; 135br Picture taken with the ROV Victor 6000 of Ifremer, at 2,500 meter depth, copyright Ifremer/biozaire2–2001; cl Kevin Deacon; 136bl John E. Randall; cl PL 137c Carlos Ivan Garces del Cid & Gerardo Garcia; 138c GI; 139c PL; 142bl PL; cl GI 144b APL/CBT; cr Bruce Coleman Limited; 152b, tr PL; 153l, r PL; 156c GI; 168bl APL/CBT; br IQ3D/James D Watt; cr PL; tr APL/MP; 169c PL; 172c APL/CBT; r GI; 177c PL; 189c APL/CBT; 192b APL/CBT; tr PL; 193b NHPA; 196bl APL/CBT; r GI.

ILLUSTRATIONS

All illustrations © MagicGroup s.r.o. (Czech Republic) - www.magicgroup.cz; except for the following:
Alistar Barnard 130c; **Peter Bull Art Studio** 23b, 34bl, 50r, 57tr; **Martin Camm** 52c tc, 69r, 78bl, 83br; **Marjorie Crosby-Fairall** 75bl; **Kevin Deacon** 69tl; **Chris Forsey** 76c; **Ray Grinaway** 68b, 71bcr br, 72c; **Gino Hasler** 70br, 72bl br tr, 73bl br tl, 74bl, 80b, 83tr; **Suzanne Keating/Weldon Owen** 104c; **David Kirshner** 14bcl bl c cl tcl, 17b c t, 18t, 20b c cl, 57tl, 67br, 91b, 107tr, 113br, 193t, 195b; **Frank Knight** 19t; **Roger Swainston** 52t, 79br, 84bl; **Guy Troughton** 104b; **Rod Westblade** 78bl; **Wildlife Art Ltd** 24tr, 26b, 86bl, 89bcr, 92cl, 102bl, 107b, 118bl, 123br, 125br, 127br, 140bl, 141br, 150bl, 157br, 167br, 174bl, 183br, 199br.

MAPS AND GRAPHICS

All maps by **Andrew Davies/Creative Communication** and **Brian Johnston**.

INDEX

Sarah Plant/Puddingburn Editorial Services.

The publishers would like to thank Helen Flint and Kathryn Morgan for their assistance in the preparation of this volume.

CAPTIONS

Page 1 Pacific double-saddle butterflyfish are usually seen in pairs on coral reefs or swimming in large schools in the island regions of the Central and Western Pacific.

Page 2 This seahorse uses its tail to anchor itself by holding onto a Gorgonian sea fan.

Pages 4–5 Beautiful, triangular-shaped silver moony fish have yellow dorsal and anal fins.

Pages 6–7 A school of lionfish swim around a reef in the Red Sea, Egypt.

Pages 8–9 A tarpon travels to deeper, coastal saltwater.

Pages 12–13 Lampreys' mouths act as suction cups to hold onto their prey and suck their blood.

Pages 64–65 A school of Atlantic salmon are swimming upstream to spawn.

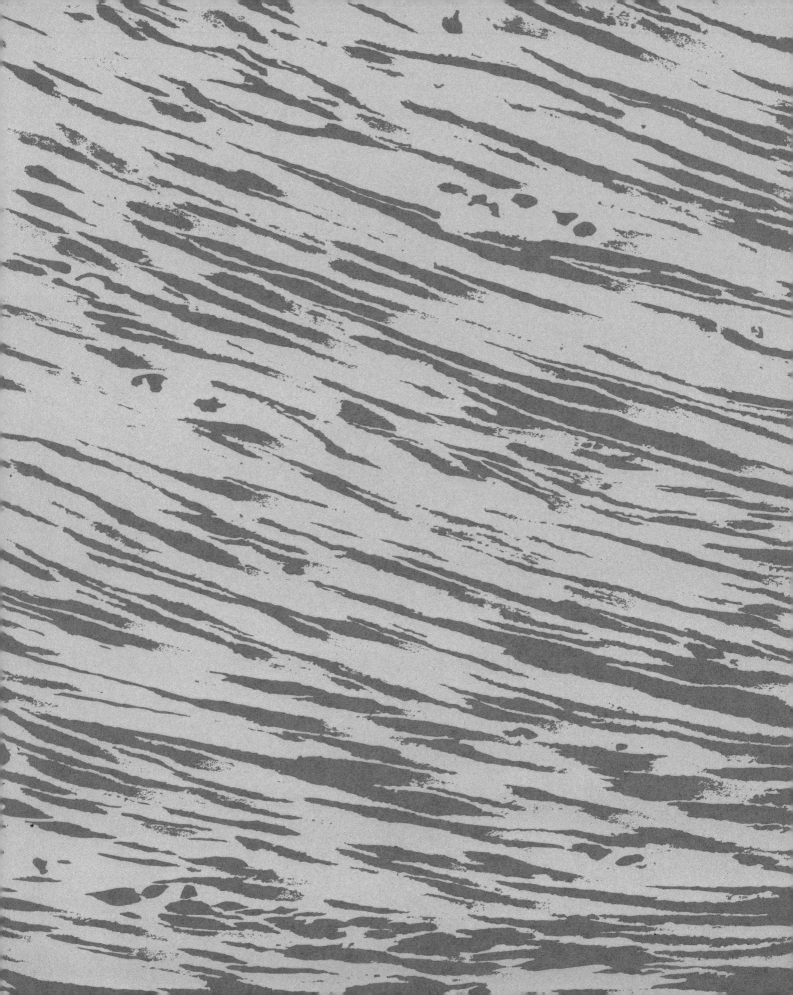